'CORKY'S WAR'

Based on the War Diaries of Percy Cawkwell, Private 63599 Royal Army Medical Corps.

Written by Ronald Fairfax

Best Wishes
Ronald Fanfax

For Jacob

MUTINY PRESS

Cover Design

"Out of Battle"

Original Painting
by
Peter Harrison

ISBN 978-0-9559705-0-4

CONTENTS

For Janet, Jane and Sally

In Memory of George Henry Fairfax and Seth Heap KIA March 1915

Ron Fairfax left school in 1956 and went into a number of dead-end jobs. In 1964 he trained as a teacher and left that to go to Hull University as a mature student. On graduating he went as a lecturer to what became Hull College. In 1989 he was made redundant and started a new career writing and presenting a series of TV/Video documentaries on Cities in the North of England, Hull at War, The Sheffield Story, Yorkshire at War to name just a few. Until he retired in 2005 he was a supply teacher in schools in Hull and The East Riding. He has two daughters, Jane a graduate of the universities of Hull and York, and Sally a Leeds University graduate. They are both products of Hull's primary, secondary and tertiary state education system. Ron lives in Hull with his wife Janet who for some years managed student services at Hull College.

Peter Harrison was born in Hull. After National Service in the RAF he worked as a printer. He gave this up to work in metal mining in Australia. After touring the world he came back to Hull and went as an undergraduate to what became The University of Lincoln. He has a degree in photography and art. Peter and Ron have worked on a number of projects together, one of the most notable being, 'Defiance' a graphic novel on Hull's part in The English Civil War.

Author's Note.

I first knew Percy Cawkwell in 1973. Percy replied to a letter of mine the Hull Daily Mail published. In it I asked readers for their memories of The First World War. My grand father served in the local regiment, The East Yorks and I wanted to contact any veterans who might have served with him. Percy was one of the men who got in touch, not as an East Yorks veteran but as an ex- Royal Army Medical Corps Stretcher Bearer.

Corky, as he liked to be known as, had recorded his memories in a series of diaries that he had kept in the field and written up in 1921.

As a result of this contact I got to know Corky very well and he became a friend of the family. Over time I had many conversations with him and I kept a detailed record of most of them.

Before he died he made me a present of his diaries and I promised him that I would try to get them into print. I approached a number of publishers but the view expressed was that the entries were not detailed enough.

For a long time I postponed fulfilling my promise and I got on with my career as a lecturer and helping my wife bring up a family of two little girls.

I did however continue my interest in W.W.1 and as part of this I interviewed many other veterans.

When in 1989 I took early retirement from further education I divided my time between making TV/Video documentaries, Supply teaching and working as a W.W.1 Battlefield Tour Guide. In the course of this work I escorted many groups through the old Battlefields and War Cemeteries of Belgium and Northern France including survivors of the war along with their relatives and descendants and I listened to and recorded many stories.

My work in this area persuaded me that Corky's story could be told in print if I took his diary and augmented it with his experiences and those of his comrades in arms.

The result is, I think, an authentic picture in words of what life was like for a soldier in the Great War. I'm fairly sure that Corky would have approved but in the end it is for the reader to judge. Corky asked that if the diaries were ever published I should make sure that the names of his family be changed. Apart from the names of his father and his brother Tom I have done so.

Ronald Fairfax
Hull
2008

Acknowledgements.

I want to thank a number of people in particular for the help they have given to the production of this work; George Fairfax, Joe Fairfax, Fred Fairfax, Ernest Fairfax, Alf Dodge, Jack Jones, Tom Lloyd, Ernest Dry, Robert Morton, Charles Budd, Philip Turner, Arthur Jarvis, John Hill, Mike Hurley, Robin Kaye, Dave Smith, Peter Starling, Sam Walters, Albert Sawyer, Brendan Bruce and Julian Halsby. Thanks also go to my long-suffering typist, Pauline Brown and to my proof-readers Val and Colin Price. A special thank you has to go to my illustrator Peter Harrison. I wish to acknowledge too the photographic archives of the imperial War Museum and those of The Canadian War Memorial at Vimy Ridge. And thanks to go to Andy and his colleagues at Fisk Printers.

CHAPTER 1 - ENLISTMENT

Saturday 28 August 1915

I suppose you could say that my war began on top of a tram. I had tried to join up with all the rest on a couple of occasions but each time I was turned down on account of my eyesight. My eyes looked normal but because of a defect since birth I could only see out of one of them.

So it was that in the summer of 1915 I was still out of uniform, a rare sight in those days. My brother Tom was in the infantry, the local regiment, the East Yorks. He had volunteered in the first rush. I was still working as I had been for a few years looking after horses and driving carts delivering the steel drums my Dad, as a blacksmith, played a part in making.

I should return to the top of the tram I was in travelling down Beverley Road, Hull, into the city to do some shopping. I was sitting in the bay of the tram when I noticed a young girl of about fifteen or sixteen walking towards the front. I had seen her sitting in the back seats when I got on and I recognised her as someone who lived locally. She came towards me and I thought, 'This is nice, she is going to talk to me'. She did. She brought her face right up to mine and said, 'Why aren't you in uniform, you slacker. Are you afraid to go to fight?'

I was so surprised I did not have time to reply. I did not have time to say that I had tried twice already. I got up to follow her but she was away down the stairs of the tram and off as it slowed for a stop. I saw her running away and turning to laugh as she met with a friend obviously waiting for her.

Both hurt and angry I suppose she made up my mind for me. I would join up by hook or by crook.

I got off the tram in town, forgot my errand and walked to the City Hall where there was a room on the first floor that was the recruiting office. Before I could climb the stairs I met a young man of about my own age who I vaguely knew as a worker in one of the firms I delivered to. I asked him if he had enlisted and he said he had just joined the R.A.M.C. He said, 'They'll take anybody, they've taken me'.

I went straight up to the corporal on the desk and said, 'I want to join the R.A.M.C.' My name, address, age and employment details were taken and he stamped the form, swore me in and said that I was to return on Monday morning just before midday and be prepared to leave in the afternoon by train for Aldershot. I asked if there would be a medical and he said not to be worried about that, I would be seen to at the depot.

I had joined up and although it was obvious I wasn't going to be part of the front-line 'going over the top' I was a soldier, non-combatant that I might be. Honour was satisfied. I walked around the town centre in my civvies, challenging every look.

I returned home and told mother and my sisters. Mother just said sadly, 'I have been expecting it but I hoped you wouldn't have to go'. It wasn't necessary to explain to her. She knew of the problems I was having. It happened a lot. At least I hadn't been given the white feather. People, mostly young girls who didn't know any better, would sometimes send envelopes to young men aged from 14 upwards. The envelopes were empty apart from a white chicken feather. When Dad came home from work he took the news much as mother had.

I didn't sleep that night. Things had happened very quickly. All sorts of thoughts went through my mind including the possibility of not coming back. Much of the optimism of the previous year had passed. It had not been over by Christmas and the war had dragged through the winter and into the spring. Spring had brought the battle of Neuve Chapelle with its high casualties and some of those had been felt in Hull. The summer had seen the actions at Gallipoli.

I was concerned as well about the effect my leaving would have on the family. I knew already that Mother and Dad would accept it. All the men would go in the end, they said. 'There won't be anybody left'. But I was also worried that the girls would have to go into war-work as my wage would not be coming in.

My other thoughts considered the medical. What if they tested my eyes and found I only had one good one, and so I would have to come back? As it turned out I needn't have worried myself about that.

Sunday 29 August 1915

I was up early and I breakfasted before anyone else. I went to church. The word had obviously got round that I was going. There were lots of good wishes and the vicar even mentioned me by name. In the afternoon I made a few farewell visits and had tea with Auntie Eve. She was older than my mother and had lost a friend in the Boer War. I got the strong impression she was rather attached to him romantically.

Monday 30 August 1915

Again up early to pack and to say goodbye, especially to see to it that I caught Dad before he went off to work. I wanted to get the goodbyes out of the way at home so I asked Mother and the girls not to come to the station to see me off.

I walked up the road to Wincolmlee to the factory where I worked and I confirmed with the 'gaffer' that I was leaving to join up. There was nothing unusual in this as chaps were doing it all the time. I went round and said my goodbyes to one or two people that I knew and with that and assurances that there would be a job for me when I returned and that any wages owing would be paid. I went back home.

Mother had packed sandwiches, hard boiled eggs, apples and a bottle of cold sweet tea. I protested at her packing clean shirts and socks as I was sure that I would have to send them back. She made me take them anyway.

I caught the tram for the City Hall, waving to Mother and the girls until they were out of sight. It was to be some weeks before I would see them again.

At the City Hall it was made plain to the group of new recruits that I joined that we were already, though in civilian clothes, in the Army. One or two were skylarking and saluting each other, until that is the sergeant or sergeant Major (I couldn't tell the difference) shouted at them in a voice that echoed through the length and breadth of the City Hall.

Our names were called out and I went to a table and drew 6 shillings and 4 pence, my first Army pay. The Officer sitting at the table called my name, Cawkwell P, and stated my number, which I immediately forgot.

When we had been paid we were told to stand in three lines and a man with white hair and a white moustache and a very pink face, dressed in Officer's uniform gave us a talk on how we were to 'disport ourselves', now that we were in the Army and under military discipline. We could not change our minds and must do as we were ordered without question. He wished us good luck and God's speed and then we were marched, or rather we walked untidily, from the City Hall to Paragon railway station where we were to catch a train to London and then to Aldershot, our depot.

There were no crowds lining the streets as in the early days of the war. People had got used to squads of young men marching down the city's roads and streets. All we got from passers-by were a few curious looks and shouts of, 'You'll be sorry' and 'Does your Mother know you're out?' from one or two khaki dressed squaddies obviously enjoying their leave in the numerous and crowded Hull pubs.

When we got to the station I began to regret that I had not asked Mother and the girls to see me off. There were dozens of people in the station, army, navy and civilian. The civilians were there to see the soldiers and sailors off after leave and weekend passes. As the London train waited in the station its engine was clanking and steaming and carriage doors were banging shut.

There were about twenty five of us in our group and we were put in carriages close together and I found out that I was the only one without someone there to say goodbye to. The lad I had met on the stairs of City Hall had his Mother and his sweetheart waiting to say goodbye to him and when they saw that there was nobody for me they wished me luck. As for me I was feeling rather sorry for myself.

On the train we settled down for what was a long day's journey and I was glad of the packing up that Mother had given me for I had neither the time nor the money to buy what was offered on the platforms of the stations we stopped at.

Before long most of my comrades had finished talking about the war and the possibility of zeppelin raids on London. I made the comment that Hull had had its share of raids. The one in June had caused a number of casualties and a great deal of damage. They became engaged in smoking, reading or losing their first army pay playing cards.

At last we reached London King's Cross from where we were bussed across the busy city along with groups of regulars and already enlisted and uniformed men, to get the train to Aldershot from Waterloo.

We arrived at the notorious Aldershot by 8 p.m. and outside the station under the watchful eye of red-capped military policemen our names were called along with our regimental numbers.

I joined 'K' company of the R.A.M.C. in their barracks. There was hot tea and sandwiches waiting for us. I collected my blankets, was allocated a bed in a line of about twenty, and I sat reading and later writing a letter home until lights out. We had been informed quite early that the delights of Aldershot were out of bounds to us until told different.

Tuesday 31 August 1915

My first reveille; I got up and washed and shaved in cold water. The weather was still warm and sunny so it was not much of a hardship. A corporal came into the barracks and told us where to go for breakfast. Hot tea, porridge and bread and bacon were on the menu.

After breakfast we were put into a queue for medical examination. It was not what you might call thorough. Not much more than the joke, 'Drop em, cough, you're in'. I needn't have worried about the eye test. I put my hand over my bad eye twice and read the chart with my good eye, nobody noticed. The vaccination followed. I didn't consider myself particularly tough but I was certainly tougher than one or two in the line who were bigger than me. When they saw the needles they just fell down in a faint.

After the M.O.s examination we lined up in the quartermaster's stores for uniform and kit. One or two of my comrades were overjoyed at some of the things issued. It seemed they had never worn underwear before and had never had two of anything when it came to clothes. They were the ones I had noticed at breakfast having second helpings as if it had been the first good meal they had ever eaten.

Back in the barracks we were shown how to wear our tunics, our hats, put on our puttees and how to make our beds and lay out our kit. I wondered if I would get the hang of it.

After a dinner of vegetable and beef stew with chunks of bread followed by rice pudding we had our first task of square bashing. We learned to form fours, right and left turns, to stand at attention, then at ease, to forward march and to halt. That went on for the rest of the day until a tea of bread and jam. After tea we had another two hours of marching up and down, being shouted at and cursed by the Corporal. At the end of it we were back in the barracks, footsore from our ill-fitting boots, with only enough energy to pack up our civilian clothes and to address them for sending home. The rest of the evening we lay on our bunks writing letters home or sitting on the steps at the door getting to know each other and talking of rumours that most of us were to be posted in the next few days to unknown destinations.

I got my first taste of the gossip and rumour that soldiers thrive on as various speculations were aired as to where we were going and what the war was doing in Russia, France, Africa and Turkey. If the rumour-mongers were to be believed they knew the facts behind everything from the sinking of the Lusitania to why the Americans were not in the war. There was even one story that King George was coming or had already been here to review troops. 'Tell him I'm sorry I was out', said one wag.

Wednesday 1 September 1915

Up again to more square bashing. At least being non-combatants we don't have to practice rifle drill but nonetheless we had to present ourselves, as a young officer said, 'in a soldierly way'. The work has been very energetic and even after just a couple of days I am beginning to feel fitter.

Over bread and jam and tea in the afternoon the gossip is that a number of us are going to be drafted. An orderly in the cook house said that new recruits have not been staying long enough to get to know the place.

Thursday 2 September 1915

Sure enough the rumour was right. This morning after breakfast the order came to pack our kit and to get ready to be drafted up north. I wondered if it was to be back where I had come from but no, about twenty of us were to go to Seaforth Military Hospital near Liverpool. It took all day to get us there. We had to go back to London then in a train for Liverpool.

It was night when we arrived in the city and although the hospital was not so far lorries were waiting to take us to the barracks attached to the hospital.

We were very tired and quite hungry when we got there but bully beef sandwiches and hot tea, as much as we wanted, waited for us. Fed and watered, it was only necessary for us to bed down, which we did quickly and without complaint.

Friday 3 September 1915

I and others are to get our first army duty tonight when we are to be put on watch on the wards.

Seaforth Hospital is quite large and has been made larger with extensions to cope with the casualties that have come in from France and Belgium. We were told what we had to do by a very stern sister. In no circumstances were we to help patients. Our job was to watch over them and take those that could walk to the lavatories, give bottles and pans to those who couldn't and to call the nurses and sisters from their room if we thought there was something urgent to deal with.

Luckily for me there were no problems on my night shift, they all seemed to be sleeping peacefully. The men in my ward had only light wounds, 'Blighty ones' as they were called. Not too serious but bad enough to be sent home to be healed and then I suppose to be sent back again. There were other wards in the hospital that held patients with awful amputations and serious chest and abdominal injuries.

Saturday 5 September 1915

I took the opportunity of my day off to look around and I went on a visit to New Brighton and Birkenhead.

New Brighton must have been a nice sea-side town in peace time with pleasant trips on the ferry across the Mersey from Liverpool. Birkenhead has a splendid park and I walked around passing many a khaki clad visitor like myself. Some of them were lucky enough to have a sweetheart on their arm.

When I got back in the afternoon in time for tea there was a letter from home with news that Tom, my brother, might be posted abroad. I passed another uneventful night on the ward.

Sunday 6 September 1915

I thought there would be a church parade on my first Sunday in the army but didn't get any orders and most of the lads in my barracks came back to bed after breakfast. I decided to go to St. Nicholas' church nearby which seemed to be the hospital church. There was quite a big congregation with officers and men, the walking wounded from the hospital and not a few nurses, one or two that I recognised.

The vicar's sermon talked much of the war and with nurses in the front row he made reference to the execution of nurse Edith Cavell by the Germans in Belgium and 'What had wars come to when women could be the victims?' I wanted to tell anyone who wanted to listen that Edith Cavell's sister was a nurse in a Hospital at Withernsea, near Hull, but got no opportunity of conversation after the service.

Monday 7 September 1915

So began a week of lectures and more drilling. My fellow soldiers seemed to know more about the purpose of drilling than I did. It seemed that drilling soldiers to turn right, left and about turn had a particular military purpose, rather than what most of us thought, it passed the time.

Its purpose, so our 'military historians' said, was to organize us in the field so that in ranks we could face the enemy and fire our muskets. But as we didn't 'bear arms' that couldn't have been the reason. It might be, said someone 'that we could frighten the enemy by pulling funny faces and chucking wound dressings at them'. There was always someone ready with a funny comment or observation. It was one of the things I was beginning to like about living together with the group. More reasonably another suggested that it was practice for the foot–slogging we would have to do when we went to France. He turned out to be right.

The lectures and talks we got explained our jobs and responsibilities. We were told about the Hague Convention and about the history of our emblem, the Red Cross. We were also told about how the nickname for the R.A.M.C. had come about. The letters of course stand for Royal Army Medical Corps but we were told that we must ignore the jibe of being known as R.A.M.C. 'rob all my comrades'. We were required under military law to protect the dead and wounded in our care from 'pillage and maltreatment' and that all articles of personal use, valuables, etc., found on the field of battle, left by the wounded and the dead must be collected and that it was our responsibility to do it. Even, it seems, the property of the dead and wounded of the enemy. It should be collected and sent back through the proper channels. There was to be no souvenir hunting.

I had not thought there was so much to being a stretcher bearer but it was explained to us that we were more medical orderlies than stretcher bearers. We would find ourselves much called on for that purpose but that was, in the first instance, more the work of the regimental stretcher bearers.

I began to get more and more interested in my work and more used to the tasks I was called upon to do in the hospital and I began to enjoy it. There was so much to take in but I was young and encouraged by remarks made by a senior officer about the fact that I seemed to read and write to a standard not all that common amongst private soldiers. I only had elementary education. I left school at twelve but was glad now for all those handwriting exercises that they used to teach us. I also read a lot and still did whenever I had a free moment. My reading habits and the fact that I had brought a number of books with me had already been cause for comment. The fact that I wrote up my diary every evening also drew comment from my comrades. One had been particularly useful for he told me confidentially that it was not allowed.

After that I was more careful whenever I filled it in. I earned myself not a little respect and popularity among my chums in the barracks, for I was able to keep notes of what was told us and to pass them on. I also wrote letters home for one or two of the chaps who seemed to have real difficulty with their 'letters'.

We had a whole series of lectures on the medical and first aid that we could give, and like the drills the lectures were given at the double. Those who gave the impression of knowing about such things said that we would get about six months of this with lots of practical hospital work thrown in before our postings for abroad. I felt that if the training we were getting went on at the pace we were going at, by six months I would feel very competent to deal with anything thrown at me in the field.

I enjoyed learning about the aid we could give very much. It was really 'First Aid' but was no less comprehensive for being that. We learned the three basic principles:

1. To preserve the life of the patient.
2. To promote recovery.
3. To prevent aggravation of the injury or condition.

But most importantly we learned that we must get the help of a medical officer at the earliest possible moment.

To assist in the understanding of the principles we were being taught, we were taken on tours of the hospital wards. Although we saw all sorts of wounds and sicknesses the beds containing soldiers recovering from amputations were for me the most moving. We were told after our visits that many amputations could be avoided if we took as our motto 'speed of delivery' and 'speed of treatment'. With this the senior medical officer who was talking to us explained that so often simple wounds became very serious as a result of delay. He illustrated what he meant by referring to a young soldier we had just seen. His right arm had been removed just above the elbow. He had been wounded by a small shell-splinter that had split the finger of his right hand. By the time it was properly treated gas-gangrene had set in and at first his finger was amputated, then his hand and then, more drastically, his arm. It was explained to us that the war in France and Belgium was being fought over land that had been manured and cultivated for centuries and was rich in the microbes that produced such infections. The wounded had to be shifted to clean and comfortable surroundings where they could get expert treatment as quickly as possible. 'The quicker they could be treated the quicker they could be got back into action and the quicker the war would be won'.

We also learned the significance of the wounded in this modern war. The medical officer

said, very gravely, that we would hear the generals exhorting us, 'to kill the Hun' but really it's more effective militarily if you wound him. A dead man gets buried, a wounded man takes up the time of many people and so puts a strain on the war effort.

Friday 11 September 1915

I drew my pay of 9 shillings and I felt I had earned it. I had got down to the hospital work I had been allocated and I enjoyed the weekend knowing I was doing a good job.

The people around here are very friendly and our khaki uniform is a 'passe partout' to the many clubs, pubs and places of entertainment that there are in the area. Liverpool Corporation has ordered that anyone in service uniform can travel free on the trams and the overhead electric railway so that enables us to get about easily.

This week-end I spent buzzing around New Brighton, Birkenhead and Egremont. I go over on the ferry from Liverpool where from the pier-head I can also get a tram from Upper Parliament Street to the pictures or the music hall.

Whatever this war has done it seems to have brought people together so there is a welcome to us wherever we go. At the back on my mind however there is the memory of the broken bodies of the poor boys and men who we have to go back to in the hospital.

Monday 13 September 1915

Another week of lectures, practicals and drill lies ahead but the weather is good as we seem to be enjoying a summer that is continuing even into September.

Tuesday 14 September 1915

The fact that I seem to read and write better than most was once again recognised when I was put in charge of number six ward. It entailed being responsible for sixteen patients and all their documentation. Filling in forms, dockets and chitties seems to be what the army likes best. Fortunately for the patients of number six ward and me, none of them is seriously ill. Most have wounds that are well on the mend with one or two suffering from stomach problems that are said to be the result of bad food and water completely ruining their digestive systems. One young man has a burn from hip to ankle on his right leg that he got from a petrol fire that filled the trench he was in just outside Wipers (Ypres), in Belgium. A year later I learned that it was one of the first times that the Germans had used a new anti-trench weapon the 'Flame-Thrower'. A soldier carried a tank of petrol on his back attached to cylinders of gas. The petrol was forced out by the gas and sprayed a distance of 30 – 50 yards. God help anyone caught in the cloud of flame. The soldier in my ward caught a splash that set him on fire from the waist down on one leg. His hands had been burned too as he tried to put out the flames. His leg was completely healed and although there was extensive scarring he had not lost any movement so it was likely that he would be sent back to France.

For recreation I catch the train to the end of the line and walk to the southern end of the river. I visited a pub right out along the estuary where the landlord said there was a place where once black African slaves had been shipped to the Americas.

Saturday 18 September 1915

Pay day again and I drew 8 shillings. I can't remember having so much money because it is hard to spend as we cannot go into a pub or tea shop without someone stands us a drink or offers us a cigarette, although I don't smoke. I am able to send Mother a few shillings each week and that I know is much appreciated.

I am still very busy with hospital work and lectures, lantern shows and practical demonstrations of the kind of work that we will have to do when we embark for France.

I never knew before that there were so many different sorts of bandages and dressings, nor so many ways to improvise a splint. We were also shown how to improvise a stretcher and how best to pick up the wounded.

Much fun was had as we experimented on each other with various bandages and of course some of us finished up looking more like Egyptian mummies than walking wounded.

I spend some of my evenings re-writing notes and effectively delivering lectures again to the ones in the group who didn't grasp it the first time. I am becoming very interested and well informed and something of a student of the work we are doing, so much so that I am known amongst our barrack room members as 'Dr Corky'.

Friday 24 September 1915

I didn't have time to fill in my diary day today, but did it later. Either I am too much concerned with the revision of the lectures attended or I am just too tired at the end of the day to put pen to paper. If I have time to do that it has to be taken up by letters home, and judging by the letters from home some sort of change of circumstance is about to happen. It is nothing to worry about but being so far away without news is cause for concern.

Most of this week has been spent at the dockside of Liverpool, checking and loading medical stores for the Dardenelles. The news from there varies if you believe the newspapers. There is optimism but the gossip and rumour is that they are already thinking of evacuating and abandoning the campaign altogether – what a waste. There was a little song at the time that summed up the ordinary soldier's attitude. You could hear it at the end of an evening in the pub when the party were downing their umpteenth pint:

18

O the moon shines bright on Charlie Chaplin
An' his boots are crackin'
For the want of blackin'.
An' his old baggy trousers
Need a'mendin'
Before they send' im
To the Dardanelles.

Whatever was going to happen we were walking up the gangplanks of a steamer with boxes of supplies that would soon be on their way there. I hope they do some good. I thought a bit differently later when many of the supply problems we had in France were because material had been diverted from France to the war in Turkey. When the evacuation took place, as it did later, much of that material was left or destroyed.

Friday 1 October 1915

Pay day again and I drew 8 shillings. The nice satisfying feeling of being paid didn't last long when we found out that we were to parade before the medical officer to be inoculated against enteric fever. Inoculations in the army we learned are a sure sign of imminent posting abroad, but we also learned that the fever could just as easily run rife in a hospital like ours where patients might be recovering from that or Typhoid fever.

There were one or two simple precautions we could take, we were told, like washing our hands after using the lavatory. This raised a laugh later on when we saw the condition of latrines in the field. We were also told to observe strict hygiene rules if in the area of food preparations. Which raised the same laugh.. We were also given a lecture on how to recognise impure water and how to purify it with chloride of lime. And there was of course preventative inoculation which lasted about a year.

As far as some of our number were concerned the time between one inoculation and the next could not be long enough. Preference was expressed for Fritz's bayonet over the 'instrument long sharp and thin' hypodermic. I acquired the habit of getting first in the queue for the needle as it did not stay sharp for very long.

The weather has turned wet and cold which has taken the edge off my enjoyment of the place. We stayed in, around the stove which was lit for us for the first time. A card game began but I stayed out of it. The same players always seemed to win, not a good sign.

Sunday 3 October 1915

I went to Church at St. Nicholas' again. After the service the Vicar had arranged tea in the church hall. I found myself talking to nurses on an equal footing for the first time. They were strictly forbidden to even pass the time of day with us when on the wards.

I didn't know whether to call them sister or nurse and I didn't know which branch of the service they were in, the Imperial Nursing service, The Queen Alexandra's or the Voluntary Aid Detachment. The V.A.D's were the easiest to talk to and I noticed that there weren't any from what you might call the working classes. At least they recognised me and were prepared to have a brief word.

In the afternoon I read letters from home and one particularly from Mother contained a note that said she had decided to move to Halifax where we had relatives. She didn't say so but I think she was afraid of more air raids and wanted to get into the West Riding where she and the girls would be safer. She sent me the new address and said she looked forward to meeting me there when I got leave. Initially Dad was to stay in Hull because of his work as a blacksmith.

Monday 4 October 1915

More drills, lectures and working on the wards doing Porter's duties. I am surprised we are not called upon to do some of the cleaning that needs to be done, but the junior nursing orderlies come in for that. They are volunteers like us and they go to their work with a will. They keep the wards very clean and tidy and they see to it that the patients have everything they need in the way of soap, flannels, towels and shaving requisites.

We do the lugging and humping and the fetching and carrying. Myself and two mates had to shift a dead man during the week. We didn't know he was dead until the nursing sister ordered us to put him on the stretcher and then pulled the blanket over his face. As we found out later we should have known he was dead because we took him from the end bed at the bottom of the ward. The nurses always put those who they know are certain to die there, so that the screens can be put up and the corpse taken away with the minimum of fuss. He was only a young lad, like us I suppose. I sometimes forget how old I am, nineteen coming up to my twentieth birthday. There is no doubt in my mind that I have grown older in the short time I have been here. Being fit and well makes you feel a bit like a 'Dutch Uncle' when you are able to comfort some wounded young lad of your own age by saying, 'you'll be up and about in no time once you've settled in here'.

This week was best remembered for the cooking lessons we got and for the instructions passed on to us relating to the provision of a 'comfort box'. I have written down one or two of the recipes, the ones we were advised would be practical to use in the field. Not only were the dishes nourishing, we were told, but they would go a long way to raising the spirits of exhausted and /or wounded men.

The first was Rice Pudding. One and a half ounces of rice, one pint of milk, half an ounce of butter, a pinch of salt, a tablespoon of sugar and nutmeg for flavouring. These quantities will make enough for about four helpings so they have to be increased in proportion as the number of takers swells. Cooking Method: Wash the rice thoroughly, put into a greased dish with the salt and sugar, then pour on the milk, adding the flavouring, and bake slowly in a moderate oven for one and a half hours. Porridge: Half a teacup of oatmeal, one quart of boiling water, salt. Cooking Method: Put a pinch of salt in the water and when boiling sprinkle on the oatmeal and stir constantly with a wooden spoon. Let it simmer for forty-five minutes. Serve with milk, hot or cold and sugar and salt to taste. In the coming years I was never once able to cook these dishes with the ingredients recommended or using the cooking methods suggested. There was always something missing. If there was rice then there would be no milk. If there was oatmeal there would be no water or vice versa. And sometimes there wasn't anything. As the jokey saying had it, 'if we had some fish we could have some fish and chips, if we had any chips'. However, as time was to tell it did not matter what the recipe was, as long as the question, 'Is there any rum in it?', could be answered positively. As far as the 'comforts box' was concerned, it was an essential item. We were often told that our reward would be in heaven if we could guarantee the availability of the 'drop of rum'.

We were to discover that cheap red wine was readily available in France and that a quantity of wine heated with sugar was an easily prepared and effective 'pick me up'. Although the use of alcohol as first aid was not advised, if there was any available this counsel was usually ignored.

Friday 8 October 1915

We have had a very jolly week playing games of football and making visits as the work has slowed down at the hospital. We have been let off the usual square bashing and have had only a few lectures on dressing and treating fractures. We were told how we might improvise splints from anything firm and long enough to keep the bones and joints at rest. The list of items suggested as splints for use in an emergency were: walking stick, umbrella, billiard cue, broom or brush handle, a policeman's truncheon, a rifle, a rolled up newspaper or a rolled up map. As usual there were funny or even ribald comments that went with the recommendations. 'Excuse me General, may I borrow your map to mend this chap's broken leg?' 'Certainly, old boy, only too glad to help'. We decided that the most readily available item to use in France, as an improvised splint, might be a rifle. As one wag said 'I understand there is a lot of them about over there'.

Friday 22 October 1915

Pay day again and the weather has now returned to being fine. Mother was right to have moved out of Hull. This last week saw an increase in Zeppelin activity. London was hit and East Coast ports took a battering too.

I will be able to get the full story of Mother's move because a short leave has been promised. There was much speculation on whether this would be embarkation leave, but we will have to see.
A week was to pass before the promise of leave was fulfilled. I spent this week mostly concerned with the patients once again in Ward 6. Their number has increased to twenty

five. One of the new patients is recovering from the effects of the gas that we have heard is being used as a new weapon. He was a young N.C.O in the Royal Artillery who was attached to a Canadian gunner's Regiment. He described his experiences in Ypres in Belgium when the Germans let off this new gas weapon. He said that at first he thought it was smoke from a gun battery. Then it began to swirl about more thickly and men came stumbling down the trenches clutching their throats and coughing. He got a lung full and thought he was going to suffocate. Luckily for him the concentration wasn't heavy and he only passed out. When he recovered he was in an aid station breathing fresh air which he said 'had never tasted so good'. He has been coughing up muck for the last few months and now he's got something that makes his lungs go into spasms when he least expects it.

Friday 29 October 1915

After breakfast I was told to go back to Ward 6 to organise the transfer of the men I was beginning to regard as my patients. They had been wakened early and those who could walk were already in their 'wounded blue'. The blue serge uniform that recovering wounded were dressed in.

A number of ambulances were lined up in the drive waiting for them and the stretcher cases went in first. There were lots of shouts of 'keep your chin up' 'don't let them grind you down' and 'see you in France'.

Most of these men had become my friends. It's difficult to avoid making friends with people when your job brings you very close to their lives. It was, as I was to discover as time passed, the best and the worst of the job.

I waved them off and went to collect my pay of 8 shillings and permission plus rail ticket to Halifax.

I got the tram for Liverpool station where I caught the train at five o' clock in the evening. I had to change at Manchester and I found the station there crowded with the world and his wife. The world being soldiers, sailors and airman and the wife, nurses, women, military auxiliaries and young women off to work, or home from work, in factories.

I had time to have a cup of tea at a Salvation Army canteen and I ate the sandwiches I'd got from the cookhouse of the hospital. I chatted with a lad in the York and Lancs regiment and a geordie in the Durham Light infantry. They both asked me if I'd been to France yet. Standing at the counter of the canteen were two young girls who told us they were on munitions in Leeds: 'we make the bullets you shoot' they both said proudly.

As we went for our respective trains, I thought about how much this war was changing things. I couldn't remember a time before the war when two young girls would have joined the conversation of two young men they didn't know, and they had been on a

22

short holiday together by themselves in Blackpool.

My train took a long time on its way to Halifax, as it stopped at every station. I had been told in a letter to get off the train at Mytholmroyd or at a village called Luddenden Foot where our new home was on the hills outside Halifax. I arrived there safely after some difficulty in the dark and the thick fog that by its smell was composed of the mist from the hills and the smoke from the town below.

I found our new home quite easily after being directed to the lights in a row of pretty terraced cottages with gardens and stone walls at their fronts. Mam had put a sign on a big piece of paper and pinned it to the door.

I was later than they expected and Mam and the girls were all in bed but they came down for a few minutes to welcome me home and Mother told me she had cooked a dinner for me and left it in the oven. Even though the fire was dying my dinner was hot enough to eat and Mother put it on the table for me before going back to bed. Home and with home cooking – a soldier's dream. After I had finished eating I lit a candle, climbed the stairs and I was not long getting into the big bed made up with crisp white sheets that awaited me. It was a welcome change from the rough army cot.

Saturday 30 October 1915

I was allowed a nice long lie in and after washing and shaving in the hot water brought up to me in a bowl I went downstairs to a breakfast of bacon and eggs and home made bread. Mother had already eaten hers and the girls had gone off to work.

One of the reasons, and the main one I think, not the air raids, why Mother had moved to Halifax was new work in the mills in Halifax for the girls. Ernest, a cousin, had lived in Halifax for some time and had found this house for Mother. It was a change from the house in Hull, there being only hot oil lamps and candles, no gas, cold water in the scullery and an earth closet at the bottom of the garden. The girls quite liked it. As Mother said, it was a change. She, it was obvious, was missing Dad but she consoled herself with the hope that he would soon find work here and anyway she could get back to Hull easily to see him and 'do' for him as she didn't trust him to look after himself.

After breakfast I got out my bike, which Mother had brought here, and checked it for rust. I then biked down the hill for a look round Halifax.

From the house smoke from the mill chimneys could be seen at the bottom of valley. Even though it was the week-end the chimneys were belching it out.

When I got down into town it was very busy with lots of traffic and mill lasses, arm in arm on the pavement, out for their dinner time. The town's industry was working twenty four hours a day and seven days a week so there was a lot of money about. The

Pubs that were nearly on every corner were full and noisy, in fact over the whole town there was the sound of activity, Railway engines were chugging and whistling, goods wagons shunting into each other, steam engines rattling and factory whistles and hooters signalling the beginning or the ending of dinner time. Walking and pushing my bike around the town I went into the market hall and bought my Mother a set of china cups and saucers to replace breakages in the move. After that I went back to the house and had an enjoyable ride over the moors.

The country here is the opposite to Hull and the East Yorkshire. Hull is flat. Here the countryside is splendid with great hills and lovely valleys that have torrents of water rushing down over rocks and by the stone walls that line every field and road. Back home I gave Mother her presents and we waited for the girls to come home from work. Mother had no news from Tom and said how disappointed she was that he didn't write more often. I was able to tell her that he would have much less time than I had for writing home as the training for an infantry man was more intensive than mine. Far more drills and of course, weapons training which we didn't do. When the girls came home we had a tea of boiled ham, lettuce and cucumbers, fresh from the garden of a neighbour and of course Mother's home made pastries. 'They'll be even better,' said Mother, 'when I get used to the oven'.

At seven o clock we hurriedly changed and the three of us went down into town that night to meet Ernest. We met him, as arranged at the gate of Syke's Mill where he worked as a supervisor, and all four of us went into a nearby Pub. As we sat enjoying our shandy beer he told me that he had no intention of joining up no matter what people said about him. He was twenty five and not yet married 'I don't have to be', he said, boastfully,' I have my pick of the crop in the mill'.

We had an enjoyable night together. There was an atmosphere in the streets of friendliness and fun with not a few squaddies on leave who fancied my sisters as they passed. They had been making the most of the free drinks which everyone seemed willing to offer in the public bars.

The fog was so thick that the bus only went three quarters of the route, so on the way back up the hill we had to hold hands so as not to lose each other.

Sunday 31 October 1915

We all went to church at Luddenden Foot and after the service we left Mother to walk home and we went down again into the town. The girls wanted to show me the mill where they worked.

We walked through the gates under the archway and into one of the weaving sheds. The noise of the looms was terrific but it didn't stop me being treated to the cheeky comments of my sister's friends and fellow workers who wanted to know who I was and whether I fancied walking out with them. Girls were becoming much more forward.

After a brief walk round the town we took the long walk back to the house where Sunday dinner waited for us. After a short rest to let it go down we went for a very energetic ramble on the hills above the house. Compared to Hull it is like standing on top of the world.

Monday 1 November 1915

After breakfast, being by myself as Mother was visiting a neighbour and the girls were at work, I passed the whole day on the hills of the opposite valley. When I got back home the girls had arrived early having wangled time off because I was on leave.

I took them as a special treat to the pictures in Halifax where we saw a news reel of Lloyd George visiting the trenches in France.

After the pictures Phyllis introduced me to one of the girls she worked with at the mill. She was about sixteen, very pretty and had been sitting in the same row as Maud, Phyllis and myself. Phyllis said her name was Edna but she liked to be called Tilly. She spent the rest of the evening with us having the last drink in a pub and including the fish and chips supper I treated them all to. As we said our goodbyes and went our separate ways I asked her if I could write to her. She said, in a rather off hand way, 'You can if you like', and as she skipped down the street she turned and shouted over her shoulder, 'Phyllis will tell you where I live'. She was an orphan and lived with her Grannie.

Tuesday 2 November 1915

I got up early so that I could say goodbye to the girls as my leave was up and I was to be away before they finished work. I promised them all that I would be back again soon.

I spent a quiet day getting my things together and then I went down to the station to get the four o' clock train to Manchester and then to Liverpool.

The journey was again slow but I was content to look out of the window and to think as I did that they seemed settled and happy. They had a nice little house in a pretty village and, most important, enough money and Dad would be joining them soon.

Friday 5 November 1915

I and others have spent what was left of the week, busy on spit and polish as there was a flap on because of an inspection by a senior medical officer.
Everyone was buzzing about like the proverbial blue bottom fly and we had to re-arrange beds, stretchering patients from one ward to another so that in the wards to be inspected the patients could sit up to attention. Those, that is, who couldn't stand to attention at

their bed ends. There was no time at all to do anything else but respond to the bawling of N.C.O's and the irritated shouts of matrons, sisters and nurses.

We are at everybody's beck and call and are ordered to do all tasks outside of simply treating the patients as nurses would. You name it, we did it. From shaving and washing those who couldn't shift for themselves, to serving meals, from breakfast to the bread and cheese and cocoa that was given at supper time, and in between we carried the bedpans and bottles to the sluice room.

In the week of the inspection we were instructed to see to it that the more 'unattractive' wounded were moved out of sight. I mean those with bodies completely covered with burns or multiple amputees and those poor unfortunate souls whose faces were so disfigured they gave you nightmares. These were men of course who were now getting the best treatment available or were convalescing. They had already spent days or weeks in much less well equipped hospitals in France and Belgium.

Friday 12 November 1915

Forty new men came into our unit last Saturday so the work load has lightened and we are having an easier time. In the evening I went with one or two others and a handful of walking wounded to the house of one of the friends of the hospital where we had tea and were entertained by the lady of the house playing the piano.

Sunday 21 November 1915

This last week has been very busy again. The hospital has suddenly filled up and ambulances have been arriving from the docks and they have been collecting patients who have arrived by train from the south. In the ward I am working in there are forty beds. They are all full and we have seven patients on stretchers on the floor. The reason for the rush is that hospitals in France are evacuating patients home to make room for new casualties from the western front.

I had to queue for inoculation again last Sunday. I felt well enough however to go to a party on Tuesday at the house of some people from Crosby. There is no end to the generosity and hospitality of people around here.

Saturday 27 November 1915

We all had a second inoculation today and the notion of the pin cushion comes to mind. It is supposed to be a booster. Sometimes we are not told what it's for. I think this one was a second anti-tetanus injection and we were warned we might get a reaction.

Wednesday 1 December 1915

The reaction didn't come until a day or so later and we all went down with sore throats and high temperatures. But it didn't take long for us to recover. Shortly afterwards we were inspected by an R.A.M.C. brass-hat, Colonel Johnstone. It was a full kit inspection and its purpose was, I suppose, to check that we still had what we had been issued with. By the end of the week we'd been issued with new kit.

Friday 3 December 1915

I drew 8 shillings and was given, like the others, another suit of khaki. I don't think it was my imagination but it did not seem of the same quality as previous issue. I didn't have time to think too much about that because half of us went down with very bad colds that confined us to barracks, croaking and coughing and not feeling very well at all.

Thursday 9 December 1915

An officer came to the barracks, lined us up and told us that we were to prepare for active service overseas. I could hardly get to the latrine never mind France. But then, as if by magic, in the afternoon we were all feeling better and beginning already to take on the role of soldiers bound for the front line.

Friday 10 December 1915

Drew 8 shillings and as we lined up for the pay parade, it began to snow outside. By dinner time it was inches thick. On the wards it was warm and cosy and we saw that it would stay that way by keeping the stoves and open fires well supplied with coke and coal.

A few of us who'd been working on the ward, including patients who could walk and were recovering, were invited to what we thought was going to be another ordinary party. We were told that a lorry was to be sent for us, that is eight of us orderlies to supervise twelve patients, making a group of twenty. We drove out of the hospital in the snow to somewhere just outside Crosby.

We arrived at the drive entrance of a very big house in its own grounds. The front of the house was all lit up with lights in every window. In the drive motors were parked for the whole of its length and those chauffeurs not sitting in the cabs of their motors were having a smoke by the pillars of the great entrance gates, their cigarette-ends glowing in the dark.

We were driven round by following signs to the 'tradesman's entrance' where the kitchen was. At the door of the kitchen, standing in the light of the kitchen lamps, were the housekeeper and the cook. We got down from the lorry and stamping the snow from our boots, wiping them on the mat, we were ushered into an enormous country house kitchen. We took off our caps, greatcoats and gloves and were told to sit down at a long pine table with chairs on either side.

The kitchen, with the electric light shining on copper pans and cooking implements, was dominated by a great black-leaded stove that ran almost the length of the room. Behind bars in its front was a glowing red fire that made the kitchen very cosy.

The cook and the housekeeper were accompanied by two young scullery maids and the cook said to us, in what I thought was an Irish brogue, 'Who likes fried eggs and potatoes?' With almost one voice we said, 'Yes, we all do'. One of the patients, looking very smart in his red tie, white shirt, and blue serge 'wounded uniform', confided in me that the invite had come from the wife of a big Liverpool ship owner and that this was their house. She came to the hospital with her Liverpool society friends and did voluntary work. He was one of the lucky ones she visited.

The two girls began to lay the table with plates, knives and forks and salt and vinegar and sugar for the great mugs of tea that was also brewed. 'I've seen to it that a drop of rum has gone into that', said the housekeeper. She seemed to be supervising the whole affair.

As we drank the strong rum flavoured tea the cook began to break eggs into a great circular frying pan and we could hear at the same time the potatoes sizzling in the oven. Within minutes there was a tray of beautiful white and yellow eggs on the table, accompanied by a pan of golden brown sliced potatoes. Then thick slices of white bread, 'baked fresh today', were spread with real butter. 'Fill your boots', said the wounded one and we began to tuck in. 'Don't stand on ceremony', said the cook, red and perspiring 'from the stove', 'Make sandwiches if you like and there's plenty more where that came from'.

With melting butter dripping down our fingers we closed the half-inch-thick slices of bread over eggs and hot potato slices; what a feast. I don't think I have ever since then eaten so many eggs and drank so much tea at one sitting. I think I ate five eggs. As our feasting drew to its close the housekeeper, cook and scullery maids sat down with us and had more moderate helpings. The housekeeper made sure, as they did this, that the two young scullery maids were not too familiar with us. They were pretty shy little things of about thirteen and had to be protected from nasty soldiers like us.

Just as we were clearing up and in spite of protests we helped with the washing up, the door to the kitchen opened and there in evening dress was our host and his wife with two small children, a boy and a girl, at their side. 'Well lads', he said, in, to my surprise the accent of Liverpool, 'have you eaten your fill?'. We thanked them both in chorus. Then, as if already prepared, the children divided us into two groups and gave each of us a half crown. Turning to leave, the family said altogether, 'We all hope you have a very Happy Christmas and you come through safe in the New Year'. Our hostess then said, pointing to the wounded as if counting them, 'and I'll see you back at the hospital'. She had a beautiful smile and was dressed in a frock that looked like silver thread, and she had a jewelled band round her hair, high on her head.

We got our coats and hats and said our thanks and farewells, reluctant to leave the cosy warmth of the kitchen. We all climbed on the lorry and as it drove down the back drive we saw half a dozen of the chauffeurs trudging through the snow, obviously making for the kitchen. I thought that in the ordinary course of events, when they drove their employers to such a dinner party that they usually passed their time in the kitchen. For this evening we had taken their place. Within six months I bet they would be in khaki like us.

As we drove back to the hospital we were in high spirits and sang a number of variations on the chorus of 'It was Christmas Day in the workhouse'.

> It was Christmas Day in the hareem, the eunuchs were standing there,
> Watching the vestal virgins combing their long fair hair
> When along came the Bold Bad Sultan and shouted down the halls.
> He said 'What do you want for Christmas?'
> And the eunuch's reply was:
> 'O glad tidings of comfort and joy, comfort and joy,
> O glad tidings of comfort and joy'.

Wednesday 15 December 1915

We were paraded after breakfast and told that we were to be taken by electric tram to Bootle Town Hall where our job was helping to examine recruits waiting there for a medical. When we arrived we found a large motley crew of civilians milling about. In spite of the fact that most of us had been in the army less than six months we were much superior in our uniforms. With our 'soldierly manner' we ordered them into lines and supervised them undressing down to their underwear, seeing to it that they arranged their boots, shoes and clothes tidily.

They were Derby recruits, the last volunteers. (Before the conscription that was to be introduced in 1916.) This was to be Derby's army after Kitchener's army. Lord Derby, a rich Liverpool 'toff', paid for the equipping of thousands of new recruits and he even had the idea of recruiting under-sized men into the army. Such men were usually rejected because of their stature. He formed units that were called 'Bantam Battalions'. We used to say, rather unkindly I am afraid, 'they can't fight and they can't lay eggs'. The 'Derby Scheme' had been introduced to 'gee up' flagging recruitment figures that were not surprising in the light of casualty numbers and that the war had lasted well beyond the Christmas it was supposed to be over by.

When we had finished with the Derby recruits it was our turn. We were given a simple medical examination and all passed fit for active service. We then filed into a room, dark because of drawn curtains, as we were to be given a talk illustrated by lantern slides on 'personal' hygiene. It was a bit like the chapter on 'Beastliness' in Baden–Powell's 'Scouting for Boys'. That was followed by a lecture on venereal disease. The illustrations, the talk and the warnings in it were enough to put you off women for life and especially French women who, it was said, did not wear underwear. I wondered if I would ever find out for myself.

From Bootle, as I had already packed, I went with others straight to Liverpool to catch 'leave trains'. I caught the train to Manchester and was to change for Halifax. It was to be the last long weekend home leave for sometime. I was disappointed that it was not to be for Christmas but vowed to make the best of it.

I was home a bit earlier this time and as I got out of the station at Mythholmroyd the weather was wintery but bright and clear. Mother and my sisters Phyllis and Maud were waiting for me in the forecourt and they took me home for a good tea. Then it was boots off in front of the fire to recount my adventures before going up for a welcome night's sleep.

Thursday 16 December 1915

Woke up to a day of nice weather and to the post which brought a letter from Tom to tell us that he had just sailed for Egypt. We learned later that he had sailed from Devonport on the 14th December in the troop ship 'Minneapolis'. Tom was in the 13th Battalion East Yorkshire Regiment, having volunteered for the 'Hull Pals' Regiment in 1914. We all spent a lazy morning in front of the fire and then after dinner we, Phyllis, Maud and myself, had a very enjoyable rest of the day rambling up as far as Heptonstall moors.

Friday 17 December 1915

I spent the weekend on visits backwards and forwards to Halifax buying things I thought I might need when I went abroad. I bought a very good Sheffield made clasp-knife with a cork screw, bottle opener, tin opener and long sharp blade, it was better than the one we were issued with. I bought a new razor that unscrewed into pieces and fitted into a small cylinder with a dozen packets of blades. I would still keep my old faithful cut-throat razor that I had inherited from my paternal grandfather but it always frightened everybody to death when I used it. Along with these things I bought a stout pair of leather gloves and a large leather wallet with a stout brass clip. I bought the girls some scent and a silver photo frame for Mother. On the Saturday I cleaned and greased the bike and stored it away in the out-house next to the lavatory and in the evening went into Halifax with Phyllis to a concert in the Y.M.C.A. Hall. There was a local male voice choir and a women soloist who led the audience in community singing.

Phyliss had told Tilly, the girl I had met on my last leave that I was home and she came to the concert. After the concert as she had sat next to me I was bold enough (unusual for me) to ask if I, could walk her home. Phyliss went on with two of her friends. As we walked up the hill she talked about the work she did and about her living with her Gran on her own. On her doorstep as we said good night she said that she was going to 'adopt' me. She had seen that idea suggested in a newspaper, 'Adopt your own soldier.' and as she said this she leaned forward and kissed me on the cheek. I left her standing at her door. She was very pretty and I fell for her straightaway. As I reached the road I shouted 'Happy Christmas' and a promise that I would write to her.

Sunday was very fine, cold but with a blue sky, and Mother told us to go out for a ramble so that she could cook the dinner. The three of us, Phyllis, Maud, and myself, went right up to Cold Edge Dams where there was still lots of snow on the high ground. When we returned home Mother had cooked a 'Christmas Dinner' with roast pork and all the trimmings. She had also put up paper chains across the kitchen and there was a decorated Christmas tree on a small round table in the window. She was, of course, very disappointed that I wasn't staying home for Christmas. Round the table I gave out my Christmas presents and got in return presents of a thick hand-knitted pullover and thick woollen socks.

As the night darkened we sat in front of the fire-light and the four of us reflected on how the war seemed to have changed so much for us just when things were going so well. Dad was still in Hull, Tom was in Egypt and I would soon be away in France. We felt just a little bit miserable.

We didn't stay unhappy for long as all together we took a brisk walk to Luddenden Foot church for advent evensong where we heard the vicar talk about the approaching goodwill season. Goodwill for everyone, of course, except the Germans. We finished the service singing advent carols and as we left Mother asked me if I still went to church while I was away and I assured her that we had regular church parades and that there would be church services in France.

Monday 20 December 1915

After saying goodbye to Mother and the girls I asked them to say goodbye for me to Tilly. Then I left very early and returned to Liverpool via Manchester where 13 shillings and 9 pence was waiting for me as pay. It snowed again and the cold and grey skies were in tune with my mood. I was much down at leaving home after my short leave but then some of my fellow barrack room comrades told me how lucky I'd been. There was supposed to be a four day embarkation leave entitlement for everybody but it had been withdrawn except for a 'chosen few'.

Tuesday 21 December 1915

After a very good breakfast of bacon, bread and tea we paraded for full kit and equipment inspection and we were passed as a full R.A.M.C. Field Ambulance.
After dinner we went in a group to a Christmas concert at the Gladstone Wesleyan club. The club was decorated for Christmas with a tree and all the trimmings. We sang carols and listened to a girls choir. It looks like being a white Christmas.

All this week we have been training and practising the application of wound dressings on each other. The different responsibilities we have are being impressed upon us. The importance of speed in the evacuation of the wounded. We are told that we have to be aware of the different chains of command in Regimental Aid Posts and how in dressing stations we must do just that, not treat the wounded. The casualty clearing station has that responsibility. The senior medical officer made us feel quite important as life savers and also how much we will be appreciated if we can provide simple comforts like cigarettes and cups of tea. I have an advantage in this as I don't smoke so I always save any cigarette gifts that I get from friends. This I find in the future reaps all sorts of benefits.

We have had a series of lectures on fleas and lice and the importance of protecting medical and food supplies from vermin and flies. As far as I can see the only way of doing anything about lice is to burn everything in sight. We were shown pictures of a de-lousing steamer. Clothes and uniforms were placed inside. It got up steam and then in theory the lice were killed. We discovered in France that the lice seemed to be almost fire-proof and certainly steam-proof.

On Thursday evening we were invited to a concert at Waterloo Town Hall, Crosby. There were lots of good songs and traditional carols and after the mince pies and tea that we were treated to, lots of handshaking, back-slapping and wishes of good luck.

Friday 24 December 1915

We had a very good Christmas tea in the afternoon with mounds of sandwiches supplemented by Christmas cake that the cook-house had made and even topped with a piece of holly. One of our number had received a packet of crackers from home and these were pulled with great ceremony. In the evening I was one of a very small number who went to church for Christmas Eve service. I knew that Mother would approve.

Saturday 25 December 1915 (Christmas Day)

Again knowing it would make Mother happy I went to Holy Communion. I had breakfast at Sand Dunes, our new convalescent home. It was a Christmas Day breakfast of scrambled eggs, toast, marmalade and tea. We ate ours after we had served the men in three of the wards.

The rest of the morning was spent in showing visitors round. It was a pleasant and profitable task being able to tell mothers, fathers, brothers and sisters, wives and sweethearts how well their boys were doing and then trying to cheer up the patients who neither expected nor received any visitors at all. Either they didn't have any family or their relatives lived too far away. Usually patients found themselves in hospitals as far as eighty to a hundred miles away from home and some families just could not afford the fare.

In the afternoon in the canteen we had a first class Christmas dinner of turkey, sausages and roast pork followed by Christmas pudding. We then went back into the convalescent

home for a sing song with the patients and nurses at Sand Dunes. That had hardly finished when it was time for a Christmas tea of mince pies, Christmas cake with sweets and chocolate. We went round the wards in party hats distributing these 'goodies' and we came across a group of nurses secretly sharing a bottle of sherry with some of the medical officers in one of the rooms off a ward. It being Christmas they deigned to wish us the compliments of the season.

Sunday 26 December 1915 (Boxing Day)

I had no duties at the convalescent home so I had a run down in the train to Northern Hospital to visit one of my old patients from Seaforth. He had lost two fingers from his right hand and there had been some dispute as to whether it had been a self-inflicted wound. Had he been accused of this it would have been very serious as it happened on active service. Lucky for him that one of his N.C.O's had been able to vouch for him and to testify that the steel door of an armoury had closed on his hand 'in the line of duty'. He was well on the mend and out of it completely, for which he had a considerable conscience. He never intended that his army service should end as it did. In the evening I attended a Church Army service which was much more informal than the services I was used to.

Monday 27 December 1915

I have had another busy week of drills, practices, training and lectures. I am feeling very fit with all the exercise. The food continues to be very good and many of my comrades have not eaten so well in all their lives. One of the recent recruits to our R.A.M.C. had been considered under weight at his enlistment. He has put on two stone and he is thinking of asking for a transfer to an infantry regiment. He told me that he was from the slums of Sheffield. A one up and one down house with six taps in the yard for twelve families, and six earth closets for the same. 'This is the first time in my life I've had three meals a day, I often went to bed having eaten only a piece of bread and dripping all day. We never had any money. My father worked in a foundry and blanked his wages up against the wall every Saturday night. I'm living like a fighting cock in the army', he said. He did get his transfer, to the Royal Artillery, and I heard that he was killed a few months later.

Friday 31 December 1915 (New Year's Eve)

I drew 10 and sixpence and after a tea, at which I shared a cake my Mother had sent me for Christmas, I went to a New Year's Eve concert at Waterloo Town Hall where the local Police band played all the latest songs. Afterwards their conductor, a fat, jolly man with a big moustache, led everyone in the hall in a rousing 'Auld Lang Syne'.

We saw the New Year in as we listened to town clocks striking midnight.

Saturday 1 January 1916 (New Year's Day)

The war was already eighteen months old and there seemed no end to it in sight. Within a few weeks I would be on the 'Western Front' in France seeing who knows how many New Years in.

The New Year started well for me. I got a personal congratulation from the matron for the work I had done with records and forms. It was a cushy number working in the office as I did from time to time. But sometimes the patient details I had to record were heartbreaking, simple and drastic amputation of limbs, operations on the face, removal of eyes, devastating wounds of the chest and abdomen and sometime operations that rob some young soldier of his manhood. All this I had to painstakingly list in pencil so that it could be altered and doctored. I had to write the time and date when some mother's son 'died of wounds in action'. Then there was the business of preparing the telegram, letter or message for the next of kin. I went from this, glad to be alive, to an entertaining evening again at Waterloo Town Hall and then on Thursday to Crosby Camp, where I was invited to play the cuckoo in a Toy Symphony that was performed. It was great fun.

Friday 7 January 1916

There is much preparation taking place for an entertainment. It is a 'do' that the officers and nurses are giving for us and those walking wounded who can make it. The canteen was transformed into a little music hall with a stage on trestles at one end. We filed in and on each table there were sandwiches of various fillings, pastries, buns and cake. That was served later with tea and, as a special treat, a bottle of beer. My tee-total principles were beginning to become more flexible. Though I had never joined the band of hope or signed the pledge, I drank very little. My attitudes towards drink had been encouraged by my Mother's tales of families totally destroyed by drunken fathers who spent all their wages on beer and then came home and beat their wives and children.
The entertainment was hilarious and some of the officers by their performances would have made more successful musical hall artistes. There was one act where a young officer impersonated one of the 'battle-axe' matrons. That brought the house down. It was perhaps as well, given the performance and our reception of it, that we were leaving altogether the next day. We were informed that our destination was Chester.

Saturday 8 January 1916

We arrived by train at Chester and the weather was splendid. It did not take us long to settle in and there was a good dinner waiting for us.

Sunday 9 January 1916

There was church parade with the 10th Cheshire Regiment. It seemed to me to be more of a military occasion than a religious one.

I had a fine afternoon off with one of my mates and we spent it boating on the Dee and then went for a pleasant stroll around the castle walls. This is a splendid old town and if circumstances were different I would have liked to have stayed here for a month or two. I am certainly getting out and about with the army and I must say enjoying myself.

We were billeted in a gymnasium in the castle overlooking the river. We put mattresses on the floor and were warm and comfortable. There were good clean ablutions plus good cooking facilities so we were well fixed up. We got out after hours very easily and we learned during our adventures a few good songs plus, appropriately, 'Rolling home'. Our pleasant stay was short lived for by Tuesday we were very busy changing kit, passing inspections and preparing to leave for London and then Aldershot.

Wednesday 12 January 1916

We arrived in Aldershot well and truly in the proper Army and we joined with 'C' company in Barosa barracks.

Aldershot is certainly the Army's town. It is full of Red-Caps, watching for deserters and defaulters, and patrolling the streets on the look-out for the drunken and brawling soldiery. As you might expect it was over-flowing with soldiers of every regiment-regulars, territorials and 'Kitchener's Pals'. It is not a pleasant place after Liverpool and Chester.

Friday 21 January 1916

The rumour was rife among the soldiers we met that something big was coming up in France. It was going to be a push so big that it would put the Germans on the run and end the inaction on the western front. One of the things that I really disliked about the army was that nobody told you anything. You could not rely on the papers and you could not rely on the gossip you heard as some of it was frankly fantastic.

Although it has been a dull wet week we have enjoyed some good route marches and plenty of opportunity to play and watch football.

After church parade on Sunday 23rd I had a walk to Farnborough I found a place to have tea. It was a bit more expensive than Liverpool but with delicious scones which I was assured by a pretty waitress had been made in the shop. While I sat at the table I wrote a letter to Tilly and told her again how much I had enjoyed meeting her. I told her I was being posted but could not tell her what was happening or where I was going.

CHAPTER 2 - TO FRANCE

Wednesday 26 January 1916

After breakfast we paraded to hand in spare kit. We are definitely sailing for France sometime today. We had a dinner of cold bully beef and bread which a regular Sergeant in the Warwicks, who was going with us to rejoin his unit, told us we would have to get used to (thankfully the tea was hot).

We marched to the station in Aldershot and then entrained for Southampton. From the railway station we marched to the dockside and embarked up the gang-plank of a troop ship at 5 p.m.

Within half an hour we sailed away from Southampton and I went up on deck when I was sure I had a space to sleep in that was warm and not too cramped. It was already dark and there were searchlights sweeping the Solent so that I could see naval craft making bow-waves as they passed us with hoots and whistles. As we got out to sea there was still a lot of traffic and a much bigger troop ship steamed ahead, with surprisingly all its lights ablaze, and passing us in the opposite direction I could see the small shape of a submarine on the surface.

I must say I went down below deck in an excellent mood, to eat the bread and cheese and hot cocoa the cooks passed around. I was sailing to France.

Thursday 27 January 1916

I woke up in the cramped space that I had managed to procure for myself the night before and I'd had some sleep but mostly it had been a disturbed night. This had been due to some noisy squaddies who had played crown and anchor well into the early hours. As the N.C.O. that should have disciplined them was one of the players there was no hope of quietening them down.

Washing and performing basic ablutions was uncomfortable. I had got up early deliberately to avoid the rush. When I got to the 'heads' as we experienced seafarers call the latrines, I found that although the crossing had been fairly calm there had been what you might call careless seasickness. The washroom and the aforementioned 'heads' had been left in quite a mess. I washed, shaved and communed with nature as quickly as I could and then I beat a hasty retreat to the mess room for breakfast in case I was ordered to play a part in the cleaning up.

After a breakfast of good strong hot coffee and bread and jam I went on deck to observe our passage into the French port of Le Havre and then into the river Seine. The river looked lovely in the fine sunshine as we steamed into the channel. I looked over the ship's rails and got cheery waves from the bargees steering vessels that were much bigger than any barge I had seen on the Humber at home. They looked very fat and French with their berets, black waist coats and moustaches. On board with them they had those, I suppose, who were their wives and children, next to them in the wheelhouse or on deck. They signalled their welcome too.

We arrived at the dock in Rouen at 9 a.m. and after collecting kit, we were paraded for a roll call in case any of us had fallen overboard in the night. Then we marched down the gang plank to the sound of a French military band on the quay playing by turns the Marseillaise and God save the King. Once on the quay, we were lined up in squads and by the left marched to a camp that we were to find was in one of the general hospitals, organised just outside the town. It was in all senses a camp. There were rows and rows of bell tents. Inside each tent were twelve stretcher beds arranged like the numbers on a clock. Our feet were to be towards the centre. We spent some time bumping into each other and there was some good natured banter as we stowed our kit. As we had no duties allocated to us the majority lay down to catch up with last night's lost sleep.

After dinner, served in our mess tins at a field cooker also under canvas, we were told to gather round so that the plans for the next day could be described to us. We were advised to get some rest as a long march was before us. We were not allowed out of the camp to go into Rouen.

Friday 28 January 1916

Last night was my first night under canvas and in spite of the cold I slept well on a soft mattress with extra blankets thrown in just before lights out at ten. The night's sleep however could have been completely spoiled had the majority of my canvas-covered comrades been unsuccessful in persuading one of our number from relieving himself by his bed, in the tent. I am beginning to discover that my general personal habits and table manners are very different from those of some of my fellow soldiers. I don't know why, we all seem to be of the same 'ordered estate'.

We got up to breakfast and then, with our kit stowed in the ambulances, formed fours for a route march. We were lucky in that it was a fine day. Marching in a very military fashion, our horse drawn ambulances and hand pushed wheel stretchers rolling behind, we made our way out of the town and passed members of the local population on the pavements who cheered us with shouts of 'hello Tommy' and 'vive les anglais'. I don't know about the others but I felt quite the conquering hero, and would not have been surprised had roses been strewn in my path and pretty girls run alongside to kiss me on the cheek.

With our brisk step we soon left the town precincts and moved into the countryside to

38

the edges of a grand forest. Our N.C.Os encouraged us to sing and it was not long before we struck up with 'It's the wrong way to tickle Mary' (a variation on the better know Tipperary} and 'Pack up your troubles'.

When we stopped after what seemed like an age there was dinner waiting for us at a field kitchen already set up ahead of us. It was to be our first taste of Maconochie's Irish stew
After the miles we had walked since breakfast it tasted delicious whatever its previous reputation. I ate two mess tins full.

We marched on through the forest on a well paved road. We sang to the great oaks, beeches and elms whose tops overhung the road like green leafy umbrellas, and managed only to frighten the birds. The forest was thick with trees and undergrowth and there wasn't a soul to hear the noise of our tramping feet except I suppose timid, wild, woodland creatures watching our passage through the leaves and branches with trepidation. The forest went on for miles.

As our progress went on the march began to take its toll, as a number of my comrades began to fall-out with blisters due to ill-fitting or new stiff leather boots. Not enough attention is paid to a soldier's feet, I decided. Napoleon said that an army marches on its stomach. It's true it does, after it has marched on its feet. I was ordered to form a team to treat those who had fallen by the wayside. I took an ambulance and collected them all in one place on the grass beside the road. The blisters some had went from their toes along the soles of their feet to their heels. In most cases the blisters had already broken and the only treatment available was bathing with a solution of bicarbonate of soda.

We dressed the feet of the half dozen concerned, put them in the ambulance and then caught up with the column. I had to make a report on each casualty as bad feet were often used, I was warned, as a reason by malingerers for being excused duties. None of the lads I saw were putting it on.

We caught up with the column just as the cooks with their kitchen were preparing the evening meal. It was the same menu as at mid-day and just as welcome. We passed the evening looking over the work some pioneers had done who had come up with the cooks. They had prepared a very tidy wash house and latrines for the use of, and pitched our tents. They had obviously been concerned for our comfort. We bedded down for the night, once again under canvas, but exhausted as we were, there was little that could have disturbed us.

Thursday 3 February 1916

We have been here two days after completing our march through the forest. We have spent a busy time preparing roads in what is a military camp that is in the process of construction and extension. It is a rail-head on a branch line from the main stations near the front. We are still under canvas but much of the camp is made up of wooden and tarpaper huts. While here we went to a gas training section where we were issued with gas helmets that were no more than canvas hoods with goggles in them. We have had to experience a gas attack of chlorine. The blokes in charge said that if we could survive being in the cloud we would be able to survive a gas attack in the field for it was five times the concentration of that usually laid down. We were pushed one by one through a door into a tunnel full of a grey-green fog. The problem wasn't breathing but seeing. I stumbled along, bumping into others, until a few of us joined up and placed our right hand on the right shoulder of the one in front, and that way we filed out of the tunnel to the door at the other end. We were instructed when we emerged to take off the gas helmets and to do the same again, but this time with a wet pad across our mouths. When the gas was first met with, in the spring of 1915 victims had been advised to urinate on gauze as this could prevent the worst effects of the gas. We all thought that it was the urine that helped but it was the fact that the gas chlorine was soluble in water. When we went back in we ran through the thinner cloud as we knew the way. At the end of the exercise we were issued with the helmets along with a gas cape and a sheepskin tabard and after collecting our other kit we entrained at the rail-head climbing into the horse boxes that were to carry us. We did this while holding sandwiches of bully. This was our meal for the night. We are to join the 4th Division of regulars 'somewhere up the line'.

Friday 4 February 1916

We passed the night in the train fairly comfortably, although I got a bit fed up with the blue fug that was generated by the smokers. We were rocked to sleep as the train chugged slowly up to Amiens, then to Albert and eventually we stopped at Acheux. The weather was dull but we were excited and happy enough on the train, having popped out for refreshments at one or two of the many stops the train made on its journey. I had my first hot French coffee and, daring though it was, a French beer. I even managed to order a coffee and cognac which helped me to sleep in the cramped and smoky truck.

We got off the train at Acheux which is in Picardy, in the Somme region of France, and from there after the light refreshment of hot tea and sandwiches we marched to a little village called Forceville. The march to Forceville took us, with a couple of stops, until nightfall. As it got dark we could see flares and flashes above the horizon over what we supposed was the Front Line. There were a number of bangs and thuds as if in a thunder storm but they were a long way off.

We were marched off the road at our destination into an old barn where the floor was covered in dry straw and we settled in and then prepared the cold army rations that were on offer for supper. We had been told not to make a fire, but our yearning for a hot mug of tea over-ruled our duty to orders. Using bits of wood prised from the walls we managed to make a blaze that warmed up mess tins filled from a well in the yard outside, and with a sprinkle of tea we made a brew. Even cold army rations of bully and biscuit taste better washed down with tea, even if it is only wet and warm. We doused the fire just in time as the duty officer came on his rounds. If only a little comforted we burrowed down into the dry straw and turned in for the night.

Saturday 5 February 1916

We are now attached to the 12th Field Ambulance and we are to assist in the setting up of an ambulance station at Forceville. The division we are to be supporting is made up of regiments including the Warwicks, The Lancashire Fusiliers, The Somerset Light Infantry and the Rifle Brigade, as, having done its stint, it is preparing to leave the line.

Monday 7 February 1916

I drew my first pay in French francs today. 20F. We are having a good time. After church parade yesterday I walked around the village. It is very dirty and neglected. The houses are mostly open and show evidence that their occupants have not long left. The countryside around is well wooded and cultivated and must have been considered good farm land before the war. We are about five miles behind what is a fairly quiet part of the line that we have only recently taken over from the French. Their troops have moved south, it seems.

I have heard that the Zeppelins have been busy again in England and they have bombed Paris. Hull has had another raid and London has been hit.

The evidence we see of the war where we are is in the air. We spend many a happy hour watching, fascinated, as aircraft fly over head. We have no idea whether they are 'ours' or 'theirs'. There have been one or two casualties for our Field Ambulance but nothing serious as far as numbers are concerned. As for the casualties they are 'wished for', 'Blighty ones'. The casualties we have had have been sustained in daylight and night-raids on the German trenches. Their purpose is to find out enemy strength and to discover whether Fritzy has any plans to attack us.

This part of the Line has been even quieter than it is now. It is rumoured that when the French occupied it they had cows for fresh milk and grew vegetables in plots near their trenches. 'Those days have gone'. This was the declaration of a Brigadier who gave our Infantry comrades a good talking to after the last church parade. The British Army would be much more aggressive, or 'he would know the reason why'.

Tuesday 8 February 1916

We were formed up after breakfast today and as we had been warned earlier we were marched for about seven or eight miles to the village of Comines where we were instructed to set up another Field Ambulance. Comines is in another French department (this is what the French call their 'counties'). It is in the Pas de Calais.

We marched along in good spirits and for miles, sang and chanted. Someone at the front would shout out 'Hip hip hooray, today's my daughter's wedding day, ten thousand pounds I'll give away'. The rest of us would shout out 'good for you, good for you, and I'll have a share' 'Is there a few quid for my dear old Mother?'. There would be another half a mile of silence except for the tramp of marching boots, then from the front again would come the cry 'on second thoughts I think it best, to lock it up in an old oak chest'. The replies to that would vary from 'You stingy old bugger' to more obscene descriptions of his miserliness. The bond felt in such circumstances between you and your fellows convinced you that anything that was chucked at you could be dealt with. Even driving snow, rain and hail did not lower your spirits.

When we got to Comin we found a much cleaner village. It was set on a hill at the edge of a wood in which were flowers that looked like daffodils and wild primroses.

As soon as we got to the place where we were going to lodge we set about making the old barn, that was to be our billet as comfortable as we could. We blocked up holes in the wall and fixed doors so that they would close. We even dispatched one of our more diminutive comrades up onto the snow covered roof to fix the tiles.

We spent the rest of the week on drills which warmed us up. There were route marches and fatigue duties. These mostly occupied us with the repair of pot holes in the roads in and around the village. It snowed heavily all the week and the temperature dropped to freezing every night. We woke up each morning to find our boots frozen and the water that had flooded the lower part of the barn was thick ice. After a quick swill and shave in icy water we were more than ready for the hot breakfast that the cooks make up for us. The steaming hot porridge and good bread with whatever jam going, goes down nicely with the scalding hot tea that, although it tastes of a purification process, is still more than acceptable.

Sunday 20 February 1916

At last we woke to a fine sunny morning and it has not rained for a week. The work we did repairing the roads has all been undone as they have been churned back to mud by lines of convoy traffic. In this week we were given a new style of pack. It is heavier but more comfortable to carry than the old bandoleer type.

I took time off and got a lift into Acheux to buy a present for Mother. I bought her a nice embroidered shawl that I could post in a big envelope. I bought a coloured postcard to send to Tilly. It was in French with a picture on it of a soldier embracing his sweetheart.

Friday 25 February 1916

I have just had a letter from Phyllis and Maud in Halifax to tell me that Mother has died suddenly, after a short illness. It is so unexpected. I did not know that she was ill. I only remember that she once complained of pains in her chest. I don't know what to do. When I asked for special leave, I was almost laughed at, until I told the M.O. what the reason was, but it was still refused. I have no one to turn to. My dear Mother has gone. I cannot believe it. She never got the present I sent her.

Sunday 27 February 1916

I have spent the last day or so in complete confusion. I am at my wits end. I attended communion in the village school and after it talked to the Chaplain. I wouldn't say he was unsympathetic but he seemed mesmerized by the death and destruction he had already seen. He kept talking of all the mothers' sons who had gone, as if there was some justice in a mother going. He seemed nervous and at the end of his tether. I left him as he said, 'Is all this really God's will?'. I went from him to seek out the Adjutant but did not get further than a Second Lieutenant who said that I would only get the refusal confirmed. Nobody was getting any leave at the moment, even on compassionate grounds. I am unhappy beyond description.

The country is deep in snow. The woods and trees around are dark and forbidding and their branches low with the weight of the snowfall. I can't even go for the walk that might clear my mind, as the roads are impassable. I wrote to Dad and to Phyllis and Maud but could not in the end put how I felt into words. I have never felt so miserable. I so much want to be home with my family. I wonder if Tom knows?

Saturday 4 March 1916

A week has passed but I have hardly noticed the work or the cold. My fellows do not speak to me beyond futile attempts to comfort me. Last night I wept as a lay down to sleep but I was left alone. I drew 20 Francs pay and if there was somewhere to go I think I would get drunk. The worse thing is not having been there to say goodbye to my dear Mother. Her funeral will have been held without me and her older boy Tom who I know, and my sisters knew, was the apple of her eye. What Dad must be going through, I don't know. They were devoted to each other like Derby and Joan.

CHAPTER 3 - THE SOMME

Sunday 5 March 1916

I went to church parade today but the feelings I had and the prayers I said were feeble in the light of the loss of my Mother.

We moved today to Haute Visée after a rough march along roads already showing evidence of shelling and through villages partially destroyed by artillery bombardment. It snowed hard with a wind behind it that drove it through our thick great-coats. We marched all day for about ten miles without a hot meal or even a hot drink so we had to make do with bully, biscuit and cold water. I felt more beat than at anytime since I joined. The march being over we are billeted about 2k from the market town of Doullens. We are in barns that we are expected to repair before we can occupy them. It was too late to start this when we arrived and so we as one fell into straw that was thick enough for us to remove the damp upper layer to get to the more or less dry stuff beneath. Luckily it did not snow that night. The sky was clear. It was fine but very, very cold. The cold made the stars that I could see through the broken rafters, sparkle like diamonds. I did not think on this for very long and like the rest soon dropped into an exhausted sleep.

Monday 6 March 1916

I awoke feeling terrible. I had a head-ache and most inconveniently, the runs. One of my mates took my temperature and it was 103. I had a very severe chill and joined the queue for sick parade and I feel that I only just made it into the temporary hospital set up in the empty village school. I was put in a bed in what must have been, in happier times, the main classroom. There were busts of classical heroes such as Caesar on a shelf around the wall. There was one space just marked with the name of Napoleon, but no bust. A pity, I thought, the French could do with someone like him at the moment.

Sunday 12 March 1916

After a week of clean sheets, hot drinks, bed rest and taking the powder I was recommended, I felt a lot better. It took a couple of days to get my temperature down and to cure the runs but I did not get the influenza I thought I was in for. But really I have no illusions, it is grief that has laid me low. By Wednesday I was still feeling weak and shaky but much brighter. Now I am back in the billet helping with the repairs that have not been finished, but it being warm and sunny as spring, it's not too much of a bad job.

We are moving closer up into action soon and have arrived at St Amand, which is only five miles behind the line. We are busy converting a large abandoned farm house into a hospital. For a change we are comfortably billeted in sturdy wooden huts that have canvas roofs. They have been set up in an orchard where in spite of the weather the apple blossoms are whitening the branches of the trees. I have been able to write home and I have replied to a letter from Maud telling me about the funeral and where Mother has been lain to rest. She is in the churchyard of Luddenden Foot. I know that she would have wanted to be in Hull but, as Maud said in her letter, the expense of that could not be borne even with the insurance that Mother had taken out to pay for her own funeral. I shall have to wait for my next leave to visit her resting place.

Thursday 23 March 1916

I am having to limit my diary writing to once a week because we are so busy. It is snowing again after three days of rain. We have been moved out of our huts in the orchard into large high, but thankfully dry, barns. For the first time since our arrival in France we have really come under fire. The aircraft we saw flying over our positions a short time ago must have been observing for Hun artillery, for in spite of the fact that our positions are well marked with red crosses German shells are landing close. Our barrack room expert on military affairs (every home should have one) told us not to worry as they were not after us but the infantry brigades of the 56th Division, located in positions around the village and towards Doullens. One or two of us wondered if that had been explained to the shells which came over, making sounds like giants tearing the air into shreds and then exploding deep in the ground and throwing up clods and clouds of earth and landing what we thought was blanketty close.

Sunday 26 March 1916

Although the weather is wet and cold I am much cheered by news from Tom that he has arrived in France from Egypt. He has come all the way from the South of France to the North by rail. He knows about Mother but Tom is not one to write his feelings down. He is with the 13th Battalion East Yorkshire Regiment and stationed not really very far away at a village called Beauquesne. I describe this to some of my mates and they tell me that there are two villages nearby called Humbercourt and Humbercamps. For a time I was kidded on that they were depots for the Hull Pals. They are actually the names of two French villages.

Friday 31 March 1916

Fritzy is certainly taking advantage of the fine weather for he has been shelling us on and off all week and it can be understood how distracting that can be. No sooner have you started some new aspect of work you have to keep your head down as a shell comes over like an express train going through a station. Today we were shelled for about two hours and I saw and treated my first war casualty. I went to the aid of a young infantry man from a London regiment who had been walking back from the canteen with a mess tin full of tea. A shell splinter sliced the calf of his left leg as if carved like a joint of lamb. The wound luckily was clean. No cloth from his uniform had been forced in and though it had cut through muscle, had not broken any bones: a real 'Blighty one'. I told him he would be taken to the rear and would probably be home in no time, but that disappointed him. He didn't want to be out of it before he had seen any action. I assured him that if that's what he wanted he would be as good as new in a few months and back in the line. The M.O. stitched him up and he was away to hospital by train in a hour.

Saturday 1 April 1916

The shelling has got worse, and with the help of the 1st / 5th Cheshire Pioneers, we are digging trenches and shelters in the chalky ground. German artillery seems to be bracketing the two villages of St Amand and its neighbour Souastre where there is a heavy concentration of troops of the 56th Division. So our expert was right.

All through the week to Sunday 9th April German guns continued to be busy but we take them in our stride and we are now able to gauge by their sound whether they are near or far. We are busying ourselves with the opening of a canteen which is going strong and has no shortage of customers.

Sunday 16 April 1916

I have not had time for church and there have been no parades that I could attend for quite a few Sundays. I have said that prayer I learned when reading about the history of the English Civil War. It is the prayer of a Parliamentarian going into battle 'I shall be busy this day, and may forget Thee, but do not Thou forget me'. It is fine and warm, truly spring, and today we move close to the Line. Myself and seven other stretcher bearers have moved up to the Advanced Dressing Station in the reserve line at Bienvilliers-au-Bois. The station is well equipped and well fortified, being half buried in a small mound. With the eight of us there are four regimental stretcher bearers.

Monday 17 April 1916

Although it has been fine during the day, so far at night it is bitterly cold. We move out of the station when it gets dark into a 'cushy little number' that we have arranged for ourselves in what is left of the old village bakehouse. We have a stove and plenty of wood stacked by the side of the oven. One of our number has scrounged some flour and yeast and has baked passable loaves which we slice while still hot and spread thickly with tinned butter and eat with slices of cheese toasted in the oven, or we cover the buttered bread with our supply of Tickler's plum and apple jam. I am informed that the Tickler's jam factory is situated across the river from us in Hull at Grimsby. We will get so fed up of Tickler's plum and apple that before long we consider communicating the information to the Zeppelin command so that a bomb can be dropped on the factory. During the week I went up to the trenches of the front line for the first time. It was raining but it was still a relief to be away from Ambulance Headquarters for a change. The trenches, including the firing trench, are all in good condition as they all are, for the most part, newly dug and the duck boards on the bottom of the trench keep your feet dry.

The village out of which you enter the first set of communication trenches is not much damaged, and there are still a few civilians selling food and drink from the front rooms of their houses. While I was on my way into the Front Line there was a disturbance in the street leading up to the trench entrance. I understood later that the cause of it was a protest from the family of a man who was taken away by the French Military Police. The man, it seemed, had been arrested because he was suspected of spotting for German artillery. There is as far as I can see a lot to target, a bombing school and a lot of high ranking brass hats milling about all the time. Certainly when Jerry opens up his aim is very accurate.

Sunday 23 April 1916

Today is the first dry day for a week. I am getting used to trench work and I enjoyed a trip up the Line a few days ago as a bearer whilst a detachment of Warwicks made a daylight raid. My job was to treat any possible casualties and with the rest of the squad with me, to carry them back to the clearing station. I gave out extra wound dressings and what were really, superfluous elementary instructions on how to use them. They had all been in France longer than I had. We wished them 'good luck' and I didn't envy them as, kitted out for the action, just young men like me, but infantry, they waited at the bottom of the scaling ladders leaning on the side of the trench, until a diversionary artillery barrage opened up about a mile down the Line. As soon as they heard the explosions they went over the top, or 'jumped the bags' as they described their climbing out of the firing line.

When they had all gone I was asked by a corporal standing by it if I wanted to watch through a trench periscope. I was told that I should be looking towards 'funky villages' (Foncquevillers)' and that a bit down from that position was the German strong-point Gommecourt. The object of the raid was to test the strength of that emplacement.

I could see through the scope what looked like shell damaged farm buildings, holes in the tiles and in the walls etc, but the largest area in view was a rise in the ground on the top of which was a big wood. Out of this suddenly erupted the flashes of all sorts of firing. The single shots of rifles, the sparking trails of mortar bombs and then firing from a number of sites of what I supposed was a complex system of machine guns. The Warwick trench raiders were in the open and about three hundred yards from the British trenches. I felt sure that they would all be killed in the hell that had broken loose but to my surprise the German fire seemed to be going over the heads of our men, as if it was a warning not to come any closer. I was brusquely pushed away from the periscope by a Warwicks officer who began to count out numbers and these were written down in a notebook by an N.C.O. standing at his side.

I heard a whistle go and a daylight flare went up. Within a few minutes the raiding party came running through a gap in the wire and they were counted in by the officer as they jumped in a heap in the bottom of the trench. Me and my squad had been steeling ourselves to the prospect of having to crawl out on top to fetch any wounded there might have been but to our relief we didn't have to. There were no casualties, thank God.

Everybody was in high spirits as we shared a dixie of hot tea that had been brought up. A sergeant went into a dug out and he emerged with a big rum jar. He poured a very liberal 'dash of rum' into the tea. We all dipped into the mixture with the enamel mugs that were passed to us and drank a good measure. I don't know about the others but I felt quite tipsy as I returned to our billet, not only from the rum but also from the excitement of the action. We left just in time, for Jerry began a very serious 'strafe' of that part of our line where the raiding party had obviously been observed as coming from.

Tuesday 25 April 1916

Some of the time I had spent in civvy street had been taken up with work as a drayman and delivery driver. I liked working with horses and horses seemed to like me, which one of the old drivers said was something that you couldn't teach. Horses either liked you or they didn't. He said if they did they would do anything for you. I became quite accomplished as a horse handler and I used to ride them out of the stables bare-back like the American Indians were said to do. I also used to get a ride when they were taken into the fields around Cottingham where they were allowed a rest, particularly the Hull Brewery horses I once worked with.

The M.O. heard of my expertise with horses and asked me if I would groom, feed and exercise his white mare. This relieved me of all my other duties. 'You jammy blankety' was the response of my associates.

The horse was not an army horse but the personal property of the M.O. He had had the horse shipped over from England, which as an officer was his entitlement. It was kept in a sandbagged stable that looked more secure than some of the dugouts I had been in. I was instructed to ride her and I rode backwards and forwards several times across the hills and valleys that were behind the line. She was lively and very fit. The tack, saddle, stirrups, etc., were of the highest quality and seemed little used.

One day I got a bit careless and a bit too close to the Line. I rode out in the open, down a road lined on both sides, with trees towards Souastre and I thought the trees would shield me from prying eyes. I thought myself for all the world like one of the cream of the army the 'Cavalry man'. In fact had I been A1 fit with two good eyes I might well have volunteered for a Cavalry Regiment. As I trotted from shadow into sunshine and back again I must have been observed by a Jerry artillery spotter. Fritz dropped a 'Jack

Johnson', that is, a shell that when it exploded caused a great blast and a tall black pillar of smoke. It landed a good thirty or forty yards from us and the trees took most of the blast but the mare, obviously not a war horse, baulked and then reared, almost throwing me.

She then set off at a lick, the bit between her teeth. She took charge and I couldn't control her. Luckily for me she galloped to the rear of the Line towards Humbercamps through Pommier. I was by turns riding on her neck, bum in the air, off the saddle like a grand national jockey, or holding a loose rein, boots out of the stirrups, legs all over the place I was more like the 'Galloping Major'. She careered down the road past a convoy of parked lorries whose drivers, leaning against the radiators of their vehicles having a smoke, jumped out of the way to avoid us. Over crossroads, narrowly missing supply carts and motor cycles, she galloped. As we rattled on pavé cobbles through the village of Pommier off duty squaddies had to leap out of the way, spilling the contents of their dinner-time mess tins. The obscene curses shouted at me were carried away on the wind.

At last after several miles behind the lines I managed to stop her. She stood just on the outskirts of the village of Humbercamps trembling all over, running with sweat, peeing and dropping her dung. I could say I felt like doing the same. It was then that I was made to realise what possible trouble I was in. A military policeman, a red-cap, signalled a colleague to stay by the road and he approached me, his hand on the holster of his side-arm. 'Where the blank do you think you're going?' he said. I breathlessly explained what had happened but my explanation went down like a 'lead zeppelin', as we used to say, for all he said was 'a likely blanketty story. I'm putting you under arrest on a charge of absenting yourself without leave from your unit and for good measure I'm going to charge you with stealing the blanketty horse. Now get down off that blanketty nag or I'll shoot you where you sit and save everybody a lot of blanketty trouble.'

I got down very nervously. I could not believe what had happened to me. I was under arrest for deserting and I knew that they shot you for that. These M.P.s were behind the lines looking for deserters and to stop soldiers leaving the line.

I took hold of the horse's rein, and with me leading it and them on either side, they began to escort me to their depot. We had not walked more than fifty yards when I had the most extraordinary bit of luck. Humbercamps was used by a Field Ambulance and a medical officer in the R.A.M.C. walked through the gate of a field straight into our path. Now, the branches of the army that there are always look after their own and he saw that I was in the same mob as him so he asked the M.P.s why and where they were taking me. The M.P. who had arrested me told my story and gave it an edge of scorn. The medical officer to his eternal credit and my salvation said authoritatively, 'Well we'll soon sort that out, I'll get on the blower to the officer concerned'. With that he walked back into the field while we waited and on a field telephone talked to my medical officer. Within a few minutes he was back having confirmed my story and I was released, much to the annoyance of my captors, and I mounted the horse again and set off back, this time at a walk.

When I told my comrades back in the billet they were unsympathetic. 'You were lucky they didn't put you up against a wall, we would have done'. The worst thing that came out of the episode was that I wasn't asked to look after the horse again.

Sunday 30 April 1916

We are having beautiful weather which has held since last week. Although I have had to turn out nearly every night because of alerts in the support trenches it has been a most enjoyable week. Spending nights in the trenches is, to some extent, uncomfortable but interesting and exciting nonetheless. Sleep was taken in a dug-out, not just long enough to sleep in but also it was dry. Wakened with a mess tin full of hot tea and rum me and my squad waited as support for regimental bearers in case a night time trench raid was planned. The nights were clear and full of stars. I remember that there was not even a pin-point of light showing and conversation was always in soft whispers. One night I was permitted again to look through the trench periscope. I saw to the north and east a star shell rising into the sky. It slowly fizzled its incandescent light out as it illuminated the whole of no-man's-land and the dense masses of wire entanglement. Then it was 'Ace of Spades' black again. It was hard to imagine that there were thousands of men out there carrying on their lives below ground like enormous colonies of moles.

Monday 1 May 1916

While I was doing my duty in the trenches last week the village has been shelled. Over three hundred shells have been counted but they have done little damage. Our Advanced Dressing Station has lost one man wounded by a spent bullet. It hit him in the back of the neck and had enough energy in it to penetrate just below the skin. It was easy to take out by cutting a small amount of the flesh of the neck and squeezing the offending missile out between two thumbs. There was hardly any blood and we quickly dressed the wound and gave him the bullet for a souvenir. That has left seven of us to move back to headquarters and when we arrived we found them preparing to move.

Tuesday 2 May 1916

After a beautiful May Day another French spring day of leaf bud and petal. The woods are green and full of wild flowers. We had a superb breakfast of fried eggs, bread and butter and tea made with untainted well water, all compliments of a very efficient field cooker. The inner man well satisfied we were marched to Leucheux, a lovely hamlet about fifteen miles from the line, just north east of Doullens. It is a pretty place, settled on the side of a deep valley near a small forest through which we marched in cheerful spirits singing or rather shouting to the tree tops. Just about everybody's boots are panned out and worn in. Feet are hardened and the M.O. has supervised a change of socks of which there is no shortage. When we get parcels from home, in amongst the cigarettes, tobacco, home made cake, biscuits, letters and copies of the local newspaper contained within them, there is, almost without exception, a pair of socks. They are usually hand knitted with love by a mother, auntie, wife, sister or sweetheart. My recently acquired pen-pal Tilly has sent me a pair she had bought in Halifax market. She told me in the first letter I got from her that she is not able to read or write so she has to have the letters she sends to me written by a friend, and the same friend reads my letters. She can't read, she can't write and now she can't knit. Her letters and parcels, however, are a treasure. As far as I am concerned I've got a 'sweetheart' who writes to me. I get letters from Tom, Ernest, Dad and the girls but to have a 'sweetheart' sending letters, even if she has to get somebody else to set her words down, bucks me up no end.

At Leucheux three clear streams flow through the well-cultivated valley and above the village is a Chateau which we are using as a hospital. In the chateau grounds stand the ruins of a twelfth century castle. The whole area is very picturesque and as yet untouched by the worst effects of the war.

Wednesday 3 May 1916

The fine weather continues. We are billeted again in wooden huts with canvas roofs and the stoves in them make us very comfortable. We are having an easy time. As I write I have brought my dinner of bully beef sandwiches and a bottle of cold tea and I sit with my back up against a tree to catch up on my diary and to read letters from home. I have sent embroidered post cards I bought in Acheux to the girls. They had pink roses and blue forget-me-nots with the words 'to my dear sisters' stitched around. To Tilly I sent one with red roses and green leaves that said in pink silk 'a kiss from France'. What I miss is that I am not sending one to Mother. I know she would have treasured it. The birds are singing a treat as I sit here and the war seems far away.

Thursday 4 May 1916

I drew 20 French Francs today (about 16 shillings). I hope that we will have a long sojourn among this lovely scenery. The work generally as an orderly in the Chateau hospital is not too strenuous. We are treating patients with minor problems that are not serious enough to send to the rear. This sector is used by battalions for rest and training so entertainment has been laid on. Last night I visited 'The Barn Owls', a soldier concert party, and they gave a good show, especially the men dressed up as women, you could hardly tell.

Sunday 7 May 1916

In the army you should never let anyone know that you are comfortable with your lot. You are sure to get shifted. I think the trees and flowers in the woods must have let on how happy I was here for our section (C) is going towards the Line tonight while the rest of the ambulance moves further back.

Monday 8 May 1916

Arrived at Bertrancourt after a rough march. We are all tired and foot sore. Marching in the damp brings it on. Our work has been to open a Field Hospital in a deserted estaminet. I am on night duty. Our army took over this section from the French some months ago.

Tuesday 9 May 1916

The weather has turned from sunny spring to being cold and wet. I do though feel fit again. In my free time I visited Acheux and Forceville. They look a bit worse for wear although the line is quiet now. Last night however our artillery was very busy. I was on night duty and having an anxious time with a patient. He was a thirty year old corporal in the Sherwood Foresters. He had a chest wound from a shell splinter and could not breath properly. He was restless and so bleeding. He was to be evacuated the next day. Our building is on a corner and as a Royal Artillery heavy tractor was turning the corner it collided with the brickwork. The noise and alarm that caused disturbed the whole Field Hospital but our greatest worry was that it might attract the attention of Fritz's gunners even at the distance we were from the line. I'm pleased to say that my patient pulled through and he was away by ambulance the next morning.

Sunday 14 May 1916

It is still cold and wet and we have had a week of it. I've also had a week of night duty and I'm getting used to it. I joined this lot, the R.A.M.C. on an impulse but I'm now discovering that I have what might be called a vocation for it. I am fit and well and young and some of the poor souls I have to treat have only my youth. The smallest thing I do brings appreciation and gratitude. Holding a cup for someone wounded to drink brings a sincere 'thanks pal' and I have discovered the gentle and tender aspects of myself I felt growing at Seaforth, along with my developing 'nursing skills'. Here on night duty in the field I am not just an orderly fetching and carrying, although certainly I have to do that as well, but I can offer treatment and, following the instructions of the M.O., take temperatures, change dressings, etc and acquire a 'bedside manner'.

The other advantage of night duty is that I am my own boss. I can cook my meals how and when I want them and I pass the time, when not attending to the needs of patients, reading and writing or chatting with the various patrols who pass. This all helps to get the small hours over and daylight soon comes. At daybreak I begin cleaning up, doing my washing so that as soon as I am relieved I can take a walk before turning in. This morning I am going up towards the line to find Tom. One of the patrols that passed told me that the 13th Battalion East Yorkshires is in the reserve line near to Engelbelmer. I can't wait to see him.

Sunday 21 May 1916

I have spent all my spare time with Tom this week, having found him with little difficulty at Brigade H.Q. He is fit but of course fed up with the Army. We talked of Mother and how much we would have liked to be altogether. It is strange that our reunion should be in France but I feel closer to him here than I ever did at home. We have spent a happy evening together with Tom sometimes breaking off from our talks to tell groups of his comrades who pass, 'This is my 'kid brother' and the last time I saw him was in Hull in 1914.'

It was my twentieth birthday on the 20 May and we celebrated it in style. I had some nice presents from the girls and from Tilly some knitted gloves with a card on which she had managed to scrawl in her hand 'with love for your birthday'. The girls had sent some tonic wine, some cigarettes, which were for me useful currency, and a large birthday cake. Tom, myself and one or two of Tom's pals ate it washed down with French beer.

I have been seeing Tom less and less as the week has progressed as we have been moved from hospital work on to a new job building shelters and dugouts behind the support lines. The rest of the Field Ambulance has moved up at Bertrancourt and me and my squad are going to a new billet at Mailly Maillet where we shall be nearer the Line and the work we have been sent here to do. It is wet again.

Sunday 4 June 1916

We are billeted in the 'Red House' a deserted estaminet. What pleasures it supplied pre-war can only be guessed at. It is near the railway crossing between Mailly Maillet and a big factory know as the Sucrerie. This region grew sugar beet and the sucrerie is where it was processed into white sugar.

The weather is fine and for a week we are to be engaged in digging and building dugouts that don't seem to me for Casualty Clearing Stations (C.C.S.) and so our job, but more Regimental Aid Posts. Therefore, they ought to be dug by Pioneers or regimental stretcher bearers. But when I offer this observation to the N.C.O. in charge he simply says "Keep blanketty digging until somebody tells you to blanketty stop'. Also quite obviously round and about there are tunnels and caverns that have already been quarried out, presumably to provide building stone for the region over the centuries. I suggest that we should use them but get more blanketty blanks for my pains: 'Ours is not to reason why'.

In all this time I have only seen Tom once but our rendezvous at a canteen set up by the 13th East Yorks, was a merry one. One of his mates, also from Hull, Billy Walker I think his name was, had some Army rum. He didn't let on to us where he had got it from. I was beginning to note that there always seemed to be some rum around.

Officially it was delivered in big earthenware jars protected by a wicker-work basket that held about a gallon, enough for 64 men. Printed into the glaze there was the Army War Department arrow and the letters S.R.D., which stood variously for Supply Reserve Depot or Special Reserve Demararer or some such, but for most soldiers the letters spelt out 'Seldom Reaches Destination' because of the frequency with which it got pinched on the way up the Line. On this occasion it had definitely not got to where it should have gone because we three, we very happy three, drank more than a pint of it between us. What dear Mam would have thought of her two sons rolling back drunk I do not know. Rest her Soul.

> Drunk last night,
> Drunk the night before.
> Gonna get drunk tonight
> If I never get drunk anymore

Sunday 11 June 1916

A fine day, the first for a week. At church parade in a field in the sunshine the padre gave a sermon on fighting the good fight. He must have had Salvation Army connections because the hymn we sang was 'Onward Christian Soldiers' and 'What a friend we have in Jesus'. I was to hear later on a different song sung to the same tune as that, it went something like;

> When this lousy war is over, oh how happy I will be.
> When I get my civvy clothes on, no more soldiering for me.
> No more church parades on Sunday, no more asking for a pass.
> I shall tell the Sergeant Major, to stick his passes up his blank.

I was to hear this song sung with more verses with even more naughty words. I don't know who made them up. There was nothing blasphemous about the sentiment. It was just part of the way we dealt with what we had to put up with. If we hadn't let off steam in the ways we did we would have gone stark staring mad. Some of us did.

For part of last week I was again on the night shift. This time our job was to carry up a mile long communication trench the bags of chalk which had been filled from dugouts by the day shift diggers, and to empty them over the parapet hiding the fresh chalk under earth so that the enemy wouldn't detect it and so be aware of our preparations. They don't seem to be fooled for they sent over sporadic shrapnel and machine gun fire. We have lost several men wounded. It is hardly what you would call a war-like and heroic activity, carrying bags of muck, but it is just as dangerous. I had a very close call one night. I was told to grab an iron spike that was on top of the trench and as I did a machine gun opened up and bullets struck the piece of metal, making sparks in the night down the length of it towards me like a firework. I dropped back in the trench double quick.

The fact that it has rained every night and the trenches have now two feet of water in them has made a bad job even worse. The man humping the sack in front of me said, as black water swirled around his knees, 'At least it's as bad for Jerry'. But its not, so I'm told. The German trenches are on higher ground they are deeper and dryer.

Because by day break we are wet through we have to go to bed each day while our clothes are dried. I have only been able to see Tom once and I would like to get back to my proper duties as an R.A.M.C. orderly.

Near the support line there are eighteen pounder batteries of guns which have been shelled. The crews join us in our billet until the bombardment is over. One German shell caused a fire as it ignited charges near the ammunition shed. Had it gone up we would probably have gone up with it but two artillery men ran out and doused the flames with buckets of water. They should have got a medal but didn't as we were the only ones who saw it happen.

The railway line that carries the train for Albert passes this way and every night it runs within a few hundred yards of our front line. Sometimes before it curves off on its way the fireman's opening of the door of the fire box causes a flash of red light and this draws the enemy guns and occasionally they land one that cuts the line. It is usually repaired however by morning by a gang of navvies.

Wednesday 14 June 1916

I have moved up to the support lines with the other stretcher bearers and we are living in a chalk dug-out that is one of a score driven into the hill side. These support trenches are well provided for. There is a well protected field kitchen and the latrines are the most sheltered I've used when this close to the firing line. There is not the usual feeling as you commune with nature that you are in the sights of a sniper's rifle. Our dug-out is about twelve feet under and high enough to stand up in. It is fifteen feet wide so there is room for each shift to lie down. Thankfully it is dry, not like some of the communication trenches which are still half full of water. Because of the exposed chalk the area has been called, by a London Regiment I suppose, 'White City'. Although it can be seen by the many enemy aircraft that fly above observing for artillery, as it is in a deep hollow no hits can be registered. In fine weather it is quite a nice billet. Over at Beaumont Hamel things are not so quiet. It's obvious that they are coming in for a pasting.

Sunday 18 June 1916

It is dry but dull. We were out again last night with our stretcher squad up into the firing line to support the Regimental Stretcher Bearers as they brought in lightly wounded from an artillery barrage. The trenches around are much knocked about and in places the parapet has had to be built up with sandbags. It is for much of its length at least ankle deep in water and one man in the Warwicks could no longer stand, his feet were so softened. When we got him back to the Aid Post he was worried that he might get reported because he had the beginning of 'trench feet'. We put his mind at rest. It didn't matter how much grease or whale oil you rubbed into the feet, the so-called 'preventative treatment', or how many times you changed your socks. If you are up to your knees in water twenty four hours a day the skin of your feet and lower leg began to die. Sometimes the condition was so bad the skin would come away with the socks when the boots were taken off. Worse, the feet would become gangrenous, as I was to see in later cases.

Things have quietened down but there is no doubt they will hot up again soon. We are being issued with new kit and especially, it has been noted, the new box pattern gas masks, 'respirators, for the use of' and steel helmets or 'tin hats' as they came to be called. When we were first issued with tin hats we had to have a chitty and return them after each use. Now we've got one of our own each. There is definitely something in the offing as we have also been busy this week helping to take supplies up via communication trenches and the support line. It is not our job but we are expected to muck in carrying ammunition, duck boards, wire and sacks of rations. Our reward at the end of the task was a 'buckshee' sack of rations. On our return it was closely examined to see if the infantry got the rumoured extras like chocolate, boiled sweets and cigarettes. It was standard stuff, however, bully, Machonochie's stew, tinned butter, sugar, jam, bread, condensed milk and tea. No real extras but there were some jars of porridge, which made a change. The sack nicely supplemented our stores so we had some good feeds where everyone in the squad had as much as they could eat.

Sunday 25 June 1916

We have had almost a week of fine weather but some lengths of trench are still knee deep in water and we have quite a few clients who have gone sick with what I suppose is rheumatism. They get unbearable cramps and can't stand up. A few hours rest on dry land usually does the trick and then back they go. We have been backwards and forwards all week, up and down the support trenches.

I moved back to Bertrancourt last night for what I thought was going to be an uninterrupted night's sleep, but I and others were pulled out of our blankets early this morning to assist in the carrying and care of gassed cases. Fritzy had sent one over and he managed to explode some of our gas cylinders, part of a store that had been buried near a firing line, nozzles pointing towards Beaumont Hamel. We collected many cases in different states of seriousness and all this under a thunderous artillery barrage going from our side that had started while I was asleep. All along the skyline there were flashes and brightly lit explosions from what must have been literally scores of our guns. German artillery replied in kind though not in scale but enough to knock the trenches about pretty badly. Most of the casualties from this were London Regiment men but mixed up in with them were one or two lads from Hull, thankfully not Tom's battalion.

I suppose I can say that it was this night that our work began in earnest. We discovered the sometimes impossibly hard work of retrieving wounded on stretchers while wading in thigh deep mud and water. This during fire from machine guns and high explosive artillery.

Some of the gassed cases we fetched that night were so bad they could not be stretchered. On the stretcher lying down as we made to pick them up, they coughed so much, they fell off. They had to be carried with one of us on either side, a shoulder under each arm. The only thing I can say now is that we could do it because we were young and fit. We could endure a great deal before exhaustion brought us low. The infantry had to put up with conditions in the trenches two or three weeks at a time and often in a hot part of the line. What was unendurable for me was trying to do my work under intense artillery bombardment such as we had this night. How many times I threw myself down, pulling my comrades down with me into the slimy mud, with the wounded man as well, to the bottom of the trench, I can't count. Or, how often I cowered in a dug-out cut out of the trench wall even though the water was too deep, I don't know. I thought every shell that came over was aiming straight at me. Luckily my comrades thought just the same so there was no need to apologise.

In the end we managed to finish the work and the gassed were treated at the Dressing Station at Bertrancourt. We were then able to snatch a couple of hours of rest and we lay down covered completely in mud. We woke up to a hot breakfast of bacon sandwiches and hot rum flavoured tea and we were ready to go again.

Hardly had we had our breakfast when a corporal told us to congregate in front of the station and one of the M.O's gave us a run down on the plans for a massive attack that was to come off in the next few days. It was the 'Big Push' that everybody had been talking about for months. The bombardment we could still hear had already been going on for nearly twenty four hours and it would carry on until it cut the German wire and completely smashed their defences. The thousands of men waiting would then move forward, take all the German positions, allow the cavalry to make the war move again, and knock the Germans out once and for all. After his rousing talk we went back to finish our breakfast then moved up to the 'White City' support lines and waited.

Saturday 1 July 1916

We were up early at five thirty but still managed a good breakfast with hot tea before we were paraded for a kit inspection and to be told to expect a lot of casualties and hard work. By this time most of the Infantry troops had been evacuated from 'White City' and had gone up the Line in readiness for the start of the battle which was to be seven thirty ack emma. The bombardment which had been continuous since the 24 June would lift then and the word to describe what happened then was to be, 'a walk over'. We went back into dugouts and waited.

Just before half past seven we felt the shock of a fantastic explosion. We thought that an ammunition dump had gone up. It was like being on the edge of an earthquake. We dashed out of the dug-out afraid that it would collapse on us. After the battle we discovered that an enormous mine had been set off under the German Line. During the previous weeks we had been carrying bags of chalk for dispersal at the rear. We had all thought it was spoil from trench digging. It wasn't, it was from the tunnel made for this mine. Then began five of the worst days of my life. They were a rough and hard five days of stretcher work and we from our small group lost three killed and eight wounded.

I had seen the wounded already in England and some in dressing stations here. I had also seen the dead. In hospital at home dressings were clean and well fitting, a little bleeding perhaps, a stain on the bandage. The empty sleeves and trouser legs of amputees were folded and neatly pinned. The wards were well ordered and the sheets were white and if there were any groans of pain they were muffled by medicine or the patient in pain was comforted by a sympathetic nurse or an orderly like me. The dead were covered by capes or a blanket and neatly arranged. Here was another world. Nothing had prepared me for the conditions that I and others had to cope with as this great battle began. Here for the next forty eight hours it was to be a shambles, dead and wounded, cut to pieces, covered in blood, an outdoor butcher's shop. I don't know how we dealt with it.

Within half an hour of the battle beginning we were busy. At first walking wounded came out of the line down the support trenches in one's or two's. They had temporary wound dressings on shoulders, on arms, on hands. There were dressings being held over wounds in the chest, the stomach or the head. They limped alone to the 'Casualty Clearing Stations' and 'Aid Posts' or helped each other. We checked, adjusted, added to or improved what had become already bloody wads of lint and bandage. But then what at first had been a ragged intermittent line of men became a queue, then a shambling, bleeding, moaning crowd until it was not possible to move in the trenches. Everywhere was cluttered with men pushing, scrambling, falling, crashing onto the muddy trench bottom as they desperately tried to get away from the rattling, banging, cacophony that was the continuing battle, and to seek treatment for their wounds. Their curses, groans, grunts and even screams of pain added to the murderous circumstances all around. If this was what it was like in the cover of the communication and support trenches, what was it like in the firing line or no-man's-land? Already we had lost bearers, killed as they tried to bring in those not able to move for themselves. The sun began to lift into the blue sky and it began to warm up. It was going to be a hot summer day.

By mid-morning most of our time had been spent in trying to relieve the crush of men trying to get away but able to walk. For part of that time we had to hold up movement because the stations behind the line had become overwhelmed with casualties. There did not seem to be enough ambulances to evacuate them or personnel to treat them. Like the trenches, the C.C.S.'s and Dressing Stations closest to us became choked with wounded men. Over the next few hours and into the afternoon the crush was gradually

relieved, but there were still crowds of men to be dealt with. We did though have a chance to begin to evacuate those men whose wounds were more serious but who we had not been able to deal with. God knows how many died in that time, of pain, shock and loss of blood, that we could not get to because we were unable to go forward against the multitude moving back.

The trenches, in fact any place where there was some cover, became Aid Stations. I found myself in an area of sunken road that was carpeted with the wounded, the dying and the dead. Men lay thickly one against the other or sat with their backs against raised ground. We very rapidly began to run out of supplies - iodine, bandages, wound dressings and morphia. Then, as the day got hotter, water. By midday the M.O.s with their orderlies had gone away for more supplies but they did not come back. We began searching the dead for wound dressings, iodine phials or whatever else they had on them. By the afternoon we were cutting up shirts, underwear and uniforms that we had taken from them, if they weren't soiled, for emergency dressings.

There was little we could do now except to continue to carry those with a chance of survival back to the rear. There we lay them in any space we could find, or if they had already died on the way to 'White City', which happened more times than I care to count, they were unceremoniously tipped on the ground in order to free what was now becoming scarce, the stretcher. While doing this we were quickly enlisted with others to go back to speed up the evacuation of the sunken road because snipers had become active and were picking off the poor souls seeking refuge there.

Backwards and forwards we went all day while the battle still raged on above us. With shrapnel shells bursting and bullets whizzing and buzzing like steel bees in flight. Our squad was close to exhaustion. We had not eaten or drunk anything for hours. On one of our many returns to 'White City' we took a break and even managed a hot tin of tea. As we claimed this more than welcome rest we watched airplanes in the blue sky, circling and diving above the battle field and had the time to ask passing wounded Infantry men snatching a quick fag before making their own way back to the rear, how the battle was going.

We found out that in our section towards Gommecourt the attack had been a diversion. But the 'Push' as a whole had not gone well. With just the number of casualties we had seen that day we could have made that observation. A sergeant in the Warwicks with wounds in both hands, now cleaned and dressed, told us that the artillery shells that were supposed to have cut the wire had been defective and that many of them had been duds. We left him smoking his Woodbine and we got back to work that went on all that afternoon and into the night.

There were now fewer men coming over the top from No-man's-land. Those left outside were either dead, too badly hurt to move, or pinned down in hollows and shell holes by machine gun, shell fire or snipers. This gave us a respite to begin to clear the backlog and by the time it got dark we seemed to have the situation, at least our little bit of it, under control. We replenished our supplies by doubling if not tripling the quantity of water, dressings, iodine and even morphia tablets by scrounging and indenting for more than we needed.

There was now no distinction between us and regimental stretcher bearers. It wasn't necessary. There weren't any left that we could see. They had gone over the top with their attacking regimental troops and suffered the same rate of casualty. Usually they carried their own officers, if wounded. We tended to carry 't'others'. In this situation there was no distinction. They were all just 'carries'.

As the night fell there was another ordeal to come and that was the sounds made by the wounded left out in the open. A few lightly wounded and even able-bodied lucky ones managed to crawl out of the hiding places they had occupied all day and they dropped one by one over the edge of the trench, trying to ignore the bright lights of flares that criss-crossed the night sky. However, the Germans were not now shooting at everything that moved as they had been in previous hours. That left those wounded who couldn't escape. Those poor unfortunate individuals set up a pathetic noise that went from simple cries for help or indications as to where they were to awful screams of pain and muffled pleas to God and Mother to help them. There was little we could do for those well away from the Line but those closer we managed to bring in with little risk to ourselves . The work began carrying them back.

Every trench was still difficult to pass through and each job was a 'long carry' back to 'White City' and the dressing stations. There, under the lights of hand-held oil and paraffin pressure lamps, even emergency surgery was being performed. The reason for this was the hold up in traffic to Advance Dressing Stations and hospitals. Not enough ambulances and hospital trains had been laid on. Nobody from the 'Top Brass' down had been able to predict such casualties.

After hot tea with lashings of 'oh, so welcome' rum, plus sandwiches of some sort of artificial cheese slice that I had not tasted before, we went back to finish clearing up, but all that meant by now really was checking that those who were left were really dead. We snatched sleep, till dawn, in what was left of the night.

Sunday 2 July 1916

We awoke, as we had slept, in the open and ate a scratched breakfast of the same cheese and army biscuit washing it down with rum and water. My mates smoked the essential cigarette. It began to rain and we found other bearers around us busying themselves carrying away the dead and one or two wounded who had come over while we were sleeping; very generously they had let us sleep on.

We were ordered back to 'White City'. It was obvious that the first part of the battle

was over. Talking with some Londoners who had been in the line a bit to the north, they told us that the infantry had suffered terrible losses and had not gained any ground on our front. They said that many of our men did not even reach the enemy wire and those that did as said before had found it uncut and they could not get through before German machine guns caught them. They said that the still intact German wire was waist high and twenty yards thick in places with razor sharp barbs as thick as your finger.

For the rest of the day we were sent into a section to the south where there were a significant number of wounded to carry out. They were badly beaten up and were a mix of Somerset's Durham's, Warwick's and even one of two "Yellow Bellies' from the Lincolns. Their wounds were almost exclusively the result of machine gun bullets, punctured stomachs, smashed legs, shoulders and arms or chest wounds. Slipping and sliding, jolting and bumping into what was left of trench walls, we carried them back. For the most part they bravely endured the journeys we had to make, halting for rest or because of congestion. But for some their pain was unendurable. The dose of morphia tablets was too limited to ease the pain, and anyway it soon wore off. We became sticky with the mixture of mud and blood that covered us. We were so much stained it was difficult to see the original khaki of our uniforms. This work went on two more days but time didn't register. We slept when we could and ate and drank when there was a gap. Then we would have a 'mad hour' of intense activity and then a pause with perhaps a troubled sleep that brought another dawn.

Monday 3 July 1916

Two days after the attack we were relieved by fresh bearers from Field Ambulance but where they found them I don't know. I immediately got permission to go into the 31st Divisions sector, to look for Tom. This was on our left and the division was supposed to have attacked before Serre, just to the north Beaumont Hamel.

As I made my way through the lines bypassing hundreds of dirty bedraggled and exhausted troops resting, re-forming, having roll-calls or congregating around field kitchens for their first hot meal in days, I saw the flattened trenches and shelters with the still unburied dead strewn around them. This was what was left of 'Kitchener's Pals'. As I passed through these untidy crowds I became increasingly worried for Tom's safety, but I needn't have concerned myself for I learned with relief from the men occupying what had been the 31st's position that the East Yorks had been moved out to Bus-lès-Artois. Although they sustained some casualties they escaped the worst of it. Lucky Beggars.

Tuesday 4 July 1916

We returned to Bertrancourt after that rough five days. We joined with the main 'Dressing Station' there and got to work on the wounded that had been delivered there and those coming from the line in dribs and drabs. Men were still dying from wounds in unacceptable numbers. We dealt with so many men of the Yorks and Lancs and with Lancashire Territorials that I couldn't count. Many of the Y and L were from South Yorkshire and they were comforted to know they were being cared for by a fellow Yorkshireman. There was a large number of wounded lying on the ground, simply covered with blankets because there weren't enough stretchers or enough transport to take them back. There were others too who, though basically treated and with the possibility of recovering, just gave up. We did what we could, dispensing tea or water and any food they needed, including the so called 'cure all' cigarette. I didn't smoke and in some cases I thought the giving out of cigarettes unwise. Sometimes men with bandaged chest wounds were given cigarettes, and as soon as they inhaled they coughed and opened up their wounds. We also passed around the rum ration to those with light wounds, ignoring instructions about the negative effect of alcohol on blood. A tot of rum was a much need fillip. It did more good than harm. The exceptions were the ones who had a blue pencil mark of their foreheads which indicated that they had been given morphia.

By night fall we could rest and were able to make our way to a billet we'd fixed up in a cottage that had been bashed about by shelling. We made a fire in the chimney with no thought for the smoke it caused and boiled water for tea or washing and cooked mess tins full of hot stew. We were all filthy, having not removed our clothes or washed for nearly a week. We were able to shave and have a bit of a swill. As a night cap we drank hot rum flavoured tea then lay ourselves down to sleep or, more accurately, just passed out with exhaustion.

Wednesday 5 July 1916

We woke to a fine summer's day and were surprised to learn that it was already eight thirty. We had been allowed the luxury of a lie in. Everything was quiet except for the sound of motors and horse ambulances here in the village to take the wounded away to the rear and ambulance trains at Dullens. As soon as we dressed, still in the only kit we had covered with mud and blood, we breakfasted in a field kitchen set up for the Yorks and Lancs, the Lancashire Fusiliers and Somerset Light Infantry. They were of the few left after their battalions had attacked Serre. They were much subdued and what talk there was was of missing comrades who they enquired after. We were able to direct them to barns and houses around the village that served as make-shift quarters for the wounded, possibly from their lot. We were then summoned in a group and addressed by our M.O. who wanted volunteers to go over the top into 'no-man's-land' to search for wounded and to bring them back if we found any. Every member of the ambulance stepped forward. The M.O. selected two squads and I was in one of them. We waited around for the next couple of hours and busied ourselves helping load wounded into ambulances. Time passed and it looked as if the scheme had been abandoned.
Eventually we were rounded up again and we trudged to 'White City' where there were a great many troops of different units milling about and shouting to each other rumours of another attack.

We left 'White City' and went into the support trenches and then into the firing line. I say trenches but by now they were just relatively deep muddy ditches, though the fine weather had dried out the least flooded areas. These 'ditches' were full of discarded equipment packs, gas-masks, haversacks, shovels, ammunition pouches, muddied rifles and scraps of uniform and tin hats plus bundles of soiled rations.

By around two thirty in the afternoon we arrived at the point where we were to go over. In front of us was Beaumont Hamel. It was nerve wracking because we all thought that once we raised our heads above the parapet the Germans would open up. Although I'd already been under fire and seen the results of it on others this was the first time that I seriously got 'the wind up' and I discovered as the rest of the squads what it really meant. We were all blank scared and we were all breaking wind at the same time. If I hadn't been so terrified it would have been hilarious. There we were twelve of us including N.C.O.s and officers farting together at different registers. We could have been set to music.

An officer looked at his watch and at 3 p.m. showed a flag over the parapet. We went up the ladders and out of the trenches that the attacking troops had used on the morning of the 1 July.

The sight that greeted us deserved the name of 'Battle Field'. To the north and south and the east towards the German wire, the sloping open field was covered with little humps and pock- marked with shell holes. The humps were the bodies of the attackers killed on the morning of the 1st. Two officers began walking towards the wire with Red Cross Flags but we stood around not knowing where to start.

We saw movement over by the German trenches and instinctively dropped flat but they weren't setting up machine guns, they were coming out as well. Quite a number came out and they began extricating our dead from their wire and carrying them to the middle of 'no-mans-land'. It was a real truce.

We fanned out and walked forward much as was done on the day and after a considerable length of time we found eight wounded and alive among the very many dead. There should have been more of us to cover such a lot of ground. The ones we found still alive were mostly Somerset Light Infantry and Hampshires. But one was a Lancashire Fusilier. They had bullet wounds of varying seriousness but in places that had not caused great blood flow and after five days in the open the wounds had closed and bleeding had stopped. We had no time to gauge whether gangrene or other infections had set in.

Those amongst the wounded who were still conscious were almost hysterical with relief. One boy in the Somersets, shot in the upper thigh, had spent the days and nights in a shell hole as all the live wounded had that we found. He was desperate for water and he kept repeating, 'I knew you would come, I knew you would come.' He was no longer in pain but I think he would have gone mad had he been left any longer. We carried him back to the trench as with the others and they were then taken to a Dressing Station. We then began the business of burying the dead. The Germans helped us. I particularly noticed that they were no longer wearing the helmet with the spike on top but a close fitting tin hat which came down over their ears and to the top of the uniform collar at the back. It looked easier to wear than the steel helmet we had been issued with.

The dead were strewn around or in rows flat to the earth as they had fell. Their uniforms and packs had been shot to ribbons and the contents were scattered all over. Most of the dead as far as I could see had multiple bullet wounds caused after they had died. Probably the result of German machine guns whose sights were lowered to catch any movement.

There were so many dead that their burial had to be unceremonious. No chaplain had come with us (I don't know if one had been asked for) so there was no Christian burial for the ones we found, collected together and placed in shell holes. We filled so many. The graves (such as they were) were marked but I know these markers did not survive another bombardment. We collected, prior to the burials, a great quantity of identification discs. We finished what we had come out to do and on the instructions of the officers made our way back to the trenches. We left the Germans standing in 'no-man's-land'. As far as I saw nobody exchanged a word.

Saturday 8 July 1916

The last few days since our excursion 'over the top' have been spent in assisting with fairly comprehensive clearing up. We still have many wounded who have not been adequately treated. Lots of blokes still only have the field dressings put on as a temporary measure and there are many more who have had relatively effective treatment but are waiting to get transport to hospitals in France or Blighty. Things are moving but understandably not fast enough for the men who feel they have waited long enough. I am talking about hundreds.

We are also having to assist with the job of clearing the dead from Aid Posts and trenches. Just as the wounded died in 'no-mans land' there are many men who have died of wounds in all the trench systems. It is an awful job, not least because after you have been at it a few hours, and you know when you wake up in the morning that you will be doing it again, you begin to become indifferent to the unfortunate soul you have to take to his grave. I say to myself that these were sons, husbands, fathers, brothers, friends and last soldiers. Now they have become heavy weights as we uncaringly lug them around and curse the inconvenience. All the talk of Kitchener's heroic army of Pals is now just the shattered body of a youth like myself who a few days ago had everything before him.

What we also have to contend with are those we might charitably call 'souvenir hunters'. These are men who search the bodies of the dead and their discarded packs and equipment, for anything of value. I can understand rations, water and ammunition being retrieved, but under the cover of this excuse they take other things, more personal, like watches, rings and cigarette cases. It is we then, the stretcher bearers, who get the blame for stealing and the reputation of 'Robbing All My Comrades'. It is not true, it is undeserved .

Yesterday, Friday 7 July 1916, I met up with cousin Ernest who has arrived with the 21st West Yorks and he is attached to our Division. So much for his declaration that he wouldn't join the Army. When I saw him he said that the situation in the mill became impossible and in the end he decided to volunteer before he was conscripted. He was very glad to see me and I him for he had news from home and letters from Dad and the girls and a present and a letter from Tilly. His lot, the 21st West Yorks, had arrived to relieve the ones who went over on the 1st. Ernest talked about 'missing the show' and how he had wanted 'a crack at the Hun'. I told him not to be so foolish and to count his blessings he had been out of it.

Sunday 9 July 1916

I went to church parade on what was a very sunny splendid day with blue skies and a bright yellow sun. The priest was much moved when he referred to the young men who weren't there. I took Holy Communion and thought how much my life had been changed in the last few days.

We had a very welcome rest on that Sunday and I was able to wash, albeit from a bucket, but the water was hot and soaped all over it was nearly as good as a bath. I shaved and I cleaned my uniform off as far as I could. What was difficult was getting the 'Somme mud' off my boots. With the chalk and earth it set like concrete. With the rest of the hot water I tried as best as I could to wash my shirt and underclothes. When I hung them out they dried very quickly in the sun. I now feel like a new man. Others of my squad followed my example so that our billet looked like a gypsy camp, especially so with the black kettle on the coke brazier.

Monday 16 July 1916

It has been a fine week and we have spent it drilling and getting fit for more work. We have exercised practising carries wearing the new gas masks, tin hats and full kit. We take it in turns being the patient and one of our squad, a little lad from Lancashire, is favourite because he is far the lightest of us all. There is still a lot of work at the C.C.S.s and A.S.s and we are working shifts to cope with it, but it is not as it was two weeks ago although there is still the need for the operating table as emergencies arrive. I was in a C.C.S. having just delivered a carry when a young infantry subaltern came in and asked the surgeon M.O. if he wanted any morphia tablets. The M.O. surprised, said yes. The officer then gave him a box of small jars that contained altogether hundreds of tablets. His mother had bought them in a high street shop and sent them over. We have quite a few infantry and artillery detachments here at Bertrancourt and they are drilling while waiting for reinforcements. He had popped in from one of them

I got to know today the names of two of the lads who were killed on the 1st of July. They were Albert Greenwood and Frank Coker. I never carried with them but I knew them to talk to. Frank was in his middle twenties but Albert was the same age as me. I found out that they had been killed while I was walking round the cemetery here at Bertrancourt for that's where they are buried.

Pay day was Wednesday, 20 francs but it soon went. We have been over to Acheux where there is a canteen and so the possibility of buying beer, wine, and egg and chips. We have made a number of visits along with some lads of the Lancashire Fusiliers who are good company and guarantee a good sing song.

The fine weather continues. We are preparing for a move. The rumour is that we are to be sent north to the Armentières sector and then that is contradicted by new information. We are to go to Belgium and Ypres. We shall see.

Wednesday 19 July 1916

Our section went up the line for our week in the trenches. We were in the support trenches with elements of the 4th Division in front of Beaumont Hamel . During the night the Germans found the range and they dropped enough to put the wind up us. To the south there was a lot of activity and the sky was lit with the red glare of artillery explosions, Very Lights and Star Shells. The flares are beautiful to watch as they descend and although their light is unnatural in its brightness, the way that everything is thrown into relief and held in suspension until they are extinguished, absolutely fascinates me.

We spent the night taking it in turns to sleep in a temporary Aid Station that we had contrived from a 'dug out'. The regimental stretcher bearers ignored our efforts and carried what few casualties there were past us to somewhere close, but in the rear. We didn't complain and then in the morning of Thursday 20 July we were relieved by the 36th Field Ambulance and our Infantry comrades in the 4th Division were relieved by elements of the 12th Division.
Men from Suffolk, Middlesex, East Kent and other South Eastern Counties chaffed and joked with us as we carried our gear 'against the stream' in the narrow support and communication trenches.

There were no billets for us when we returned to Bertrancourt so we spent the first of two nights under the stars. The second night was after a march to Bus Les Artois. I was lucky, the lad who was usually up on the horse drawn ambulance had hurt his hand so I sat up with him and took the reins. I did not have to march. I slept out however with the rest because my temporary driver's position did not entitle me to sleep in the ambulance. That privilege only extended to him. When I tried to sleep on the damp ground I wished for the exhaustion that always came after a long march. That usually guaranteed sleep.

There were tents and huts at Bus but no room at the inn for us. A Sussex Regiment had nabbed all the cover. There was some advantage to this, as we discovered in the morning, for we were able to avail ourselves of their Field Cooker and we enjoyed a hot breakfast of porridge, bacon sandwiches in freshly baked bread, with hot sweet tea, and it didn't taste of chlorine, petrol or more unmentionable flavours. It was the best grub for days. There was the added bonus of hot water for a 'swill' and a shave. Fed and watered, washed and shaved, with the sunshine drying out the damp and aches and pains from uncomfortable sleeping quarters, life felt good again. After breakfast we gathered up our traps and moved off for another march, our destination Doullens.

CHAPTER 4 - ON THE ROAD TO BELGIUM

Sunday 23 July 1916

Almost immediately on our arrival we were paraded in preparation for getting on board a train so we had no time to taste the delights of Doullens. It was a town well behind the lines and therefore liberally served with the kinds of diversion so dear to the 'wanton soldiery', that is estaminets, cafés, canteens and perhaps, perish the thought, places of ill-repute.

On board the train we found ourselves with plenty of room and we settled down, as we correctly judged, for the night. We were bound for Cassel in Belgium. Sleep came easy as we put our feet up and we were lulled by the slow rattle of the train's progress north.

Monday 24 July 1916

We arrived, and after a breakfast of bully, biscuit and disappointingly cold tea we de-trained at the bottom of the hill that Cassel is on top of and we, like the Grand Old Duke of York, marched up it.

The hill rose steeply above the plain and around we could see a number of turning windmills. We marched through the old town, down the hill on the other side to the village of Herseele on the Poperinghe to the Ypres road. We rested for two days and we were billeted in the barns of a small farm. We had a lazy time and even played cricket and football in the fields of the farm where hay had just been cut. The farmer's wife sold us fresh eggs and then, seeing that we had no means of cooking them, fried them for us in an enormous frying pan on a trivet over an open fire in the field. She had two little daughters who shyly peeked around the entrance to the barn, watching us busying ourselves arranging kit, etc., but ran away when we called to them. Only once did we entice them to come closer and that was with the promise of chocolate. The lad who gave it to them was startled when they thanked him in what sounded like German. They and their parents, of course, speak Flemish which to the untutored ear sounds like German.

Wednesday 26 July 1916

We regretfully had to say goodbye to our first Belgian billet and we set off on the march to Proven. Feeling fit and rested we were soon singing and chanting replies and echos.

One example went like this: from the front would come the call-

> Sister Anna, you carry the banner.
> (Reply, single voice, plaintively)
> But I carried it last week
> (Loud chorus)
> You carry it this blanketty week
> (Reply as before)
> But I'm in the family way
> (Loud chorus)
> You're in everybody's blanketty way

So we marched on. Another favourite was a parody of the advertisement for a notorious cure-all of the time. Singing it passed many a fatiguing mile. There was a patent medicine I think called Lydia Pinkham's Elixir.

> So drink, drink, drink of Lydia's Pink, a plink a plonk,
> So efficacious in every way
> So drink, drink, drink of Lydia's Pink, a plink a plonk,
> The saviour of the human race.
> So drink, drink, drink of Lydia's Pink, a plink a plonk,
> And all the papers will show your face.

> Now little Bertie, he bashed his Bishop,
> He bashed his Bishop, which was a sin.
> He took a dose of Lydia's compound
> And now his Bishop is bashing him.

> So drink, drink, drink etc.

> Now little Gertie, she had a siezure,
> She had a siezure, she couldn't pee.
> She took a dose of Lydia's compound,
> And now they've drained her
> Into the sea.

> So drink, drink, drink etc.

Mile after gruelling mile we sang such songs, and so managed to bear soft feet in hard boots, tired legs, the pain and irritation of webbing straps biting into our shoulders and the uneven cobbles of French and Belgian roads. Sometimes roads were only paved in the middle so the outer ends of the squad had to march on very uneven surfaces.

I hoped my dear departed Mother, who never said anything stronger than damn, and that rarely, wasn't able to hear how her youngest son had coarsened. How he used vulgar, if not obscene language that would, in the words of a Sergeant Major I was to meet, 'cause an Archbishop to kick a hole in a stained glass window'. I hope she knew that it meant nothing except a way of enduring hardships difficult to bear and that the themes of songs and stories were merely ways of cementing the essential comradeship that was the only positive thing in this 'lousy war'.

Thursday 27 July 1916

We have arrived in Proven, Belgium, where we have taken over a convalescent camp. Our patients are for the most part recovering from light wounds and trench maladies such as, chills, typhus, dysentery, trench feet and not a few 'nervously exhausted'. The weather is fine so the tents they are in are dry and fairly comfortable. We are kept busy receiving casualties by the railway which was built and is manned by British railwaymen so it reminds us of Blighty.

In the convalescent camp most of the patients seemed to come from London Territorial Regiments and they have never been to, nor have even heard of Hull. They call me 'Yorkie', and seem fairly philosophical about the prospect of going back in the line having not earned the cherished 'Blighty one' only a period of rest. Their descriptions of the war around Ypres paint a grim picture of mud and blood with the Germans holding onto their positions behind unassailable concrete.

From time to time German aircraft fly over and systematically bomb the towns to the rear. They are genuine air-raids with planes in formation force. They are, however, soon seen off by our R.F.C. and watching the fighters diving and turning high up in the blue is a regular pastime. The German air force try for the railway here and have dropped bombs near to the camp in spite of huge Red Cross indicators on the tents and on the ground.

There are patients in the hospital of all age groups and some quite old boys as well. There is one young patient who definitely should not be here. He is a boy of scarcely sixteen. To enlist he lied about his age and was only fourteen when he volunteered. Although nothing is certain, he is likely to be sent home when the shell splinter leg wound he is recovering from is healed. His parents have already requested his release, so I'm told, but he maintains that it will be his choice to go or stay. He insists, without any hint of bravado that he wants to go back into action. The opinion of the more mature patients on either side of him is that 'he needs his brains washing'.

Sunday 6 August 1916

I drew 20 francs pay and I'm having the good time I predicted. The village is very pleasant, as are the people. Most of them seem to speak English. There are places to go for a fry-up and the Belgian beer that's made around here is very good. Some of it on

73

offer is dark, almost like English beer and there is a curiously white beer that has a very interesting taste.

The weather is still holding good and all around on the village farms the crops are a treat to see after the desolation of French farming in the Somme valley.

We have now taken over the local Convent school as a hospital. The Sisters have loaned us a room in their house for an operating theatre and their Pastor has opened up his garden for our wounded to sit and walk in. We are very well liked by the population and everyone tries to help us.

I am at present on night duty, which is no hardship in this weather. As the ward is in one of the permanent buildings in the Convent school with a hard wooden floor it is easy to maintain. There is plenty of fresh water 'on tap' and the school latrines are clean, disinfected and a pleasure to use, but they are not a place where you can sit and contemplate the secret of the universe as you do your business, for they are the standard hole in the floor that you get in France and Belgium. However once you get used to them they are, so they say, healthier and it is more natural to squat. The important thing for me is the luxury of being, 'far, far from German snipers'. Like the little song I heard here:

> Far, far from Wipers I want to be
> Where German snipers can't get at me;
> Down in a dug-out, warm, dry and deep,
> Waiting for whizz-bangs to send me to sleep.

We are well behind the lines so are not bothered by the artillery that can be heard in the distance. When I am relieved I can wash and shave and have a good breakfast which I cook for myself in the kitchen. I then stroll back to my billet, a small out-house in the yard of a neighbouring farm. I preferred it to the canvas I was offered. I have made up a bed with an old mattress 'won' from the school, and I sleep the sleep of the just, being able to take off boots and uniform - against 'Kings Regs' when you're in the trenches.

Sunday 13 August 1916

We are still enjoying fine weather and also a good time, spending our money on egg and chips and Belgian beer, which is still affordable. On Thursday I had some free time and I cadged a lift on a lorry into the next village of Rousbrugge. It stands on the Yser canal. The village is used as a recreation and rest area by Belgian troops who have the line to the west of Ypres. They are sociable and pleasant men to mix with and generally speak passable English. I learned that most of them were Flemish and not French speaking. They, French speakers, are the 'posh' ones as we might say and they come from around Brussels. The men here are generous and want to show their hospitality to 'Tommies'. I visited a very well appointed Military hospital sited in the village where I was told there were English nurses, but I didn't see any. The Belgian Red Cross nurses were very pretty but a bit stand-offish. I suppose like ours, they only talk to officers. I spent some time during my sojourn there watching anglers all along the banks of the canal. There were women, children, old men and soldiers busily as we say 'drowning worms'.

Monday 14 August 1916

We have just been given the first letters from home in weeks. The mail has been following us around and has only just caught up. It is quite unusual for the mail to be late. Maybe the disaster in July is to blame. Tilly writes (or rather her scribe) that she is having a pleasant summer and she hopes I am having the same (well, apart from the war on the Western Front, yes). She also told me that she had had a birthday. Dad, Maud and Phyllis have sent me a parcel of cake and sweet biscuit that has been bashed about but it is still edible. Fortunately the five hundred cigarettes that accompanied it were in a tin. They have nicely augmented my 'currency' bank.

I went on a visit to Poperinghe which for some reason has been made temporarily out of bounds so I had to be careful. The town is quiet and not much damaged although the Germans shell it, long-range, once or twice a week with H.E. There are lots of civilians and plenty of shops and bars whose proprietors are disappointed that there are not more British soldiers for customers.

Sunday 20 August 1916

The weather has changed and it is dull and wet. I'm still on night duty and having a decent and comfortable time as before.

One of the 'nervously exhausted' patients had a very bad night last week. He had a nightmare that was so severe in its effects that I thought he might go mad and harm himself. Whatever, it was proof that he wasn't 'swinging the lead'. He has got into this state before and has had to be restrained. Although he disturbs the rest of the ward, they are not critical or scornful. They sympathise with his condition and tell of how he was buried in mud for days under constant bombardment. When he was pulled out he was in a terrible state, unable to speak, trembling from head to foot and having completely lost control of himself.

Yesterday we had a sports meeting. It was successfully promoted in a pasture close to nearby hop-fields. I won a second for sprinting a hundred yards and our section took seven prizes altogether. We were highly satisfied.

Thursday 24 August 1916

We packed up and the Ambulance as a whole moved through Poperinghe to Remy sidings where we are to run a rest camp in huts. Just across the road from us are two

British and two Canadian casualty clearing stations.

Sunday 27 August 1916

The weather is now fine and my preferred night duty is still working well. I have gone so far as to swap duties with a mate in my squad. I like to have plenty of time to look around during daylight. After a few hours sleep, my time is my own. I have been over to look at the Canadian clearing stations and I find they are very comfortable. I met with one of my Canadian counterparts and he was very keen to show me round their facilities. I must say they are of the standard that we would usually associate with an Advanced Dressing Station or even a small rear hospital. They even had volunteer female nurses from home.

My new Canadian 'mate' proudly showed me blood transfusion equipment and volunteers giving blood. I had only heard talk of this process and to see it in action was fascinating. While I was observing a transfusion from a donor to a flask, to a patient, one of the orderlies dropped a pint bottle of the blood. The Canadian M.O. supervising the operation upbraided him for his carelessness and then instructed him to learn something from it. On the floor were the contents of the bottle, one pint in a widening pool of red blood. The M.O. said, 'If you saw a wounded man lying in that amount of blood you might think he was done for because he'd lost so much. Don't forget,' he said, 'he has another eight or nine pints inside him.'

Sunday 3 September 1916

I just had time to buy a very pretty purse for Tilly in one of the many shops in Poperhinge before we got the word to move again. The move this time was to Wormhoudt, which is a French/Belgian frontier town. We arrived there on Thursday by steam tram, a very enjoyable and memorable trip.

Our section is now billeted in an empty school and very comfortable it is. We are a bit crowded and have to step carefully over still sleeping comrades when we go on duty, but the conditions are good. The latrines are modern and hygienic if still of the hole in the ground type but we can shave, bathe and wash, as civilised people should. Each morning, as he shaves, Fred Earnshaw, a recruit who says he is in his late forties (I think he's well over fifty), shouts out, 'Do the poor people have this?' 'Yes of course they do,' is the chorus. Fred's reply is, 'Well it's too good for them.' This question and answer, it seems, comes from the fabled conversation of a virginal Royal Princess to her new husband on her Wedding night.

Wormhoudt is still a very clean town not having yet had any Army from any side as permanent guests. It is so far from the line that not even very long range artillery has bothered to introduce itself. That may of course change given the fortunes of war. It boasts a theatre and we have already been to a show given by a visiting concert party called 'The Flanders Follies.' At that show we heard the old songs like 'Tipperary' 'Pack up your troubles,' and a rendering of 'If you were the only girl in the world' by a female impersonator. 'She' went on to sing in duet with a lad in khaki, songs that were new to us. They were 'Keep the home fires burning' and 'There's a long, long trail a-winding.' These songs went straight into our personal repertoires and we sang them in many of the numerous estaminets of Wormhoudt, nearly every one of which boasted a piano.

The weather keeps fine and country life goes on as normal with hop-pickers and harvesters very busy. Tomorrow the plan for our squad is to do a tour of the town so that we can explore the shopping streets on which we have seen a jeweller's, a draper's and a shoe shop. Our intention is to look for presents for family and friends.

Monday 4 September 1916

The mail brought awful news this morning. I could not believe it. It was so unexpected and in a ordinary letter. I was already on duty carrying a lad from the ambulance to the hospital when the letter was handed to me. It was news from Dad at home of the death of Tom. Dad wrote that Tom had been killed by shrapnel whilst on sentry duty in the Somme area on the night of the 23rd August.

I wanted to go where I thought Tom was stationed. I knew it was unreasonable and the Corporal told me, as gently as he could, that there would be nothing I could do. Tom would already by buried.

I have never felt so low. I thought we would both get through it and come home together. It is ridiculous to think about it but I am bothered by thoughts of how Mother would have coped had she been alive. I wished so much that I could be at home with Dad and the girls but there is no chance of that. I was told by the Sergeant Major not to bother to ask.

Tuesday 5 September 1916

I am feeling very fed up and I have been placed under arrest by the S.M. for refusing to drill. He shouted at me and did not seem very sympathetic at all. As I stood there he pointed to the hospital saying, 'How many young lads have died in that place and how many more will die before this blanketty lot is over.' I know that he wanted to keep my mind off thoughts of Tom so that I wouldn't brood. He had no choice but to punish me. I got fourteen days number two Field Punishment. He said that I should think myself blanketty lucky for, 'If I hadn't blanketty noticed there was a blanketty war on and refusing an order was a serious offence, I was lucky not to get blanketty shot.'

Sunday 10 September 1916

I have been in detention for the last few days but I am having an easy time. The hard thing is trying to get over the bad news. My thoughts keep going back to my boyhood. Tom was a good brother to me. I could always rely on him to look after me and of course being the elder boy and the first born he was the apple of Mam and Dad's eye. He was called after Dad, Thomas Walter. My mates in the ambulance are very kind and caring. They see to it that I lose no comfort through being in detention.

I've received letters from Maud, Ernest and a further one from Dad in which he tried to comfort me by saying that I'd seen Tom before he was killed. I don't suppose Tilly knows about it yet but I can't bring myself to write to tell her. She never knew him but I had written about him to her.

Because of a kind act by the very S.M. who put me on detention I have been able to write to Dad and the girls to tell them that although Tom was badly wounded he didn't suffer before he died. The S.M. found out through the M.O., I suppose, that Tom was buried in the St Vaast Military Cemetery, Richebourg. There is a large R.A.M.C. unit there and they recorded that Tom was brought in unconscious and that he died while being treated. The S.M. had gone to a lot of trouble getting the M.O. to telephone to find this out. Of course as far as I was concerned this might not be the whole story. I had been party to letters to parents and loved ones that described the most peaceful of passings when the reality was that their son, husband, brother, fiancé, what have you, had been blasted to bits or had lingered horribly mutilated or been forgotten on a stretcher as he bled to death or drowned in his own fluids as gas gnawed at his lungs. Death here, in this war, was not the rose-tinted 'going to sleep' of postcards and romantic books. This was a war of flying flesh, slashing metal and earth shattering bombs. Tom knew this as an Infantryman as much as I did as a stretcher bearer. What happens here doesn't have much to do with what they think at home. It is another world.

Monday 11 September 1916

I am still technically under arrest but I received the same sudden orders to stand by and shortly afterwards we moved off towards the coast. We passed through Berques, a fine old fortified town with double walls and a moat, that was further protected by a belt of marsh. We marched over one of the old draw bridges that led through towered gates into the medieval town and the population, most of whom seemed to be on the streets, gave us a rousing greeting as we stamped the cobbled roads. They were disappointed when we did not stop.

Our long trail continued onto Uxem where we billeted in farm out-buildings. We had time for rations of biscuit, bully washed down with tea, brewed on a fire we made in the yard before we turned in on clean dry straw.

Tuesday 12 September 1916

We were roused from a sound sleep at 3 a.m. and still half in it we were formed and marched off with our destination being, we were told, Dunkerque. Rumour spread through the ranks quick as a rash that we were going to catch a boat to Dover. We certainly needed something to cheer us up at that time in the morning as we were given no break to eat breakfast or even to relieve our natural functions.

We passed through Coudeherque and along a canal bank where we rested for an hour, in time for a field cooker to catch us up and to serve hot stew and tea. We then went on to Dunkerque, arriving at 9 a.m.

We marched straight through the town, to the sea front on the south side of the harbour. Here we 'fell out' and as the sun, sea and the wind still had the warmth of summer in them we were soon enjoying the bathing. We had a high old time on the beach, picnicking on bully in fresh French bread bought in the town, supplemented by apples bargained from a street trader. We even managed to persuade labourers at the business of repairing a harbour wall to boil us tea on the fire they were using to melt tar. All that was missing were the donkeys and the sticks of rock. In spite of myself I felt cheered up. I consoled myself with the certain knowledge that Tom would not have blamed me.

At night fall we marched back through the town of Coudekerque, fresh and revived, and were billeted in very comfortable barns that seemed to have been prepared for us on the farm of one Monsieur Van Steenberg and his family. They could not do enough for us. They fed us eggs for supper which we ate with bread and butter and then jam, washed down with a gallon of tea with added rum from our ration.

We rested there for nearly three days and we saw to it that we left it as we had found it. We cleared out the straw from the barns, burned it and filled the latrine ditches in so carefully, you could not see where we had been.

Friday 15 September 1916

We moved from Couderkerque back to Wormhoudt once again, only passing through Berques as we did before, once more disappointing the townspeople. The weather was splendid. My spirits rose to the point were I joined in a version of Mademoiselle from Armentières that I had not heard before;

> Three German officers crossed the Rhine, Parlez Vous,
> Repeat, Repeat
> They blanked all the women and supped all the wine,
> Hanky, panky, Parlez Vous
>
> They came upon a way side inn, Parlez Vous,
> Repeat, Repeat
> They blanked on the mat and walked right in,
> Hanky, etc etc

Pray, landlord, have you a daughter fair, Parlez Vous,
Repeat, Repeat
With lily-white blanks and golden hair,
Hanky, etc etc

Each time we passed a hamlet, farmhouse or isolated cottage, the occupants came out to see what the noise was. They stood, some holding the hands of little children. As they did we roared out the choruses, the only words they would understand being Mademoiselle, Armentières and Parlez Vous. Mine was the loudest voice of all as I sang, tears rolling down my face, imagining as I did that poor dear Tom was marching alongside with me.

Friday 15 September 1916

At Wormhoudt we stayed in our recent billet, the school, and there prepared for what was obviously going to be a big move. As always rumour took the place of information and they ranged from 'going home' to 'peace talks'. After two days of packing, loading, cleaning and then burning rubbish, we moved to Esquebech where we were lined up for the train. The weather was fine so we would be dry and comfortable for the journey.

CHAPTER 5 - WE RETURN TO FRANCE AND PICARDY

Monday 18 September 1916

We arrived at Amiens back in France proper and the Somme. That was after a very roundabout voyage touching Cassel, St Omer, Calais, Boulogne and Abbeville. To have gone more directly to Amiens would have brought us close to the Front Line and Jerry's aeroplanes and artillery. Railway lines and trains were a favourite target of his. When we stopped at Calais there was much excitement as the Division had been rumoured to be going home. But we only got out of our horse boxes, forty hommes, eight chevaux, to stretch our legs, relieve ourselves and buy a coffee at the canteen on the station. At Amiens we were marched to a temporary baths and ablutions unit were we took it in turns to bathe and shave. Then scrubbed, with hair combed we where given fresh uniforms while ours where put in steam boilers to fumigate them and de-louse them. We where then told that because there had been a mix up over our billets we couldn't go straight to them, so we could spend the day in Amiens. We were ordered very firmly to be back at the tents we were going to spend the night in for a roll call at nine o' clock. There were to be dire consequences for any late-comers, skivers and boozers. They really needn't have worried, they knew what they were doing. We were all 'boracic lint'. We hadn't been paid for two weeks.

Amiens was a sort of Army capital city. There were railway sidings, Army H.Q., Flying Corps H.Q., R.A.M.C. H.Q. etc. etc. Because of these factors the town was full of Officers of all distinctions and these of a number of different Armies, French,, British, Belgian, Portuguese and so on. As one wit said, 'The only officers not in evidence are the Germans, and it won't be long before they're here.'

The city had a magnificent Cathedral although much of its structure was under sand-bags. Down the hill from the Cathedral to the canal which had barges on it now being used for carrying the wounded was the oldest part of the town. The canals were once also part of a system of floating gardens where market produce was grown. One of the streets in the old quarter was called Turpin Street. I thought Turpin was an English name. Bold Dick the Highwayman, legend has it, stayed at a pub at Welton, near Hull. Maybe there was a relationship.

We tramped around the town envying the officers and their V.A.D. girlfriends who were taking advantage of the many restaurants and cafes that the city had to offer. Eventually we found a Y.M.C.A. canteen passing on the way to it a long queue outside of all things in France, a fish and chip shop. The distinct aroma did not make the cheese and biscuit rations we had to eat any more appetising. We ate them washed down with weak Y.M.C.A. cocoa. That was all we could afford.

As we had no money left most if not all of us returned early, changed our uniforms and made ready for sleep in the bell tents allocated. After a fine day we could look forward to a dry comfortable night. We turned in only to be turned out for the nine o clock roll-call. To the S.M.'s and Duty Officer's utter amazement nobody missed it.

Tuesday 19 September 1916

All up on a beautiful morning to a good breakfast of bacon, bread and tea. Eating and drinking our fill put us in good heart for a march to Villers-Bocage, a village on the Amiens - Doullens road. It was a fine day and we measured our step on the part cobbled highway. As armies of old we were prepared to 'march a day' on the breakfast we'd had and we stepped out. I shall never forget that experience, marching in step in fine weather, fed and watered, with mates who would lay their lives down for you, singing and chanting our bawdy songs. On that day, as on others, the cry from the front was 'It won't be long now.' Echoed at the back with, 'one more clean white shirt.'

Sunday 24 September 1916

The splendid weather with what we would call in England an 'Indian summer' saw us still in the village of our destination, Villers-Bocage.

We are 'old sweats' now and know when we are being prepared for action. The drilling and carrying practice being doled out assures us that we will before long be going up the line.

The Battle of the Ancre or the Battle of the Somme, take your pick, was still going on and had been for months since the awful days of July. I wasn't able to find out what progress, if any, had been made. Nobody at our level or rank knew what was going on or why. It was around this time that we learned and sang over and again to the tune of Auld Lang Syne the answer to the question 'Why are we here?'

> 'We're here because we're here because we're here because we're here' and so on.

Or we sang to the tune of Come all ye faithful:

> 'Why are we waiting, why are we waiting,
> Oh why are we waiting, why are we waiting.'

On the outskirts of the village an enterprising French woman had set up an estaminet in a very large barn. It had a piano and rough wooden tables and chairs. She had even fixed up on trestles at one end a sort of stage, so we spent many a happy hour drinking very cheap vin rouge and enjoying 'turns round the room'. We have some very good singers and comedians in our lot, enough for entertainment to last all night.

On one such night when our amateur 'concert party' was in full swing, who should walk in but Ernest. He was there for a night before going up the line the next day with the West Yorks. I was able to stand him a drink and outside in the garden, in the late summer evening, we talked of Tom. Ernest had met some lads of the 13th Batalion East Yorks some weeks ago after they had come out of the line and they said that just Tom and one other bloke had been killed that night of the 23rd of August.

We went back in the barn and had another drink to absent brothers and absent friends. We didn't talk any more about it. It was always best to let it lie and think about only the good things and the day to day business of survival. Dwelling on such loss made you more miserable. Men went down that road and we had all heard of self-inflicted wounds, desertions and not a few suicides. There was no shortage of means of doing that..........'eat, drink and be merry, for tomorrow...........'

Monday 25 September 1916

We marched to Corbie, fifteen miles, about 5 or 6 hours on the road. The hot weather made marching very difficult and the last stretch which brought us through the town and two miles past it, lasted an hour and a half. It was a gruelling plod. At the end of it we thanked the memory of the Quartermaster who had organised boot repair at Villers-Bocage. There would not have been a boot unbroken nor foot un-blistered at the end of that slog if the Army cobblers had not done their necessary work. St Crispin deserves a prayer of thanks.

Corbie was an absolute hive of activity with the French and the British using it for convoys, ammunition and supply dumps and artillery parks. There were C.C.S.s, rest centres and facilities for evacuating wounded by road, rail and barge. It had safe havens and secure shelters in caves that honeycombed the area. We are under the less protected cover of canvas pitched on chalky ground in a valley below a steep hill boarded by a canal and ringed by a number of deep pools or lakes. On the other bank of the canal the French are stationed.

Sunday 1 October 1916

The last few days under canvas have not been unpleasant. There has been some drilling and carrying practice, gas masks off, gas masks on. But we have had free time. During this time we have enjoyed some bathing and several visits to the town where we met, talked and drank with, for the first time 'Johnny Frenchman'. They call themselves 'poilu', or, 'the hairy ones'. At least that's what they used to be called, until they had to

shave their beards off to fit into the new gas masks. They were very interested in trading and had lots of Jerry souvenirs, pistols, bayonets, helmets etc. They also had a lot of red wine which they were issued with in metal bottles. They did not drink water. Bully beef, which they insisted on calling 'singe' (it means monkey), was what they were after. They were also interested in tinned stew.

The next day, after our first meeting, we arranged a 'rendezvous'. We arrived, stocked up with tins of bully and Maconochie's stew. Our stores had been obtained from a chain smoking cook at one of the field cookers serving us. My store of cigarettes, (I thought at the time that I was the only non-smoker in the British Army) proved very useful and I was recompensed by my share and with cash adjustment.

After much haggling and light hearted bargaining, during which we quickly learned to count in French along with the words for 'not enough' and 'too much', we finished up festooned with the straps of wine 'bidons', a pistol, pickle-hauber helmets and enough bayonets to take a Jerry trench. We were told by our French comrades to keep the bidons out of sight. The expression they used was ' planquer', which means 'hide it'. It was Army issue. I also obtained three loaves of fresh French bread in the shape of barrow wheels. What a change that made from teeth breaking biscuit. We were to see more of our French allies for we got orders to leave our tents and move into town.

Monday 2 October 1916

We moved last night into the chateau in the centre of Corbie. A section of it is a rest centre for Officers. I went to a concert given by a military band in the ruins of a very old church. The church had been demolished by time rather than Fritz. The band was from a London Regiment and they rounded off their evening with a lively party in our billet, the stables of the chateau. Our contribution was the contents of one or two of the bidons we had swapped for bully.

Sunday 8 October 1916

Another week of hard work in this crowded town. It must also have been a hive of industry before the war for there are a number of empty premises and enterprises plus what looked like the remains of a motor factory.

Work in the chateau and C.C.S. varies from the cushy to the backbreaking. There is a regular intake of wounded from the Front Line trenches. The surgeons and nurses are busy with quite major operations and amputations. The war in this part of France is still going on. On one particularly active shift in the early evening we carried in a young Officer from a Scottish Regiment. He was still in his kilt and below it his right leg was horribly damaged. We carried him from a horse ambulance right into the operating theatre because there were no trollies. We were told to wait by one of the many nursing sisters as we would be needed to take him to his bed. We were not standing around more

86

than fifteen minutes before we were carrying him out again to his bed. Still unconscious from the anaesthetic, still muddy from the trenches, his leg was now off at the thigh and thickly bandaged. I had witnessed amputations before closer to the line where in minutes the leg, arm or hand was sliced round and then sawn off, but I had thought that what I'd witnessed was an emergency operation. I'd expected it to take longer in a proper hospital. It didn't. Fifteen minutes and a young man was crippled for life.

My little squad met up with our French 'poilu' friends again for more bargaining as they had plenty of wine and we had more contraband bully. One of them, the one who had the most effective English, was called Bertrand. He promised us a special evening at a place he knew so that was arranged for the next night when we were all off duty.

We duly met and they took us to a private house down one of the still undamaged streets of Corbie. We arrived at the front door of a relatively smart house and they led us through the door and into a large front room. On the sofas around the room were sitting four young women aged between twenty and thirty and an older lady who could have been their Aunt or even their Mother. What was this, a brothel? It couldn't be, there were queues outside such places, the ones where the common soldiery were welcome, that is. Discrete places like this were for officers. We were soon disabused. It was nothing of the kind. The older lady was the aunt of Bertrand, our French soldier friend. The young women were two cousins with two friends. All four young ladies were married with husbands at the front. The tins of bully and stew were for them and in exchange they were going to give us a party but all was to be respectable and above board.

They brought out the gramophone and played music to which we danced and they sang songs and we sang old and new ones. We drank red wine but we were on our best behaviour. What a treat to have your arms around the waist of a young women and to be close enough to smell her powder and perfume. All those men at war, wounded and fit and no women, the only consolation perhaps, a letter and at best a photograph from a friend, sweetheart, fiancée or wife at home. At worst a few of the 'saucy' French postcards, much thumbed and dog-eared as they went the rounds. Here we were, laughing, singing and drinking with nice looking French ladies. Language wasn't a barrier, it never is when people are getting on with each other. The war seemed very far away. One of the songs played was a revelation to me. I knew the tune straight away, but of course could not understand the French. I asked one of the girls to write down the words for me in French and for Bertrand to translate it if he could. The words to the song were:

'Si tu veux fait mon bonheur,Margerite,Margerite.
'Si tu veux fait mon bonheur,
'Margerite donne mois ton coeur.

Translated;
'If you want to make me happy, Margerite, give me your heart.'

The version I knew went like this;

> 'Sinty voo dee arbanar,Margerite, Margerite.
> 'Sinty voo dee arbanar,
> 'Margerite dunn moy Dunquerque.'

I had heard the tune sung dozens of times on the march and shouted out over Belgian beer or French vin rouge in many an estaminet but the words I knew were totally different. I found out that they were nonsense. I can't think of any explanation except that the talk of British Tommies was splattered with examples of words that only sounded like French and we used them without thinking. Napoo, sanfairyanne, oompettypoo, even the wine we drank was unaccountably called 'plonkay'. These words hardly got near the original French pronunciation. But the words to 'Margerite' took the biscuit.

We left the house saying goodbye and promising to return and to keep in touch and thanking everybody for their hospitality. Meeting the French would never be quite the same again.

Monday 9 October 1916

With the memory of that evening still with us we moved again. We arrived at a camp situated near our old front line. Now about ten miles behind. Well after the first days of the July/August battles the Germans retreated to a new highly fortified line of defence. All that 'no-man's-land' and all those trenches that we had fought over the Germans had simply 'up-staked' and abandoned.

Where we were was a regular war scene with bell tents, ridge tents and bivouacs scattered everywhere. Dozens of fires where flickering and blazing on the hillside as hundreds of troops brewed up or boiled stew, oblivious to the possibility of an air raid.

Although the line was well ahead, at the front the guns were rumbling and flashing and the sky was lit by flares and searchlights. There was mud of course, we slept in it, covered only by a wagon sheet. However, we slept, that was something. Our expectations were that we would reach the Line tomorrow morning.

Sunday 15 October 1916

This last week has seen us involved in a great deal of activity as we have moved very close to the front at Les Boeufs. Over the past few days a number of attacks have taken place night and day and we have had little sleep being almost constantly on the move, bringing back wounded under fire and having to traverse the most awful ground. The only cover we had were the pre-war sunken roads used by farmers to get to their fields. They always lead towards the German Line, in this case on the ridge across at Le Transloy.

The journeys backwards and forwards were sickening as we had to trudge through the most awful waste of war. There were dead horses everywhere in the mud, in various states of putrefaction, and as they rotted they became part of the landscape. Daft as it sounds, on a battle field you had to watch where you were putting your feet, and this carrying a groaning mature man who couldn't keep still because of his pain. One false step and the most obnoxious stench was released as a distended belly you thought was solid ground, caved in.

During the day, if it was fine and at all warm there were the flies to contend with. They were great fat green or bluebottles and they infested the bodies not only of horses but those of the unburied dead. Sometimes all you could see was a great black buzzing swarm settled on rotting flesh. The unspeakable things that had once been men had lain out there for months when this was 'no-man's-land'. Some of them would have been killed in the first days of July. They were now only recogniseable as soldiers by their ragged tattered uniforms, rotting kit and battered rusty steel helmets. Our instructions were that if we found any dead we should retrieve their identification disc, but surely we had to be forgiven for not reaching past what sometimes were skulls with scraps of skin hanging from the jaw into the collars of rotten shirts of filthy sodden cloth, where the identification disc might be hanging round a skeletal neck. Where we couldn't reach, or we couldn't bring ourselves to reach, the composition disc that every soldier had round his neck we took the personal identity bracelet that it had become the fashion to wear round the wrist. They were unofficial and often the present from a loved one at home with a message on as well as the name. At a pinch they were accepted as evidence that a dead man had been identified Sometimes under the shirts and uniforms of the more recent dead there could be seen the trembling movement of bodies quick with maggots doing their work.

So we waited for orders as to who we were to fetch and carry in a trench hastily dug in the featureless mud. The Aid Post that we took our charges to was in a part of the line that was once a German dug-out. But dug-out seemed an understatement once at the bottom of the forty steps that lead to corridors with doors to rooms off that had been lit, when occupied by Fritz with electric light. It was unbelievable. It was like an underground hotel. You had to admit that Fritzy had known what he was doing when he built his defences on the Somme.

The Infantry are in the valley in between Les Boeufs and Le Transloy waiting for our artillery to clear the ridge before they attack again.

If we win this battle we will capture a desolate countryside. Where there were once the rolling hills of agricultural France with villages, cottages, churches, farms and woods there is not a house nor a recognisable tree standing. The ground is a turmoil of shell holes, broken kit, rifles, equipment, wagons, dud bombs, smashed artillery pieces, shell cases, strewn cartridges, and unmistakably, the corpses of the fallen.

The villages of Carnoy, Guillemont and Ginchy which we passed through on the way here are just great heaps of stinking ruin. Un-typically, as we tramped here there was no singing.

Behind us as we wait, our guns are massed in line for a distance of five miles. When they open up the roar is terrible. The sound over head is like that of a hundred express trains, streaking through a station. As the shells explode the German lines disappear into clouds of red, yellow and purple smoke and flame.

It is no surprise that old Fritzy is feeling the strain, for every day a few men sneak into our lines to give themselves up. One of our jobs is to 'guard' the ones who get near to us. We are then supposed to take them to the rear, but we do this by enlisting them as bearers for the wounded. Our lads don't mind having a Jerry on either side of them with a shoulder under each arm as long as they get to treatment as quickly and as comfortably as possible. The Germans we see look haggard and beat, all they can say is 'Wasser, Bitter' 'Kamerade' 'Danke, Danke'. I did hear one say 'Cigaretten?' but all he got in reply from an unsympathetic 'Yorkie' was, ' Blank off, tha can smoke thee bleedin' own!'

There are some surrendering Germans who give the impression of feeling lucky to be alive. They have a reason for being nervous for there are elements of our troops who have a reputation for dealing harshly with prisoners, treating them brutally and even from time to time sticking the bayonet in. This applies especially to Australians. I heard a story and I don't know if it is true about a group of prisoners being escorted across 'no-man's-land' when they and their captors were caught in an artillery barrage. It was said that the prisoners were all summarily killed.

We continue day after day staying in this period, longer in the line than the usual four to five days. We are granted the concession by a young R.A.M.C. Officer, who happens to be passing, of not having to 'polish up'. Even our senior N.C.O.s can't believe their ears. We've not seen him before and we don't, significantly see him again. Someone probably pushed him in a shell hole. It was noticeable that as he delivered this statement to the couple of squads who were in the post at the time, having a well earned rest and a welcome 'wet and warm' cup of char, that his uniform was immaculate and you could see your face in the polish of his boots.

Sunday 29 October 1916

The last fortnight has been very difficult, cold and wet with new attacks by our Infantry almost every day. Stretcher cases had to be carried down in pitch darkness over narrow tracks marked with white tape between shell holes. The distance we had to travel for each case was nearly two miles.

Two days ago we came down from the Line. What a nice, lousy, starved, dirty and worn-out lot we were but, instead of a hot meal and the possibility of getting a bit cleaned up, we had to go about trying to find our camp which had been shifted, without our knowledge, further back in the sea of mud. When we did find our camp we had to doss down where we could but that made little difference for in our exhausted state most of us slept for two nights and a day – straight. Only stirring to relieve ourselves, drink rum laced tea, then back to sleep again.

Sunday 5 November 1916

After our rest, which was hardly long enough to dry our clothes, we moved to the main Dressing Station at Carnoy. I was feeling a bit dicky so I went sick before we set off. The M.O. in his generosity said that I would be allowed to ride on one of the ambulances and that he was certain that I would feel better when we got to our destination. It was no good. The roads were so bad and crowded that we had to abandon the ambulances and arrange to return later to pick them up. There were lorry convoys of supplies, nose to tail, being overtaken by caterpillar tractors towing howitzers and, in between, motorcycle riders, solo and side car, nipped in and out of gaps that opened up in the traffic. Added to this were columns of troops marching to the rear one way and to the front the other. These columns had to avoid pioneers trying to re-make a road holed by shells and cracked up by vehicles. All this was in mud that was ankle deep so there was no crunching tramp of feet or swish of wheels, only a slushing, slapping sound as a river of mud, once a road, was disturbed in its course. The horses, pulling limbers, carts and wagons, were stoically enduring their work, ignoring that they had dried mud up to their bellies. And as for the poor ammunition mules, they looked very scruffy as they plodded on their way. If it was possible to make these conditions worse, there was the occasional explosion of a long range shell.

The only highlight on this weary march, and I was feeling worse at every step, was that we passed parked 'land crabs', or 'land ships' as a new military machine was called. They had caterpillar tracks on either side, with machine gun and cannon poking through apertures in their armour. They looked like something that might win the war for us because it was obvious that they would crush flat the infernal barbed wire that held up any possibility of movement. We were to come upon what became known as the 'tank' later when we were given special training on how to get wounded crew members out of them.

When we got to Carnoy I was still no better and I had a temperature of 103. The M.O. diagnosed trench fever and I was given an anti-typhus injection and sent to the hospital in Corbie.

I was pretty bad and don't remember the journey much except the stopping and starting of the motor ambulance and the young guardsmen in the bunk above dripping blood on me from a wound in his shoulder. I do remember the clean sheets of the hospital bed. Who would forget that? And I remember the hot bath and the shaving off of four days growth. There I was in my clean pyjamas and I got a quick glimpse of a couple of pretty nurses. I had paradise enough.

Within a couple of days I was up on somewhat shaky legs and helping the orderlies with ward duties, especially the tea making. Within another day I was making my own way back to Death Valley having hitched a lift on an A.S.C. lorry that was delivering supplies to hospitals in the sector. The back was stacked with bully, cheese, tinned butter, sugar and sardines as well as blankets and medical gear. My driver was gasping for a smoke so I arranged a tin of each from the list and some tea I hadn't spotted to change hands for a portion of my cigarette bank. His enthusiasm for the trade was undisguised and besides it was His Majesty's property, not his. With my not having the smoking habit I always felt that I got the best of the bargain.

The A.S.C. wallah dropped me off where I knew my squad would be billeted and I soon found them squatting round a fire in a mud hole, brewing up and chatting about the rumoured move to the rear and rest area. I was welcomed as the prodigal, especially as I was bearing gifts of 'tuck'. We were soon snacking on sardines and bread and butter and I was being congratulated as a 'toff'. It was worth the few fags that it cost.

CHAPTER 6 - OUT OF THE LINE

Sunday 12 November 1916

We are away from the mud of the Somme and Death Valley is simply a memory at last. Now we are set up in the Manoir de Penthieu. It is a fine old house at Blangy-sur-Bresle. Our new billet is between Abbeville and Tréport. To get here we spent three gruelling days on the road re-tracing our steps through to Amiens and past it. Then after that a night in a slow train of carriages that looked as if they had been in the wars as well. Hardly a window was intact and the doors had been ripped off. We were however able to doss down and there was tea and sandwiches in French bread waiting for us at the stops we made. With that, and being able to lie full length, the edge was taken off the long time the journey took.

Our arrival late at night in a downpour of rain was not eased by having to form up in front of the house to be issued with rations and blankets. We stood there waiting and the water dripped on us from trees and broken gutters. Inside we found a hall big enough to have done this exercise under cover. Outside was as dark as the interior. What was the difference? Ask the Army.

Never underestimate the resourcefulness of the average squaddy. Our damp blankets and great coats were soon drying in front of an enormous fireplace that a quick scrounge had filled with wood and our cooks quickly had the ancient stove in the kitchen heating water for a brew. When it was prepared we drank it, milked and sugared with tinned condensed, and laced with the life saving tot of rum that our Sergeant, redeeming himself, produced like a magician. So to bed, in the dry, with a comfortable warm feeling in our innards.

We are now splendidly fixed up and having a fair time. The latrines, ablutions and kitchen are well served with clean fresh water that has never been acquainted with chlorine, petrol or mud. There is fine country around, totally untouched by the war and nearby a nice village in which we spend our time off. The locals are very welcoming and we can drink the plonkay that is on sale at every door. We eat eggs and chips round the stoves of the village old ladies. They will put on such a supper for a few francs.

We have had another bonus in that at last our C.O. has left us. He was not the most popular amongst his ranks of men and his place has been taken by someone who so far seems a very decent chap.

We have the minimum of drills and practices but we still see the necessity of keeping fit and ready for action even though we are enjoying a week's rest away from the cares of the world and the war.

Sunday 19 November 1916

We are still nicely settled and we all feel well rested. It is difficult to convey the comfort of not having your night's sleep persistently interrupted and then not having any opportunity to catch up on 'shut eye'. Here we go to bed at lights out and don't wake up until reveille. There is tea and breakfast waiting for us. We can bathe, shave and use the latrine at our leisure. It will all put us in good heart for whatever tasks lie ahead.

We are back at work, if you can call it that, for in the hospital for Officers we are now running there is only one patient. When I think of the Aid Posts, Clearing Stations and hospitals I have worked in where the only place to put a stretcher was on 'sky hooks' I don't understand how our patient arranged to have this place to himself. I have the job of 'bath attendant' so with only one bather to attend to I have plenty of time to look around.

The weather is variable, frosts, snow and rain with bursts of splendid sunshine in blue cloudless skies.

One or two of the neighbouring villages are occupied by detachments of Indian Cavalry and I have spent many an interesting hour talking to them about one of my favourite subjects, horses. A good few of the men have not seen action yet, for the promised break-through, when they would ride on through German lines, has not come yet. They are finding the weather difficult. It is not the cold, they say, but getting used to the changes every day.

Some of the others, as far as I could note Sikhs, have already endured a Continental winter in Belgium and they know what to expect when they go up the line to the mud and the cold.

Sunday 26 November 1916

Life at Blangy is still good. I get a lot of time to write my diary, write letters, and to read the books I have begged, borrowed and stolen. I am reading Hardy's Tess of the D'urbervilles and I think I am in love with Tess. That almost perfect combination of light duties, comfortable billet, good hot food, hot tea on tap, plus the significant bonus of not being shot at cannot last. If it went on until Christmas and we stayed here we would be 'quids' in.

We are still making the most of what the village has to offer. To serve our needs one enterprising villager has opened his house as a little 'club'. There we have taken to drinking a fizzy French wine that you can buy there. At one time I would have said it was champagne but its not the real McCoy. It is though quite palatable except that you have a 'bit of a head' the next morning.

Tuesday 28 November 1916

I received letters from Dad, Maud and Phyllis at home and one from Ernest, who has had a week's leave in Halifax. Tilly sent me a card. Ernest in his letter wrote that his lot had been opposite Transloy on the 12th November, just as we left. Dad has written to ask if I have been to where Tom is buried so I shall have to write back to say, no. Tilly's message was brief but to the point. 'I miss you, I love you', and she wrote it herself. Her missives do seem to be getting shorter and less frequent. The girls seem to be much taken with fellows that they are walking out with and I wouldn't be surprised if wedding bells are not in the air. I also had a letter from someone who had volunteered to write to me from the Church in Hull. What I should write in reply is that my church going has dropped off somewhat and that I am not quite as sober in my habits as I used to be, plus reference to the fact that there is an important community of my fellow man that I am supposed to hate to death. ' C'est la guerre.'

Thursday 30 November 1916

We have a new man in 'C' section who, as soon as he was settled in, volunteered to bake for us. He persuaded the cooks to let him borrow the oven in the kitchen for half an hour and with ingredients 'he had about his person' he had in that time drummed up hot scones for tea. We ate them with butter and Tickler's plum and apple. There were unfortunately no currants to be had 'not even for ready money', but they went down well just the same. He has suggested, bless his heart, that he could bake a Christmas cake if we scrounge the ingredients. He gave us a list.

Sunday 3 December 1916

A and B sections moved off today leaving us to evacuate what patients we had. They have gone now by motor ambulance to Abbeville and beyond. We are still enjoying life in this 'cushy little number' but the threatened move is coming so we will have to like it or lump it.

Saturday 9 December 1916

After a week of sweeping, scrubbing and packing we are ready to move 'somewhere down south'. That was the reply when we asked where we were going. It sounds like the title of a Kentucky Minstrel show.

We are very disappointed to be moving so close to Christmas. Had we stayed here we might have had a tree and decorations just like home. 'Maybe Father Christmas might have come down the chimney' was the plaintive cry. 'I should cocoa', 'Don't you know there's a blanketty war on?'. These are the words of encouragement we get from our Sergeant. Our reply, out of his earshot of course is 'Yes Sergeant, No Sergeant, Three bags blanketty full, Sergeant.'

Monday 11 December 1916

We are on the move to join our unit as promised 'Somewhere down south'. But we all know what that means, we are going back to the Somme.

At first we thought it would be a 'quickie', the move that is, for the first part of the journey was by train, albeit in carriages that as before were in need of repair. Back home they would have been confined to scrap. But for us they were 'Pulman' luxury. Anything was better than 'Shanks' Pony'.

Our thoughts on a quick journey were soon dispelled for we were shunted into a siding after the engine's first chugs and rattles. There we stayed for a day and a night on bare rations with no hot food and no hot drinks, even the engine boiler was cold. It was freezing in the compartments but we had been warned of the overnight stop so each one of us with any sense had 'won' an extra blanket. But it rained in. A man who appointed himself section scrounger, he was a middle-aged man from Rotherham called Bert Thompson, and I became quite a pal of his, went through the window onto the track and came back dragging a railway wagon cover whose only disadvantage was that it smelled of horses. We didn't mind for it covered the ten of us in the carriage. So, buried in blankets and great coats, snuggled together for warmth and under the tarpaulin, the cold was kept out and the rain that was dripping through the broken windows was kept off. We slept maybe only for several hours, but we slept.

Tuesday 12 December 1916

Came the dawn and it had been so cold in the night that the water had frozen on our canopy. The morning was misty with the frost still in the air and only a pale grey light where the sun on the horizon should have been. With each sunrise came the 'dawn chorus'. It was not the sweet song of the nightingale in the valley below but the coughing and rauking of the early morning smokers as they lit the first gasper of the day and choked on the first puffs. As, with eyes bulging, tongues out, they seem to be choking, the usual remark was, 'Come on, cough it up, it might be a gold watch'. Sympathy at such times was not the strong point of my comrades.

As we shuffled and fidgeted ourselves awake the call came to de-train and we opened the doors to jump down on the track. We had to line up and have the roll called, but as we stamped the circulation back into our feet and clapped our woolly gloved hands, the clank of dixies, 'was heard in the land.' There was to be a mess tin of hot stew for each, followed by hot tea and rum (in the same tin). After that the standard phrase that normally summed up such complete satisfaction was, 'Well if they come steady..........' I shall not, dear reader, attempt to explain its meaning. We got back in the train and had to settle down to another day and night of waiting. But this time we did get hot drinks and hot food. So with cards to play, cigarettes to smoke, the fat the chew and, as far as I was concerned, a book to read, the time was passed.

Wednesday 13 December 1916

This morning after breakfast, with much rattling, puffing and spinning of wheels, the old engine set off and we began to chug through a countryside that showed the signs of early winter. There was frost in the furrows of the deserted fields and the leafless trees had branches that showed black against the grey mist.

The train began to slow to fits and starts, upsetting the cards on the knees of the nap players. We stopped, I don't know where, once again in sidings and in the daylight hours we were there, watched supply trains and ambulance trains, passers by having obvious priority over us.

We had just resigned ourselves to a night once again in a stationary train when our carriages were jerked forward and we began to rattle along slowly. Rations had been issued so we ate bully, biscuit, sardines, cheese and jam. Only cold water to drink. I distributed pieces of chocolate from a store I had been keeping for Christmas and was almost 'canonised'. We rolled over to sleep but this time just under our blankets as we had cut up the canopy to cover windows that were letting in rain and wind.

Thursday 14 December 1916

We passed through Amiens in the early hours and towards five in the morning arrived at Albert. It had taken three days to make a journey by train that would, in peace time, have taken a morning.

The winter weather has set in. 'The frost was cruel' to quote the old carol as we formed up off the train to begin a march in light snow to our billet.

As soon as we began to march our feet got warmed up and the vigour of our movement got the blood coursing through our veins. Within a short time we were in good enough spirits to sing in spite of the falling snow:

> If you want the old battalion,
> I know where they are,
> Repeat, Repeat
> Repeat first line
> I know where they are,
> They are hanging on the old barbed wire,
> I've seen em, I've seen em,
> Hanging on...................

We only managed one rendering before there came the stentorian voice of the S.M. 'Quiet in the ranks.' They didn't like that one.

By previous standards it was not a long march, and within two hours we had arrived at our billet. It was a large plank-built hut wrapped round with roofing felt and standing in a sea of mud near a place called Bronfay Farm (or what was left of it). We were back making mud pies on the Somme. But not to worry, for just as we deposited our kit on the bare boards of our new home sloshing through the mud came a horse drawn field cooker. Within minutes we were listening to the spluttering of frying bacon in an enormous pan with the spitting of falling snow adding to the sound. Bacon sandwiches and hot tea, how easily our loyalties were won over.

Sunday 17 December 1916

We are in an area that was part of the join between the French and British lines and we have now taken over a French camp of about a dozen quite large well constructed huts. We have orders to make them into a Corps Rest Station for upwards of a thousand patients. The huts are, to say the least, a bit 'untidy'.

In this weather of by turns frost, snow, wind and rain, the country is miserable. We are in between Bray and Maricourt and across the Somme valley is Sailly Laurette.

In rear areas such as we are in, with so many troops about, trips to villages close by for diversion are not that enjoyable. In the estaminets it is a crush and the prices charged even by Divisional canteens are exorbitant. The profiteer is not only at his business back home. There are plenty in evidence here. Bartering is still a possibility and we have Christmas in mind when seeking out those in need of cigarettes and the extra rations that we have 'obtained'. Mr. Bun the Baker says he will stick by his promise if we can get the 'makings' of a Christmas cake.

Sunday 24 December 1916

A fine sunny day that dried up the mud somewhat. Everybody is hard at work at the camp. We are putting down planks and duck boards. These lead to the ablution and latrine block. We are arranging and repairing stoves for warmth and fitting out a recreation block. As we do this we are all looking forward to working here as we can see that it is all our own work and we are only occasionally disturbed by the odd stray artillery shell to remind us that there is still a war on.

The rumour is that there is to be a Christmas truce but as usual there is more hope behind such rumours than fact.

At tea time Christmas Eve Mr Bun the Baker was as good as his word. He baked us a cake. We'd collected ingredients for him out of parcels from home to which we added local flour, eggs and of course rum. He didn't like the French flour we scrounged. In his expert opinion it was ground differently but he made do. The other thing he made do with was the oven. No bribe would persuade the guardians of the field cookers to give him access for his baking so he improvised an oven from a bin. He put the bin horizontally over bricks, fitted it with bits of iron for a grate and then covered the bin with thick clay mud. There was no shortage of that. Then making a fire underneath with wood we provided, the smoke of which came out of an old pipe at the back of a chimney, and this he had to regulate carefully so that it wasn't seen by Jerry spotters, he put in his cake and closed the front of the bin with a bit of flat tin. His baker's nonce told him when it was done and out it came. It was a bit black round the edges, but nonetheless a large Christmas cake and home made. With that and the contents of parcels that yielded everything comestible from mince pies to marzipan, we had a very nice Christmas Eve tea. We then sat round the stove cosy, content and holding mugs of tea, we thought of home.

There was no Christmas Eve truce. We had to turn out to go to Bronfay to bring back casualties from a Welsh Regiment to the dressing station which had been dug into the hillside. Fortunately for everybody, there weren't many and it only took a couple of squads to bring back three wounded who needed carrying and two who made it on their own. They had been wounded by a Christmas present from Fritz's artillery.

The night was clear and very cold. The mud was frost frozen and we slipped and slid as we tried to keep the boy steady on the stretcher we had. After a few hundred yards we realised there was no point in care, he was dead.

Monday 25 December 1916

We are not on duty today. We rose late to a breakfast of bacon and bread with fresh tea. As we got up Bert, as usual, was very cheerful. With a big smile on his face he said, 'I slept like a baby last night, I pissed the bed and woke up screaming for my mother.' It is very cold.

After breakfast we began preparations for Christmas dinner, which each hut is organising for itself. No shells have come over since last night. After the carry, as we made our way back to bed last night, or rather this morning, a star shell was shot high in the air. I didn't know if it came from their side or ours but I wondered if it signalled the rumoured temporary cease fire.

As we were getting things together there was the timely arrival of mail from home. There was quite a bit left in our hut and it was a nice Christmas box. Parcels of goodies had already been delivered so this lot was mostly letters and cards. The cards went up around the hut and then there was a silence as letters were read. I had a letter from Dad and Maud just saying that I would be missed and one from Tilly telling me that she and pals from the mill were going to have a night out this Christmas.

We then sat down to a Christmas dinner of potatoes, onions and a stew with what looked like lumps of beef in it, but the neighing and clippetty clop sounds made with cupped hands betrayed a general lack of confidence in the identity of the meat. 'Think yourselves blanketty lucky that you are not in the trenches.' said the cooks who delivered it for our collection. And as they left they had a chorus of 'And a merry blanketty Christmas to you too.' ringing in their ears. Whatever it's origins we ate it, and with contraband bottles of plonkay wine and 'oo dee vee' added to the camaraderie around the table we had a good time. One of our number had been an Officer's 'Batman' before he blotted his copy book. He said that the officers would be having goose, pâté de fois gras and champagne on their menu. It is alright for some.

By the time we had finished other squads began arriving in our hut and altogether we had a good 'sing song' that was the usual mixture of soldiers' ballads with traditional Christmas carols. We then moved the party into the village where we had a riotous spree that resulted in so much making merry that military and regimental policemen on their usual patrol became nervous that there might be a general outbreak of 'going home.'

Tuesday 26 December 1916

We were given no time at all to recover from our 'morning after' feeling. For as soon as reveille was sounded we were sent orders to pack up and before you could say 'hangover' we were, much to our disappointment on the road to Sailly Laurette. The 19th Field Ambulance took over a camp that was 'all our own work.'

Sunday 31 December 1916

We have been told firmly that there will be no 'excused duties' for New Year's Eve and that there is to be no partying. I don't think we are in the mood for it anyway. The job we have been on this last week since Christmas was over, has been cleaning up conditions in the village. It is in a filthy state. Latrine discipline, not to put too fine a point on it, has been ignored. There is waste food, cheese slices, half eaten bully, rotting biscuit, and general army rubbish including mule and horse manure that has simply been left. There are rats everywhere. We are not in a good mood, especially after all the good work we did at Bronfay. Quite a few of us are already on 'fizzers' (charges) for insubordination. We have renamed ourselves the Royal Army Shit Shovellers. Our only consolation is that we are doing it in fine weather.

Sunday 7 January 1917

After a week of working to clear up the mess someone else has left we have now moved with C Section to Chippilly, the village next to Sailly Laurette. Here we are converting another old camp of huts into a Field Hospital. We are also extending the communal cemetery. It is to the north of the village and from it you can see the valley of the River Somme. Chippilly is about thirteen or fourteen miles from our new front line at Le

Transloy, so we are well out of the action.

The Hospital we are fixing up will provide a place away from the front line where patients can rest and recuperate and where the more seriously wounded can have a pause before going to the coast or even to the fabled homeland 'Blighty.'

Sunday 14 January 1917

Still fine but very, very cold. The line is quiet so there are few casualties reaching us. We are getting on with our hospital building.

The huts we are erecting are substantial and well made. They are specially constructed in England to be shipped out in sections so that they can be put up on the spot. They are waterproofed and their well fitting windows and doors keep out the cold and the wet. They would make nice houses.

Our task is as before, but the work is cleaner. Our situation is better drained, being a bit higher. We do however, have to keep a close eye on the materials and supplies we have, especially anything burnable. We have been told that there is a fuel shortage across the whole of the line in France. The shortage is not on the German's side as they occupy the French and Belgian coalfields. In this severely cold weather any timbers we leave about tend to 'walk'.

I had to go a few miles closer to the line to Maricourt to get some gear for our hospital and I got an idea of how the cold is effecting the boys in the Line. The Advanced Dressing Station there has a number of cases of very bad trench foot and frost bite along with chronic influenza patients, trench fever and measles. The men in the trenches are standing twenty four hours at a stretch in fifteen inches of frozen water. There is nowhere to lie down, nowhere to make a fire, if there was any fuel, and food from field kitchens is cold when ration parties do manage to get it into the line.

Back behind the lines at Chippilly the hospital is beginning to take shape. We have finished the baths and latrines with quite a bit of help from some Royal Engineers who kept telling us that they could have earned a fortune at home if they had stayed in protected employment. 'We were told we would be sorry when we volunteered. We should have listened'. Shouldn't we all?

We are trying to keep warm in our free time by playing football and rounders. Football is as much passionately followed here as back home. Our Corps is now in the final for the Divisional Cup and being the 'home team' we hope they win it.

Mr Bun the baker, who is still baking his bread and cakes in spite of the fuel shortage, is a keen footballer and even had a trial for Rotherham United before he came out. He suggested over tea and hot buttered teacakes fresh from his 'bin oven' that we should play football instead of going to war.

We all assured him that his suggestion would be sent to the proper authorities, especially as 'we all knew Lloyd George and Lloyd George knew our fathers.' Andy Jackson, of another squad, an astute Liverpudlian who could always be relied on for a merry quip, said that the problem would be if the Germans were losing they would mount a maxim in the goal mouth.

Tuesday 16 January 1917

We have acquired two dogs at the hospital. They were found wondering about, scavenging for food and were becoming a bit of a nuisance. They were probably abandoned by a refugee farmer. They are proving useful in what is truly an international sport of the Western Front. I know the French go in for it, we do it and I can't think the Germans don't indulge. The sport is rat hunting. There are so many that the Pied Piper would have enough work until his pension, even though Hamelin is Fritz-side.

It is not just their numbers for they scurry about in groups of four or five, perhaps they are family groups, it is their size. 'I saw one the other day with a cat in its mouth' is not so much an exaggeration, and they get everywhere, the hospital, latrines, kitchens and our billets.

So along with our truly French dogs we are hunting them out, so far the kill is twenty but another twenty will take their place.

The problem here that encourages rats, is waste, There is so much waste food, particularly the cheese slice and the teeth breaking biscuit. Mind you, the waste biscuit problem maybe solved by the fuel shortage. Three or four biscuits, set burning by a drop of oil in an old bully tin punched with holes and whirled round the head on a piece of wire, will soon give off a glow easily hot enough to warm hands or heat a mess-tin of water for a brew of tea.

Sunday 21 January 1917

A padre came to give Sunday service at Church parade. He had obviously only just come out from England and was not quite used to the language that the men come out with. At dinner time he showed his Christian fellowship and he asked to eat at the table with us. He was shocked and non-comprehending when a soldier in his hearing, while proffering his mess tin to the cooks, was heard to say 'Oh blank, not blanketty Mac blanketty con blanketty ochie's blanketty again.' A Sergeant at one of the tables stood up and said 'Right you lot watch your language, we have a man of the cloth as a guest!'

The weather is dry but fairly frosty and in the wind it is even colder. Our hospital is now open and we are busy with patients. The ward I am on for night duty is already full of young men with trench maladies and not a few with artillery wounds. Shells bursting on the frozen ground give a greater spread to fragments.

I am busy all night with bottles and bed pans, not only for those who can't get to the latrines but also for those who don't want to, as its too cold. I am not going to grumble. If the patients get out of bed the door has to be opened and that lets Jack Frost in. As it is the frost is on the inside of the windows. There is not enough fuel for the stove and the best place is in bed under the blankets. I wish I was there.

Sunday 28 January 1917

We have now had a week of the hardest frost I have ever known. It has been fifteen degrees below zero. Even the French say they have not known it as cold for twenty years.

The water tower to the hospital so expertly erected by the Royal Engineers is frozen up and in danger of cracking. Getting clean water is a job in itself. The dogs have gone to warmer climes but then so have the rats. We wait for water carts but by the time they arrive they have frozen up.

For me, on duty at night, keeping warm is almost impossible. I sit in my great coat wrapped round with two blankets, but I am still cold. I am very pleased to see the daylight.

Once during the week I braved the cold and went outside because I had heard Archie Guns and the noise of aircraft engines. Over head, caught in a searchlight beam, there was a squadron of big German planes. High up in the black sky with stars twinkling in the frosty night I could see them as dark shadows and their German markings were clearly lit. Dots and dashes of sparking tracer arched upwards in what seemed slow elevation. I had no thought of how dangerous it might be had they dropped bombs, standing as I was staring skywards as if I was watching some aerial show on a Bank holiday. The A.A. fire made them fly higher and they were driven off.

Thursday 8 February 1917

We started out today early after a hot breakfast of porridge, bacon, bread, jam and tea. We were ordered to go to Bray and make for the line east of Suzanne where we were to 'assist as necessary' along with two more squads of bearers. I was particularly sluggish after only three hours sleep.

The weather is still cold and although we were promised wheeled transport, it did not turn up so it was 'shanks' with a hand cart to carry our gear and equipment. 'Corky and Co, bearers to the gentry, stretchers provided.'

We halted for the night and one of the three C.C.S.s in the village kindly provided accommodation and a hot dinner. We bedded down early.

Friday 9 February 1917

We were on the march again to Suzanne but not before we had been treated to a full English breakfast of porridge, bacon and eggs, bread and jam and lashings of real coffee. Some people have all the luck.

The only thing that can be said of the tramp to Suzanne is that it got our blood moving on a very cold day. The frozen ground rang to our boots and there was not the least 'give' in the surface, which made for hard marching.

We arrived at Suzanne in daylight and were shown our lodgings for the night, a bell tent in a camp with many others. We had an extra store of blankets on the cart so our caravan was happy to rest.

For reasons of supply difficulty we were told at dinner time that rations were short so we were asked to use our own. Of course we protested just in case the plenty that we had provided for ourselves attracted the dreaded and voracious 'scrounge fly'. We fed ourselves on our usual fare of bully, cheese, sardines and jam with the bonus of a batch of bread that Mr Bun had baked for us. 'He shall have a 'putty medal' for services to humanity' said Bert Thompson. 'And no less a person but the King shall present it' we all chorused........for

> Last night we dined with the King
> And he did a peculiar thing
> He stood on a stool
> And pulled out his blank
> And said 'If I play, will you sing'.

The Royal Engineers in Suzanne had set up a picture house in a barn and so in the cosy fug made by a hot stove and tobacco smoke we watched Fatty Arbuckle and drank some vin plankay that we swapped for a couple of fags.

When we got back to our tent we found that some of our blankets had been 'won in a raffle' and the locked box we kept our rations in, had been forced. Our hope was that the missing tins and our last loaf of fresh bread had gone to 'the needy not the greedy'.

Saturday 10 February 1917

The thaw has just started and the road we tramped along to Clery, where we have been directed our Aid Post is, was already muddy and the melting snow and ice was dripping off the trees in the wood we marched through. We are now in a sector part of which was once held by the French Army. The evidence of the hard fighting both armies endured, French and German, is all around us and under our feet as we go up close to the line. There are many dead about, still unburied, and most of them are French. Rifles lie discarded like sticks and the rubbish of soldiers and battle is thawing into a carpet of packs and rotting cloth.

At the Aid Post we are warned of the work we have to do. Apart from the day to day 'wastage' as ordinary casualties are called, a big attack is expected in a day or two.

At the Post there are a number of men suffering from influenza and dysentery. Really they are simply victims of extreme cold. It seems sick parades in the line are getting longer. But why wouldn't they? Four or five days in the open under fire, no warmth, no cover, no hot food, standing in freezing water, anybody would be sick. It is a wonder that the whole army doesn't come down with something.

The thaw continues and the mud is knee deep again. It flows over the top of our rubber boots and before long we are caked with the freezing stuff.

Towards ten, in order to pick up 'a carry' we had to go up to positions held by the 33rd Division, Royal Fusiliers, Welsh Fusiliers and Worcesters, etc. The German Line here is called the Hertzfeld trench. Across from there we picked up our casualty, a Welsh boy with a stomach wound from a splinter. We looked at it in the light of an Officer's torch and it did not look deep so we left the metal splinter in as it kept the blood from flowing. We gave him morphine and somebody lit him the inevitable cigarette. I wished he hadn't for his cough attracted attention and something or other began buzzing past us. A sniper I suppose, aiming at the sound.

That was only the beginning. We had gone up to near the Line with two squads making eight men and we had two miles to carry. That is two miles of supposed trenches to walk in.

They were old German communication trenches and had once been tidy and deep with duck boards and revetting. All that had gone as fuel for braziers. Now these trenches were just deep muddy ditches with sections blown in by shells and long stretches collapsed by the thaw. The stink of decomposition that usually went with a big freeze had returned and already the rats had come back nosing their way across pools of the thaw. Their fat shapes leaving ripples behind in their wake.
Some lengths of trench had not been walked down for weeks and dead lay on the muddy floors or were under the water that now flooded in. Slipping and sliding on god knows what we plodded and sloshed our way back, cursing the war, the mud, the casualty and eventually each other.

At one point in our journey just as a grey cold dawn was breaking we were so startled and frightened by what we saw we almost abandoned the stretcher 'to hop over the

bags' and to run away over the top. As we clumsily manoeuvred our charge around a traverse we saw a tall figure, as we thought standing, at the entrance to what had been a dug out. Our fear changed to curiosity. We looked closer. It had once been a man but he was now dead, but erect. We couldn't tell if he was German or French, most of his uniform had gone and his body was now beginning to thaw and droop. He seemed to be caught on something at the back. It was a broken rifle with a bayonet still attached. He had been transfixed by it, the point through him and then firmly embedding itself in the gap between the concrete posts holding up the entrance to the dug out.

We arrived at our Aid Post exhausted and to complaints such as, 'Where the blank have you been, you've been out all night. Have you got a woman?' Taking turns to carry, the eight of us had taken nearly seven hours to travel approximately two miles. For the last few hours our casualty, overdosed with morphine had lapsed into fortunate unconsciousness.

Thursday 16 February 1917

I don't think the expected attack came off. I don't know, they tell us nothing. We are still busy with the daily grind and the thaw, though nearly finished, is making it worse. There has been no rain but the mud is still knee deep. It gets everywhere, especially in food. We are covered in it and don't really get a chance to clean up. It's possible to be charged for taking your clothes off to clean them when you're in the line. We do have to shave, which is uncomfortable, to say the least, in cold water. I have Grandad's cut throat that I can sharpen. The others have to put up with razor blades that have seen better days. There is still a fuel shortage and the nights are still very cold. We are managing to sleep fairly cosily wrapped up warm on the bed frames left in an old German dug-out that we are using. At least we are off the cold floor.

The one night when we had more than two hours sleep at a stretch was rudely interrupted in the early hours by what sounded like the artillery barrage of a counter attack. The enormous force of the explosions rocked our dug-out to the point where we thought it might cave in so we rushed up the steps to the outside. It wasn't German artillery but one of our own ammunition dumps going up. Although it was some miles away we could see smoke, flames and sporadic explosions in the early morning light. It is the second big dump that German air-raiders have found recently.

There was another kind of hell let loose afterwards as we had a mad scramble to assist in bringing out casualties, of which there were four hundred.

When we got to the limits of the blast the dump was still burning, spitting and farting as smaller bombs went off, and the area for hundreds of yards around was littered with unexploded shells that had been thrown up by the blast. The R.E.s were already there collecting them or defusing them. Men were wondering around dazed and shocked, some bleeding from the nose and ears, but all they got if they could walk was the instruction 'sit down a bit, have a rest and then go to the Aid Post down there'. There were too many severely injured to take time with 'walking wounded'. There were severe burns cases, blast victims, men with injuries from flying metal and cases of extreme shock, so extreme that we had to tie one poor sod to the stretcher because his convulsions and trembling kept throwing him off. Once again we had some long and difficult carries. The light railway that there is running down to Clery was soon busy and full with wounded passengers.

Friday 17 February 1917

It took us days to sort out the shambles of the exploded ammunition dump and there were still bombs going off forty eight hours after with consequent casualties.

There is nothing more true than the phrase 'it is an ill wind' for in all the tragedy of death, suffering and injury 'bounty had fallen from the skies'. Near to the ammunition dump there had been other stores and these had gone up in the explosion. The result was a short sharp shower of tins of rations and stores of all sorts, including rolls of somewhat scorched blankets. Tins of bully, butter, bacon, stew, sardines and bags of sugar were all over the place. We had to gather it in before the M.P.s put the area 'out of bounds'.

Apart from some damaged bags of sugar everything our scavenging found, though dented, was intact. It was not the case with the rum jars. They either didn't survive the blast or they and their wicker basket were smashed as they landed, but you can't have everything. 'Manna from Heaven' was never so appropriate a quotation for the material we were able to 'rescue'. Of course it all had to be collected and returned to the Quatermaster's stores, but in that classic phrase 'Blank that for a game of soldiers'.

Sunday 25 February 1917

We are now at Twelve camp, the journey to which has brought us to a hill overlooking our old hospital near Chippilly.

Last Friday we were relieved from the line by the 8th Division which has West Yorks, East Lancs, Sherwood Foresters and Lincolnshire Regiments amongst others in it. We set off once we had reorganised to make for Suzanne early on Saturday morning, then we marched here in the afternoon.
We are under canvas again and being issued with poor rations. There is gladness in our hearts that we can supplement them with dips into our 'found' stores. Fresh bread would be nice but there is a struggle for it in the village where there is a French baker. The price is high and we can't afford it. I scouted all round the village and did in the end find a farm house where a couple of stale loaves were going spare in exchange for a tin of jam.

Sunday 4 March 1917

The weather is fine with just a hint of spring. We are at Villers-Bocage, a small village where we rested for a few days last September. On Wednesday we marched Chippilly to Corbie staying again very comfortably in the Chateau.

We spent a few pleasant days getting settled and having access to hot water and hot food. I took the opportunity of having a bath. I found an enamel hip bath during a scrounge in a roof space above where we were sleeping at the top of the Chateau. We were in small bare rooms that I suppose were used by servants in the Chateau's heyday. I soon had it filled with hot water that I painstakingly carried in bucket after bucket up the steep stairs and I luxuriated in it. I did this until the duty Officer popped his head round the door and had me out of it so that he could requisition my prize. My protestations that I had promised my mates the use of it after me were laughed off. As his Batman emptied it out and then carried it away I stood there still soapy in my 'Birthday suit', cursing the officer class - under my breath of course.

There are two theatres in operation here but we missed their performances. We did hear though the band that played in the square and it gave us plenty of Martial music.

The shops here are well stocked if we had the money to spend in them.

On Saturday afternoon our Corps played in the final for the Divisional cup and we won three-one.

Our march to Villers-Bocage today was a pleasant one in fine weather. We passed on the way through the small communities of Pont Nouvelle, Sant Gratien and Moulin Le Bois. There were cheery greetings from civilians as we went on our way. In Moulin Le Bois the villagers who turned out to wave us on were in their 'Sunday Best'.

Monday 5 March 1917

Drew 20 Francs today. We are to leave Villiers-Bocage to march to Boeval where we are to stay the night. It is still very cold and when we wake we have to break the ice on water before we wash.

We started our march and were soon stepping out in the spring sunshine and in good voice:

> Whiter than the whitewash on the wall
> Repeat
> Wash me in the water that you washed your dirty daughter in
> And I shall be whiter than the whitewash on the wall

Followed by

> One staff Officer jumped right over another staff Officer's back
> And another staff Officer jumped
> Right over another staff Officer's back
> They were only playing leap frog
> Repeat

At Boeval we were lucky to be billeted on some very nice French civilians. After we had stowed our gear Bert Thompson, who was sharing the billet with me and I sat in their kitchen in front of a blue tiled stove and ate egg and chips with fresh French bread and butter and drank tea while we talked.

The man of the house was about and had already been discharged from service in the French army. He had been in the French army equivalent of the Engineers and had sustained a back injury while building a temporary bridge. He walked with difficulty. What was unusual was that he spoke very good English. The explanation for this was that before the war he had been a waiter in the posh London restaurants of the Savoy and the Dorchester hotels. I expressed surprise that he wasn't working as an interpreter. He said he had suggested this when injured but the French authorities had been indifferent and had not used him, very much their loss.

We talked into the night about all sorts of things, about French culture, life and history. I told him that not far up the road was Crecy where the English had fought the French and to the north was Agincourt. Both those battles were in the Hundred Years War and I expressed the hope that this one wouldn't last a hundred years. I was surprised to learn that the man and his wife had not heard of Crecy or Agincourt. Obviously French school history missed them out.

That night we slept in a bed with sheets, absolute and utter bliss. The bedroom was bare except for a big wooden bed and a metal stand that held a bowl with a big jug underneath. On the wall there were two faded photos in oval frames of two old people. They were the grandmother and grandfather of our host.

Tuesday 6 March 1917

I personally woke up the next morning feeling better than I have felt in a very long time. Bert and myself took it in turns to wash and shave in the hot water brought up in a jug by the wife. We then went downstairs to an already cosy kitchen where we breakfasted on fresh bread, butter and home made strawberry jam washed down with bowls of sweet milky coffee.

When we left we vowed to keep in touch and said regretful goodbyes, leaving our rations of bully, jam and sardines on the kitchen table. These were for some reason, gratefully received. The meat, I think, they didn't get much of it.

The next leg of our journey was to Nouex and we were somewhat shocked when we were told it would be a long march of twenty six kilometres. By the end of it we were knackered and we more or less only shuffled into the barn allocated as our sleeping quarters. We spent a few minutes rearranging the dry straw that was to be our bed. What a contrast from the night before. None the less we got our heads down straightaway, lifting them only very briefly to accept the dixie of hot cocoa that came round accompanied by sandwiches of stale bread and cheese which we wolfed anyway, then oblivion until reveille.

Wednesday 7 March 1917

On a cold and frosty day we made a brief march to Outrebois, near Doullens, where our job was to finish the hospital started by another Field Ambulance. It had been set up in another empty Chateau requisitioned by the Army.

After dumping our gear in the outbuildings of the Chateau me and Bert chose billets in the village surrounding the Chateau park. We were hoping for the same standard that we had experienced in Boevel. We were disappointed and found ourselves offered a shed next to the outside 'cabinet' of a cottage lived in by an old lady. She demonstrated early on that she was only interested in the billeting allowance and she did not make us welcome at all.

Sunday 11 March 1917

We have now got our hospital up and running in the Chateau. The building is in good condition with large rooms that lend their dimensions to well proportioned wards. Our Medical Officer is proudly claiming that it will be at least as good as some of the hospitals on the coast. He even goes so far as to say that it might be as good as some in England. We have no patients yet and it seems heartless to wish for them solely because we want to try such facilities as the newly equipped operating theatre. We have been told that female nurses are on the way to complete the picture.

The village around the Chateau is small so there are no cafés or estaminets yet but down the road Doullens has the promise of a night life.

Sunday 18 March 1917

This week has seen a tragedy, if you can talk in such a way with a war on that is killing thousands. But this tragedy was personal. Two of our men were found dead in a saddle room at the Chateau where they had set up their billet. Their room was just the right size for two with good windows and a well fitting door and they had made themselves very comfortable, too comfortable. To make the place as warm as they could they had taken in a brazier made from an old bucket and filled it with coke that they had filched from the Chateau boiler room. When they bedded down for the night they left it burning and as they slept the fumes from it did their work.

They were good mates and they had been with us in the Ambulance for a long time and we had endured some sticky moments together. What a pity that they should die in this way when shot and shell had not been able to find them out. We had a service for them at which I said a few comradely words and we buried them in the local churchyard down the hill from the Chateau at Outrebois. The M.O. is to write to their people. If I come out of this I shall go back to visit their graves one day.

Wednesday 21 March 1917

We are now at Ourton, a village between St Pol and Bethune. Last night we had all settled down wrapped up warm for sleep when we received sudden orders to move. With much cursing, fumbling confusion and disorganisation we formed up ready. We marched all through the night and I think I was asleep most of the way for I remember very little of the march except that the road was very bad and if I did 'wake up' it was after falling, as others did, into the pot holes that broke up the road surface.

We passed through a small town called Frévent where there were lines and lines of motor coaches ready to speed hundreds of troops to Berlin, as one wag suggested. More likely they were for use as ambulances. Then we went on to Ecoures where we rested and I stayed asleep for another three hours.
We arrived at Ourton in daylight after what could have been described as a forced march. We had completed approximately fifty kilometres in twenty hours, night and day. I am thinking about joining the French Foreign Legion.

Thursday 22 March 1917

I have been lucky with my billet again and I have found a nice 'civvy' billet in the cottage of two old folk who treat me like their son. It's a pity there is only room for one.

Army work has begun again with practices, drilling and lectures. We are told by an R.A.M.C. Officer that speed is of the essence when getting casualties out of the line. We have decided he must be 'just off the boat' and ought to get some 'service in'. The last thing we need is someone like him ignoring our experience and telling us the blankety obvious. A week up the line should sort him out.

There is a rumour circulating that the Tsar of Russia has fallen and that Russian troops are leaving their lines and going home. What it means, if true, is difficult for us to sort out. Does it mean that the Russians are pulling out of the war?

Certainly here we are not pulling out for we seem to be on the verge of another 'big push' and we and the troops and equipment on the move through here, in the direction of Arras, seem to be preparing for it. If there is one in the offing let's hope it's not a 'cock up' like the Somme and the Ancre. Its difficult to put a finger on it but there is a sense of anticipation in the air, no excitement only a pleased confident determined feeling, whoever you ask and whoever you talk to. Meanwhile I am enjoying the comparative luxury of my 'civvy' billet.

Sunday 25 March 1917

I woke from my 'box bed' behind a curtain in the kitchen of 'my little grey home in the west' to the warmth of a stove on which there was fresh coffee and fried eggs. I know the eggs were fresh because I collected them after the chickens that I mind had laid them. I also help with weeding and digging the garden. It is such a change from my army work.

After breakfast I went to church in the village and although it was of course Roman Catholic and so I couldn't take Communion, it was good to be among the villagers at worship. My French wasn't good enough to understand the sermon or the reading and I couldn't sing the hymns but nobody minded, especially not my hosts, who had invited me. It was the first time I had experienced any sort of church service for weeks.

CHAPTER 7 - ARRAS

Sunday 1 April 1917

Troops have been moving forward all this week towards Arras and although there is nothing certain so far we expect to be on the move any day now for the south, where we are convinced we will take part in another attack. All the Division is busily and keenly training for the coming action.

According to my hosts the weather is extraordinary for the time of year. Spring was very late and they have not known temperatures so low with such cold wet weather in their living memory of many Aprils. Whatever the weather, I am insulated from it. I am cosy by the bright glowing fire in the kitchen, drinking hot sweet tea made with pure well water and enjoying egg and chips. Added to these pleasures my French is coming on 'leaps and bounds'. Is there a war on? I ask myself.

As if I needed confirmation that there was a war on came in the distant sounds of a massive bombardment in the south. I learned later that it was greater than that artillery barrage before the first day of the Somme. It was directed at a new heavily fortified series of German defences that they have withdrawn to.

Monday 2 April 1917

We are on the move and I have had to leave my friends in the billet. Last night they showed me a photograph of their only son who had been in the French Infantry and killed at Verdun. He was the same age as me.

We left the village with a rousing 'bon voyage' and 'bon courage' ringing in our ears as we went up the line to have another dab at Fritzy.

The weather is cold but fine. I am not, however, and have some stomach problems so I am going up the line in style in the ambulance wagon, but I'm sure I'll be alright when the fun starts. Is it something I ate?

Good Friday 6 April 1917

Bright sunshine on this Easter Day but there is no time for celebrating it. My squad is cramped in a dug-out near our old front line, with the Germans about a mile away. Our artillery is still giving them a pasting and keeping their heads down but there is still no proof yet that the barrage has been any more effective at cutting the wire than it was on

the 1st July 1916.

Easter Sunday 8 April 1917

At home I would be in church, shaking hands with my fellow church goers and saying, 'He is risen' He is risen indeed'. There is not much evidence of Him here if He is risen. Hell has come on earth in the form of our artillery and the Germans are in the inferno.

Monday 9 April 1917

I have never been this close to a creeping barrage before and I marvel at how accurate the gunners seem to be,

We snatched some sleep last night and woke this morning to sleet and cold rain. We had packed our traps by seven and moved forward as the battle opened up. We are now part of an operation that includes the French.

The Germans are not staying still under the onslaught and are giving almost as good as they are getting, sending salvo after salvo over us, some shells of which have found the dumps stocked up in anticipation of the attack. We have halted on our own front line outside Arras.

Monday 15 April 1917

I am back with a few stretcher squads in our own line enjoying the rest, the first since last Monday. The attack was a success in all sectors, so we are told, but by far the most importance achievement has been the taking, by Canadian and Scottish forces, of the German fortifications on Vimy ridge to the north of us.

In our sector we advanced five miles and we stretcher bearers couldn't keep up with the pace. As soon as we had delivered a casualty back at our C.C. station and then went forward, the Aid Posts had shifted further on.

We have passed through St Laurent-Blangy, and Athies to Tampoux and then in another spurt to the outskirts of Rouex where we set up a station in the ruins of a chemical works. I actually saw the enemy fleeing, as if taken by surprise, and much to everybody's relief they did not hang on to a railway embankment which would have been difficult to assault, for just one dug-in machine gun kept us at bay for a time before the crew dismantled it and then they upped and left. I'm close to front line action again here. It gives a good idea of what the Infantry have to put up with when attacking out of the line. Just as on the Somme most of our casualties at this stage, the ones we have had to carry back, have had machine gun bullet wounds to the upper body, lower abdomen or legs. Men are mowed down like wheat as they 'hop the bags'. If they get it in the head it is usually 'curtains'. These we tidily lay down in rows on the nearest flat bit of road so that they can be buried later.

Our Division took away several batteries of German guns, including some howitzers, but the horses they used became casualties too. Broken legs, spines, great gashes in their bellies from shell splinters, leave them writhing and roaring with pain. They have to be finished off with a spike in the head and they are left to rot and to be hives for flies.

Exploring trenches and dugouts after 'mad hours' of carrying yielded plentiful souvenirs but we had to be aware of 'booby traps' left by the Hun in the desolate wasteland he abandoned in his withdrawal.

The fortifications he built in this part of his line were just as robust as the ones we found on the Somme last July. But not only were they militarily strong they also seem to have been built with thought for the comfort of the men that occupied them. It seems daft to say it but they had been able to make them cosy and so deep and well constructed that below, down steps into tunnels with dugouts off, I'll bet all you could hear above was the dull thud of exploding shells.

In one little subterranean 'sitting room' we found some coffee, still hot, the occupants had left so quickly. There was black bread, a jar of what looked like dripping with pieces of the meat at the bottom, a long sausage and cardboard boxes of dried fruit, raisins, apples and prunes. Nothing was poisoned or spoilt as we had been warned. With my squad we sat candle lit around a little table and we tucked in while at the same time opening fresh mail and parcels stored on shelves. We did hope that there would be more food in the parcels but they were obviously presents of hand knitted socks, gloves and mufflers. They would come in handy anyway.

The letters were no use, no-one could read the language except that some contained newspaper cuttings and photographs, obviously of sweethearts, sisters or mothers. Some were of women sat holding babies with two or three smaller children around them; the families of the men who once occupied this hole. I learned a German word that seemed to appear often at the end of the letters we took out of their envelopes, or it was written across the bottom of photographs, 'vergestmeinnicht'. In English 'forget me not'. It was at times like these that we might begin to wonder what all this bloody mess was about. What had we got against these people? What had they got against us?

Such thoughts were soon dispelled as we were called out again to recover casualties and to dress their wounds but we were eager to come back to the comfort and security of our better 'ole' to sleep the night.

In that week the work we had to do was as usual across trackless country, impeded by trenches and shell holes. We were further hampered by unbelievably fierce snow storms and these in April! One thing we did notice was that the wire, usually always an impassable obstacle, was now crushed flat by the weight of 'the tank'.

We had snow storms some three days and nights in succession as we went forward with the attacking troops. Being with the forward troops meant suffering the same counter bombardment as them. On our return with a carry, stumbling and scrambling, we crouched or simply dived flat, all four of us, as shells burst around, shrapnel above or machine guns sought us out. At such times the stretcher case, if not delirious with morphia, would scream out pitifully as his extreme discomfort was multiplied by being thrown to the ground. If he had the voice to say it we were called all the 'bastards' under the sun. But it was either that or be stretcher cases ourselves, as some of us were. Forty four stretcher bearers were casualties in that action. The 10th Ambulance lost forty, we lost four. There was no information regarding the reason for their heavier losses for we were in the same action, unless it was that they were grouped for rest or to receive instructions and a German heavy fell amongst them.

Our rations for the fourteen days from the 9th April were the poorest we have had thus far and for some days we were on half rations only supplemented by our looted German stuff. I only remember twice when we had hot tea and only three issues of rum. The rest of the time we drank water, which tasted of chlorine. Had it not been for my personal circumspection in secreting a French 'bidon' of very rough Calvados bought expensively in Ourton, from a farmer friend of my hosts, my little squad would have had a very hard time of it. Eating basic rations of bully and biscuits brought only one advantage as far as I could opine; constipation. Performing one's natural functions in the field was fraught with all kind of dangers. Wherever latrines were dug, Fritz found them out either with artillery or snipers.

Without putting too fine a point on it, in such circumstances you were a bit vulnerable. The basic latrines built by pioneers were dug as eight to ten feet trenches, about a yard wide and between three and six feet deep. Across this ditch a wooden pole was laid on supports and there, precariously balanced, you communed with nature. In quiet times, because the pole would support three men at a time, you might pass the time of day with your neighbour. Subjected to bombardment machine gun or sniper fire was another story. I learned, so as to avoid the latrine, what might seem like a disgusting trick. I got it from a party of Yorks and Lancs who in peace time had been coal miners. It was at times, however, a very 'convenient convenience' These ex-coal miners did in the trenches what they had done down the mine. They did their business squatting over a shovel and then threw it over the top.

Friday 19 April 1917

Reveille this morning woke us from a good sleep after a relatively quiet night. We managed to get down by about two and were, unusually, not disturbed. There was some fairly fresh bread for breakfast with jam and hot tea the first for two days; very welcome.
We were ready again for the fray but to our relief we were told we were moving to the rear. We did this not unwillingly for as Fritz's 'morning hate' built up even we amateur

artillery spotters could tell he had brought up more guns. We set off and skirting to the south of Arras passed through Archiecourt. Our traffic was going one way and lorries, men and guns were going the other. We moved along what can only be described as a valley of destruction. Both sides of the road were lined and piled with smashed gun limbers, dead horses, wrecked motor lorries, bent and twisted artillery, some broken down tanks and all this mixed in with the ruins of the village and town houses that had been crushed by German guns. Much of what we were passing was what was left of convoys that had been travelling forward to supply the big push. It was a picture of the useless spendthrift strategy of the war. As we limped, exhausted, on our way, as if to emphasize the waste, the drizzle, driving wind and grey skies were suddenly blasted by the vast row of an ammunition dump going sky high.

Our progress was so slow, hindered by the traffic jam of battle and the necessity of frequent stops, that we only covered half of our route, our destination being Wanquetin, about sixteen miles from our starting point. By night fall we reached Dainville but when we got there there was 'no room at the inn'. The town was so crowded with troops that the only shelter that we could find for our squad, was under a wrecked wagon. We spread a tarpaulin on the muddy ground and rigged a torn cover from the wagon around the broken wheels to keep out the wind and were about to settle for a miserable night when Bert Thompson came back from a scrounge to say that he had found a field cooker in a barn, brewing up tea and cooking hot stew. Once again my store of cigarettes proved a life saver. Ten Woodbines procured us a mess tin of stew each, a loaf of bread and hot tea. The cooks wanted ten more for a tot of rum but we thought that exorbitant. We went to our make shift beds with the warm glow of Maconochie's in our bellies.

The wet dripped down the cover and in spite of our ground sheet tarpaulin the cold struck up from the bare mud, but we were wrapped up and all huddled together for warmth. It never seemed to get through to the Army that we would trek through mud, blood and barbed wire, often doing much more than our duty, if we knew that at the end of the day there would be a simple hot meal, a hot drink and a weather proof billet, if only with dry straw. Most of the time we couldn't even expect that. Officers, on the other hand, had everything that was going. Every one of them had a batman/servant. For the Officer at the end of the day there was almost invariably a cooked meal, a hot drink and a dry bed. We knew this as a fact from men who had been Officers' servants and had been relegated to the ranks for some misdemeanour or other. As it was, for us on that night, though damp and cold, we slept.

Saturday 21 April 1917

On the move again, back, and reformation. After a meagre breakfast, for no arrangements had been made for this unexpected stop, we tramped on feeling miserable. Billeting arrangements had been made further on for us at Warles or some such place. Therefore we could not join the long queues at the field kitchens, cookers or canteens set up for troops who had to breakfast before filing along the broken roads to the front. Our cooker

was way ahead, probably waiting for us.

Still undaunted, we put our best foot forward and we stopped after about ten miles where the cooks were waiting for us with last night's stew warmed up and this morning's bacon. Welcome as this grub was it was accompanied with gruff expressions of 'Where the blank have you been' and 'We were thinking of feeding it to the blanketty pigs'. These phrases, unlikely as it might seem, hid genuine worry at the possibilities of us having got seriously lost or, more seriously, being hit by some long range shell and decimated.

Wanquatin, our destination, we reached in the late afternoon and the tents for our stay awaited us like a crusader's camp. Our caravan was to rest only the long weekend before another move.

We spent the rest of the day and the next Sunday, 22 April, at rest or cleaning our kit and ourselves. There was a general replenishing by Medical Officers and their assistants of depleted supplies. Wound dressings, bandages and iodine were indented for and distributed to orderlies and morphia and tetanus serum plus new disinfectants were allocated to the M.O.s. Anti-tetanus serum was now in plentiful quantity, as last year there had been a serious shortage which added to the casualty list when lock-jaw set in after wound infection.

The weather is now fine and certainly not so cold. With that, being under canvas is quite comfortable. Mail has caught up with us. I have letters from Ernie, Maud and Phyllis. Tilly's cards get more and more brief but at least she is trying to write them, but she did send me a rather nice photograph of herself, which I showed around proudly. Doing that of course evoked comments that were from the tastefully complimentary of her prettiness that is, to bawdy reference to what they would like to do to my 'sweetheart'. I expected it and was not offended by comrades whose coarseness often hid a very sensitive soul. You could rely on them when the going got rough.

The food parcels we got with the marvellously efficient mail are a welcome addition to basic rations though we do have a kitchen here that in the fine weather fries bacon and eggs and even the popular favourite, chips. The meat pastes, cakes and sweet biscuits that we get from home do ensure that satisfying feeling, along with a hot cup of cocoa at the end of the day, of having eaten fairly well.

Wanquatin is at a crossroads that in 'peace-time' would have been a quiet backwater. Now there is a constant coming and going from north, west and south of lorries, armoured motor cars, horse drawn carts, motorcycles and guns pulled by steam tractors or horses. Add to this lines of troops who rest for a while and then move on.
We chat to those who cadge fags or mugs of tea and as many of them are fresh from Britain we hear all kinds of rumour and speculation being passed on. At the time I noted some of the stories:

'German troops in league with Fenians had invaded Ireland. That turned out to be based on news we got from an Ulsterman that last year some Fenians had taken on the British Army in Dublin.

'There are French, British and German deserters who have formed gangs and they live altogether in the abandoned dugouts on the Somme. They have their own women and they terrorise the the neighbourhood'.

'The Russians have pulled out of the war and their Army has mutinied'

'Douglas Haig has committed suicide and Lloyd George has taken over'.

'There is going to be a general strike in England'.

'Every time we fire an artillery shell a penny royalty is paid to the Germans through Swiss banks because Fritz owns the patents on the fuses'.

'The French Army is close to mutiny so we might have to take the Germans on by ourselves'.

Some of these rumours were the usual bull-blank and some turned out to be true, certainly the ones concerning the French Army and the Russian, but the one that made us prick our ears up was that 'the Americans had entered the war'. It was confirmed very quickly to be true, and it was like a bomb shell. The phrase, 'It will all be over by Christmas' returned to our lips and we were more or less convinced that we would see the sights of Germany and Berlin before long.

Monday 23 April 1917

We struck camp and set off to march over country roads, shattered, cracked and pot-holed by heavy traffic. It was twenty kilometres to Bulencourt where we stayed for the rest of the week in clean, dry, weather-proof barns.

In the fine late spring weather we finished cleaning and re-fitting plus we had the added bonus of being de-loused and after this we received carefully repaired, but clean, underwear. Whenever this concession was granted we always searched the newly acquired garments for the stains and patches that might indicate that they had been taken from a casualty, especially a dead one. Patched holes in a vest near the heart or stitched tears round the crutch were carefully scrutinised. Damage in this last quarter stimulated in the mind of the superstitious soldier the greatest fear; the award of the D.S.O., 'Dicky Shot Off'. We often discussed what wound we would prefer - 'a nice clean bullet in the head,' 'being suddenly blown to kingdom come, never knowing what hit you' and so on. But what was terrible to think about was the loss of your 'manhood'. We had seen all the catalogue of wound types in our work. The D.S.O. was the most feared.

Saturday 28 April 1917

We are now in a large Army hut in a field near the road between Arras and St Pol. We have been told again not to become too settled for we are likely to move in the next forty eight hours. We don't usually get so much notice and knowing what we are going to do seems to have put everybody in good mood. They are raring to go. God knows why.

Sunday 29 April 1917

We had a proper and organised church parade this morning but after it Cecil Duffield decided to entertain us with his version of a service. He had us standing in our hut with him before us like a padre, telling us which hymns we were to sing. The versions we sang were 'We are Fred Karno's Army' (The Church's is one foundation). and 'When this lousy war is over' (What a friend we have in Jesus). He then delivered two readings and they went like this:

> The readings this morning are taken from Genesis, Chapter 1, Verse 1
> And Isaiah Chapter 10, Verse 6

> 'And God said let there be light and there was, and you could see it for blanketty miles'.

> The next reading is taken from Isaiah.

> 'He was known as Isaiah because he had one eye higher than the other and one day he came unto Rachael and he quoth her saying 'Rachael how much will it cost of me to lay with thee?' and Rachael quoth Isaiah and she did say 'Twenty sheckels'. So Isaiah did pay her twenty sheckels and he did lay with her. Some months hence Rachael came unto Isaiah and she quoth him saying 'Isaiah I am heavy with child, what steps art thou going to take?' And Isaiah quoth Rachael saying 'Blanketty great big ones' and he disappeared into the desert.' 'Let us pray. Now go in peace my children'.

It was, as you might say, blasphemous, but there was no harm in it. A favourite saying was 'You've got to laugh or break your heart'. My favourite verse from 'When this lousy war is over' was:

'When this lousy war is over,
I'll be sailing o'er the sea.
I will soon be in our parlour,
With my tart upon my knee.
She will tell me how she's missed me,
I will kiss her on the mouth
And at last she won't resist me
As my hand is moving south.

Monday 30 April 1917

Two squads including ours left Third Field Ambulance and we were taken by Ford motor ambulance whose canvas roofs had been replaced by steel sheets to guard against shrapnel. We motored to St Nicholas to the north of Arras, there to be attached to the 2nd Battalion Lancashire Fusilliers. The last time we passed through here, Easter Monday, it was our front line. It had become now a military camp in the rear with transport lines and dumps of stores.

During the day we kept our heads down because of sporadic shell fire but that night, under cover of darkness, we went variously by lorry, cart and foot, skirting Arras through St Laurent-Blangy to establish an Aid Post at Tampeaux.

We established our Aid Post in a cellar in what was left of the village. We came under occasional shell fire. Our front line is about one thousand yards from here but persistent bombing raids and attacks take it gradually forward to the next objective, the chemical works at Rouex.

The cellar we are occupying is now pretty strong after we put more beams above, supported by beams, brick and stone as pillars. Outside on top we have laid beams, corrugated iron, doors, window frames, floor boards and brick rubble from the demolished house that was once over the cellar we are in.

Wednesday 2 May 1917

Our reinforced cellar is standing up to repeated bombardment during the day and we feel reasonably secure as we cook up stews and hashes from bully added to the preserved vegetables that were in jars arranged in plenty on the shelves down below. At least those that are not unbroken. There are also lots of pots and pans so we are making genuine attempts at real cooking. We only venture out at night.

Saturday 5 May 1917

We have been busy after dark as we go out and clear the wounded. It is not a long job as the motor ambulances are able to come along the cleared roads right into the village. This is the fastest turn round situation I have been in. A carry is fetched, brought back down, and it goes straight into the ambulance with wound dressed. The same goes for the ambulance barges on the canal near by. The casualties are carried straight onto the barge, then it's a smooth ride to hospital. Just the kind of transport for a wounded man as every jolt by road could be agony.

Sunday 6 May 1917

In the early morning we at last got down to sleep after a hard night's carrying the most pitiful cases I have seen for some time. The new troops we are encountering are untrained and unprepared for artillery bombardment. It seems that some scrambled 'over the top' and were caught in fire while trying to get away. Only someone who has never been under such fire could have the cheek to point the finger of blame. Nerves of steel are necessary when enduring it without flinching and so far as I know no human being has yet been born with them.

We sleep with uniform and boots on, gas helmets within easy reach, and use our kit and packs as pillows so we are ready to go if the call comes. We usually get up fairly late in the morning after having slept through the sound of splinters from H.E. raining down on our 'roof', and then we pass the day drumming up and, in the case of my mates, smoking, that is of course unless any casualties occur in the village,

Monday 7 May 1917

One day this week, and I haven't noted which, a company of Cavalry came trotting into the village. Our Aid Post had been cleared away and cleaned up and we had been up off our floor where we slept, an hour or so. Somebody surely should have known how keen Jerry artillery observers were. They were so much on the Q.V. that you might believe that they could see round corners. So a company of shiny Cavalry, fully kitted out and presumably ready to ride through the German lines, would make any Fritzy artillery spotter think that all his Christmases had come at once.

German gunners began at first to range in with a Jack Johnson or two and then started to register with puffs of shrapnel bursting overhead. We watched the scene from the protection of our reinforced cellar. Horses reared as they were peppered with the small lead balls of shrapnel shells. Some fell with their riders hit too and then high explosives, five point nines rained down. There was pandemonium as horses and men were blown in the air in pieces.

When the smoke and dust settled and the barrage was over, no horse or rider was left standing. Most had been killed or wounded. Those not hit had either run away in panic, riderless, or been galloped out of range down the street of the village.

We came out of our cellar to do what we could and we tripped and slipped among the bloody shambles that had once been the pride of the Army. That's what the Cavalry were described as being. We had to work quickly picking up those wounded who we thought had a chance, for Jerry knew that that's what we would do and he would start again. He did just that as we had got the twenty or so we thought we could save, down the steps of our Aid Post. More H.E. came in but the explosions simply redistributed the fragments, big and small, of the men and horses left in the square. The Officer who had ordered them to form up as they did in full view of the enemy should have been shot for incompetence.

We waited until dark and got the wounded we had treated out into ambulances but not before three more had died of shock from loss of blood.

Thursday 10 May 1917

The Lancashire Fusilliers, or what was left of them, came out of the Line today, but our two squads went in again the same night with the 11th Brigade, who relieved the Fusilliers. The 11th Brigade was made up of Somersets, Lancs, Hampshires and the Rifle Brigade. They went into action immediately and they attacked with bayonets fixed and captured the chemical works and occupied Rouex by the next morning. Our work with them was very hard and dangerous as we had long carries through heavy barrages of fire. One of my squad was killed. It was my old mate Herbert Thompson. The other two of the squad were rendered useless from the shock of a shell which landed almost right beside us as we were carrying a case back.

The blast of it picked me up as if by a giant's hand and threw me down into a shell hole. I was dazed and on all fours in what I thought was a water pool at the bottom. I lit a match and saw that it was the blood of a lad from the Lancashire Fusilliers who was laying dead on the side of the hole, with his head on his arm as if sleeping. Recovering myself, in spite of bleeding copiously from the nose, I scrambled up the side and cautiously looked over the edge. Two of my squad were clinging together, gibbering like monkeys and jumping up and down, shouting hysterically, as if dancing, over the up-turned stretcher with the casualty under it. Bert was on his back, talking to himself. I slid out of the hole and scrambled over to Bert. In the dark I felt his tunic and it was covered in thick blood. He had been caught by a shell splinter. I decided to leave him where he was and to sort out the others.

It was a black night and we were in the line of the barrage. I told the two 'Dervishers' to blanketty snap out of it as they were drawing fire and I got enough sense out of them so that they put the carry back on the stretcher and we got him, in spite of there being only the three of us, over the railway embankment. It was the nearest bit of shelter.

Leaving these two with the casualty, as they now seemed 'compost mentis', I went back for Bert. I found him in a hole which, in trying to crawl away, he had slipped in to. I helped to pull him out and although he cried out in pain, he could just walk and we managed to get to the embankment across soft earth furrowed up by shells. We got as far as that but he couldn't make it up and across. All he wanted to do was lie still. He whispered , 'I knew you would come back for me, you silly bugger, now leave me here and look after yourself'.

I tried to find his wound, which he said was in his stomach. I struck a match to see but as soon as I did a machine gun from quite close opened up on us. I did have time, however, in the brief flare of the match to see a great hole under his arm. It was a cavity from his arm pit to his waist and it was wide and deep. I caught a glimpse through tattered uniform of splintered white rib bone, torn flesh, blood vessels and what must have been his lungs. My gorge rose. I was horrified and all I could do was to try and plug it with the spare shell dressings I had in my pack. They just disappeared as bloody wads into his body.

On his back, looking up at me as I adjusted his helmet to make him more comfortable, he said, 'By God, Corky, we've supped some stuff, thee and me, 'aven't we?'. I tried to encourage him not to talk.

'We've had some good times though, dunt tha reckon, eh?' I told him that we had and we would see more when we got back home. His reply to that was;

'I've told thee before, owd love, never try to bull–shit a bull-shitter, so, Corky, me owd duck, write to me missus for me. Tha's good with thy letters. I was never any good at school, allus gettin' t'slipper, the bastards'.

For want of something to say, I asked him if he was in pain, not that it would have made any difference, as I hadn't any morphia, so there was nothing I could do. How he could talk with such a wound God only knows. His voice was now a hoarse whisper.

'When tha writes, tell me mam I allus loved' er'.

He began to shake from head to toe. Then he went rigid and, like a child, tried to lift his hands as if going into the arms of somebody. He cried out 'Oh Jesus Christ, Corky, this is it.' And then he died.

The machine gunner must have heard him shout for he started up again. I couldn't manage him on my own so I had to again reluctantly leave him to go to seek some more bearers.

Getting over the embankment in one piece I shouted into a Regimental Aid Post of the Hampshire Regiment dug into the bank that I wanted a lift with a wounded man.

The first voice that answered me was that of a man with whom I'd been in training at Seaforth and I had not seen him since we both left there. He was a good chap and in spite of the heavy fire, went with me over the railway to make sure that Bert was dead.

It was quiet enough now for us to drag Bert as far as the Aid Post and we went back, enlisting the help of another squad to carry the wounded man we had been fetching. I and three others carried Bert's body while the two lads from my original squad, still shell shocked, limped behind.

Friday 11 May 1917

We had an uneventful day and I needed it. Bert had been a good mate, always cheerful. He could always be relied upon to scrounge what was going and he always shared whatever good fortune he came across. He never shirked work and was always sympathetic when younger inexperienced kids got the wind up. I would miss him.

Our N.C.O. knew Bert well and I had no difficulty persuading him to let me off duties so that I could be at Bert's burial. I went with a section of Pioneers to Athies, just up the road, and that's where Bert was buried, along with half a dozen others lost at the same time.

As I set off for Athies from Tampeaux our Field Ambulance was clearing wounded cases by road and canal barge. Suddenly Jerry artillery opened up and two motor ambulances were blown away and a shell landed in the bows of one of the barges. It looked as if it might sink with it's cargo of casualties. Another shell landed on the canal bank and killed three more of our people. Jerry was shelling anything that moved, even though the transport was marked with large red crosses, and there were Red Cross flags flying. Had I not been on my way to Bert's burial I would have been on the canal bank, working. There was an Angel on my shoulder.

Sunday 13 May 1917

I have moved back with our Field Ambulance to Haute-Avesnes where we have set up a hospital well behind the lines from Arras. It is at a cross-roads to the south of the Arras – St Pol main road and nicely out of the way of traffic moving east. I spent two nights in a Horse Ambulance until I was found a billet under canvas. We look as if we will be here some time.

Sunday 20 May 1917

We have been a week now at the hospital at Haute-Avesnes. We wake in the morning to a white mist that soon clears and then we have had sunny warm days. We seem to be escaping from a rumoured food shortage. The food is good and plentiful and the cooks try their best to ring the changes with soups and stews. We have even had the treat of sausage and chips a couple of times, though nobody asks what the sausages contain. 'It is a military secret known only to the top brass, code word 'bangers'.

The hospital that we are running is for the Divisional sick so some part of our work is to see to it that the boys simply get a rest. They might have 'gone sick' for all manner of reasons and there are a few sympathetic M.O.s who recognise that what they really want is rest, in a bed and 'out of it', if only for a few days. So unless some ambitious C.O. desperate for a medal or the 'Honour of the Regiment' needs them for a trench raid, they are prescribed a few days in hospital and 'the mixture as before', and by jingo it does them the power of good.

Sunday 27 May 1917

It is Whitsuntide weather and around here as it is unmarked by war, it is beautiful. Fruit trees are blossoming and every leaf is summer green. The surrounding villages are bright and peaceful with carefully tended gardens of both flowers and vegetables in rows.

We are having an easy time and to some extent getting over our last nightmare in the line. I have enjoyed especially several trips to Aubigny, a village a few kilometres away, where the people are welcoming and generous with gifts of wine and apples.

On this beautiful Sunday morning there was a church parade and for me the first time for weeks that I have reflected on faith. I seem to be neglecting my commitment and excusing myself by saying that I am too busy and that I am being a Christian in action in my daily work. Which is true. But I know that there is no substitute for Communion. During the service I thought much about Bert. He had never been to church in his life apart from baptisms, weddings and funerals. If anybody had asked me I would have said he was a Christian man, 'by their deeds shall ye know them.'

Drew 20 francs at a pay parade and I mention this, having not referred to pay for some time. It increasingly goes nowhere. Prices are going up but our pay is not. There is much grumbling 'in the ranks'.

Wednesday was my birthday. I had an enjoyable enough time and my mates passed the hat round or as our French comrades say 'Le cat' and we bought bottles of fizzy wine that passed muster as champagne. After a couple of bottles we were merry enough to have a bawdy sing song but before we could get it under way a young lad from a Scottish Regiment began a rendering of 'There's a long, long trail awinding' and that changed the mood completely. It was a memorable, early summer evening. There was a bunch of rowdy young men 'the wanton soldiery' getting drunk, sitting amongst the tables and chairs of an improvised estaminet. There we were in a foreign land, being quietened by the tenor voice of a fresh faced youth singing a song so evocative of home. There wasn't a dry eye in the house. It was my twenty second birthday and the second I had had in France. How long now?

> 'Take me back to dear old Blighty,
> Put me on a train to London town.
> Take me over there,
> Drop me anywhere,
> In Liverpool, Leeds or Birmingham,
> Well I don't care.

> All I want to see is my best girl,
> Cuddlin' up together we soon will be.
> Aye tiddley ighty, take me back to Blighty,
> Blighty is the place for me.'

Sunday 3 June 1917

I got letters from home and from France today. Dad and Maud, as well as sending cigarettes for my store, write of meat rationing and of supplementing shortages by getting rabbits from 'someone in the village'. Ernie is fed up and in his letter told me how he wants to go back to work in the mills where work mates he left behind, are doing shifts of twelve hours a day, seven days a week, and earning a fortune. It seems as far as his opinion goes that nobody at home, unless they have lost someone, gives the war a second thought. Tilly sent me her usual, 'hoping this finds you as it leaves me' card but she did say she misses me. I miss her and everything about her and I said this to her in a letter that I wrote, but I can't come on too strong as she has to have my letters read to her.

Mind you, you can't come on too strong in letters as the officers censor them or even just don't send them. You have to be careful what you write. I certainly shouldn't be writing this diary. I would be for the high jump if it was found, as it is against regulations.

Sunday 3 June 1917

We are still enjoying fine weather here at Haute-Avesne. The food is good and though we are pretty busy the work is not too hard. I only find the time to write my diary up once a week.

A lot of new recruits have come into the Division as replacements for the ones lost in the battle of Arras, which I suppose is still going on. Certainly we have no shortage of patients. There is a rumour that new recruits 'go sick' more often than those who 'have got some service in' or their 'knees brown', as Army parlance would have it. It isn't really surprising. You have to be hardened to the prospect of trench life otherwise you get into a 'funk' or 'get windy' pretty quickly. Nobody blames them.

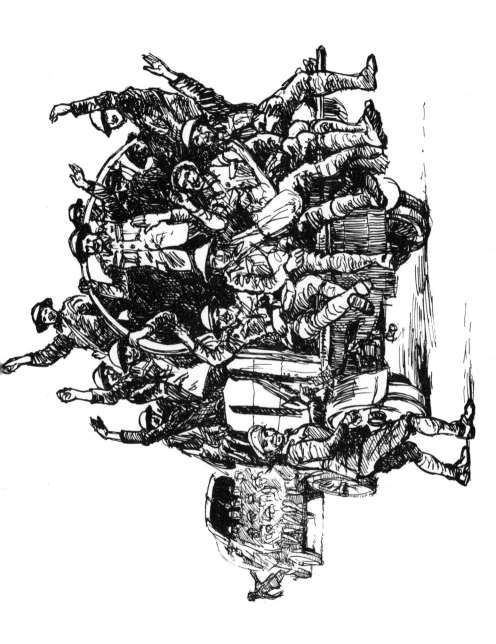

I have being doing work this week that has made a bit of a change. I was told to help prepare a pair of horses for the Divisional Horse Show. My experience and assistance was welcomed by the ambulance farriers, for they were new to their job. By the time we had finished the horses were in fine fettle. The Army Service Corps took an ambulance wagon, a general service wagon and a small cart along with them to the show and carried off two firsts and one third prize. You could have said almost that you were at an English County Fair and that there wasn't a war on.

Sunday 10 June 1917

The fine, sunny, summer weather continues but there has been a change for us. We have been moved to a camp at St Nicholas near Arras ready to go up the Line again. Last night we were taken in our Ford ambulance cars for about twenty kilometres to join the 10th Division. Twenty kilometres took us, with clear roads, about half an hour. On foot that would take us a day. We have become motorised. For part of the journey we were transferred to motor lorries, great six wheeled juggernauts with canvas hoods that are said to be replacing the horse, but I'll believe that when I see it.

The first night we spent in large deep caves under Arras. There are hundred of yards of them, some recently excavated, but many lengths of the system were dug out in the Middle Ages. Now we use them for Stores, Aid Posts, Communication Centres and even Under Ground Barracks, complete with kitchens and ablutions. The caves can be entered by stone steps down from almost any building in the centre of Arras.

We have been attached to the 10th Division because although there have been reinforcements our Field Ambulances haven't had an allocation. So the squads, including mine working at the hospital, have been collected to make up Medical Orderly strength in the line.

Our time in Arras brought us into contact with some chaps who had come from Belgium the day before. They had been working in the Ypres Salient and they told us that enormous mines had been set off under the German lines and that this signalled a new offensive in Belgium. If they can be believed and there is going to be another push at 'Wipers' then it will take the strain off our work down here. Now that we have a tented Sub-Division running at Savy Berlette, plus the hospital we have just been transferred from at Haute-Avesnes, a decline in the number of casualties to be treated would extend limited facilities.

Monday 11 June 1917

We are still in reserve at St Nicholas and as Neuville St Vaast is just up the road I can visit Tom's grave. A little along is Athies so I can also pay my respects, from time to time, to dear old Herbert. There is plenty of traffic of all sorts so I can easily jump onto a lorry or even a motorcycle and side car. Holding up a packet of fags by the roadside usually brings some wheeled transport to a halt.

There are open air baths just a walk from our billet which is in the cellar of a big old house. The cellar has been extended into the Arras cave and tunnel system, so we have more than enough room. I walk along the tunnel up some steps and I can, before breakfast, take an invigorating swim with a few mates as keen on swimming as I am. We go during the day and sometimes catch the summer sunshine. Another thing not to be underestimated is the sheer physical pleasure of being clean again.

Wednesday 13 June 1917

We have had a long quiet period, and I took advantage of it today to make a long walk over to Vimy ridge. Part of the way I hitched a ride in a lorry. Then trekked the long pathway up to the ridge. On either side it was gouged out with huge craters and generously scattered with scores of unexploded shells, either on the surface or marked with signs all over the place warning of their presence and advice that transport should keep to the path.

What an enterprise it must have been to capture the ridge. I was shown the entrances and tunnels used by the Canadians whose forces were largely involved in taking the ridge. The excavations go down hundreds of steps to three or four levels. Out of these tunnels, on the day, Canadian troops poured in their thousands, much to the surprise of the Germans. There was the usual intense barrage but instead of having to cross yards and yards of open field, the attacking troops coming out of the caves so close to the line were on the German trenches in minutes. The trench systems are still in good repair. The preparations for taking the ridge were made in secret and they took almost a year.

I came down from Vimy and saw signs for Oppy, another strong point in the German line. Dad had mentioned in a recent letter that men from Hull in the East Yorkshire Regiment had been badly beaten up at a battle here before the line was breached. I wanted to confirm this but I didn't get far before an M.P. stopped me and said that the village and the wood where the strong point was most concentrated, were out of bounds because of unexploded munitions, particularly gas shells.

I returned from my walk, or rather ride, because I cadged another lift, and I was invited to six rounds in the ring with a P.T. instructor I had befriended who is teaching me how to box. After a vigorous four rounds I packed it in. I got changed and decided to treat myself to dinner. I walked into town and found an estaminet open and serving meals. I ate a very good dinner of roast duck at a table in the open as the sun went down. After half a bottle of good French red I drank a glass of what I was assured was home made apple brandy, or Calvados. I am, as the sayings go here, 'living like a Lord's bastard' or alternatively 'a fighting cock'.

Tuesday 14 June 1917

Much of today has been taken up watching air fights. Fighter plane activity has, so I am told, increased over Arras in the last month. Planes with Black Cross German markings dive and turn, 'beating up' Arras with machine gun fire and light bombs. They are then taken on by our boys in the R.F.C. High up in the sky their machines spiral, twist and climb, trying to dodge the guns of attacker and defender alike. We have seen German and British planes brought down in smoke and flames, their crashing and burning signalled in the distance by great clouds of black oily smoke.

Sunday 17 June 1917

We are still in reserve at St Nicholas. The squads of bearers who have gone up the line before us have had such a quiet time that they have preferred not to be relieved. Their longest stay in the line will benefit them later by a longer stay in reserve and we stay out of it for a bit longer, so everybody wins. It is so quiet at the front that it is safe to say that the battle of Arras is slowly drawing to a close. There has been no news of any big actions and the casualties that are coming down in dribs and drabs are now just close to the number to be expected on any ordinary day on the Western Front.

Sunday 24 June 1917

We are back again by Motor Lorry to Haute-Avesnes. If we have much more of this riding in style, we will forget how to march. More seriously our feet will get soft and the next time we are called upon to 'foot slog' will be murder.

We are still running the hospital until the Division comes out of the action.

During the week our Ambulance was reinforced by forty new men. Because it is so quiet they have yet to have their 'baptism of fire'. To be quite honest, and I don't want to slander my fellow man or my comrades for that matter, for that's who they will be, they do look a puny if not a dozy lot. The recruiting authorities at home are I am afraid, 'scraping the bottom of the barrel'.

One old friend who has joined us again is Billy Bun the Baker. I welcomed him back, being the only one who recognised him, with cries of 'I thought you had bought it'. Where had he been, but seconded to a group of Officers and N.C.O.s who had paid him half a franc each extra a week to bake them bread, buns and cake. He came back with a collapsible metal oven that can be put up and taken down in minutes complete with its chimney. The blacksmith at his 'posting' had made it for him. He will soon need his own mule to carry his gear. He had not had 'a carry' since the last time I'd seen him and he'd only been transferred back because the Ambulance squad that he was supposed to be working with had been getting put out by his privileges. Their loss our gain, we are already scrounging round for cheese scone 'makings'.

Sunday 1 July 1917

It is now twelve months since our 'Big Push' on the Somme. Since then I have spent about twelve weeks under fire, often in very dangerous and exposed situations. It is as much as some Second Line Infantry Battalions. I count myself very fortunate in not having been hit yet, touch wood. The time table for the P.B.I. is usually four days in the Front Line, four days in the Support Line, eight days in Reserve and four days rest. Rest usually means carrying and carting ammunition and supplies or even digging trenches. They need to be kept out of trouble. I don't think we in the R.A.M.C. work to the same time table for I personally have done longer times in the Front Line, under fire. But I don't tell everybody, they'll all want some.

We are still at Haute-Avesnes, under canvas and looking after the Divisional sick which now includes coping with a serious dysentery outbreak.

We are quite comfortable in our tent at the moment but we have to concern ourselves with it being windproof and waterproof for the weather has changed. It is unseasonably cold with a strong biting wind.

Living in such close contact with eleven other men, as I am in the bell tent we occupy, you might imagine that there would be 'fall outs'. In all my service so far I cannot remember any serious quarrels or major disagreements. Once or twice when new men, replacements, have been dropped in there might have been a bit of a squabble as they 'fitted in' but mostly we get on well. What makes things work, I think, is humour. We always start the day off or finish it with a laugh, even when we are dog tired or blank scared. I can remember dear old Bert once, as an example, saying as we were being bracketted by all sorts of shells, making all sorts of noises, while carrying a patient and in desperate fear for our lives, 'I think they'll be droppin' Grand pianos next cos we've had the rest of the blanketty orchestra.' Even the wounded boy on the stretcher said, 'Don't make me laugh 'cos it hurts when I do'.

Tuesday 3 July 1917

We have moved from our canvas billet back to the tunnels under Arras where we are assisting in the transportation of patients to the hospital at St Jean in Arras. This work leaves us plenty of time for swimming during the day at the baths. My swimming style and speed is much improved. In the evening Arras has a lot to offer. Although still in range of Jerry's big guns and aeroplanes the town is thriving as an entertainment and recreation centre for all manner of troops.

It is a big town with a railway and a canal and before the war was probably the main town of the region. The most interesting part of it for us is the main square. It is a large central paved area of about two hundred to two hundred and fifty yards square. In the square there are many repaired shell holes and some pits fenced off because of unexploded bombs. It has been under attack since the beginning of the war and the houses that front the square which have three, four or five storeys, have had their decorated fronts knocked about a bit. In peace time it was a centre for weaving and the making of carpets and tapestries and it's been engaged with these crafts since the middle ages. Someone better read than me passed on the story from Shakespeare's Hamlet about somebody being stabbed while hiding 'behind the Arras': that is the tapestry. When I told this to someone else they were not impressed. 'Stabbed behind the Arras, very painful'. Well, as they say, you learn something new everyday and a day without learning is a day wasted. Obviously my fellow soldiers don't realise 'what a wonderful thing education is'.

Around the square every available room or hall is used for some sort of recreation, from eggs and 'pompidoo fritz' (chips) served out of the window of someone's house to classy restaurants that only the Officers can afford. An example menu might be, soup, hors d'oeuvres, pate de fois gras, preserved duck, cheese, gateaux, with white wine, red wine and congnac. 15 francs, nearly two week's wages for a Private Soldier.

Almost every other hall is staging some sort of show from films in a bare room to music hall in the Arras theatre. We have been entertained by Fatty Arbuckle at the pictures and amateur singers and comedians in an estaminet, and with a piano in what was once the Mayor's meeting room. Some of the comedians had a nice line in sentry jokes;

Sentry:	Hearing a sound, shouts, 'Who goes there?'
Voice:	Out of the darkness, 'I'm the Army Chaplain'
Sentry:	'Halt or I fire'
Voice:	'I'm the Army Chaplain'
Sentry:	Fires, walks over to the body 'Who do you think you are kidding? You must think I have just dropped off the boat …I'm Charlie Chaplin silly bugger'

There are those amongst us who say they have found other sorts of entertainment in the more shady parts of the town. But in seeking for female company they often get something else. Getting a dose, as the 'clap' or 'crabs' is humourously referred to, like everything else it's not taken seriously. Only the victim has to do that. He is put on a charge and any possibility of leave is stopped until it is cleared up, if it does. The whole range of infection was on offer from pubic lice to syphyllis As for meeting respectable Arras girls, if there are any around, we don't get a look in. They gravitate towards the higher paid Australians and Canadians or to the officer class. I remember a story on the theme;

Artillery man with medals is asked by drunken squaddy
what he got them for; 'Gunnery' Replies the gunner.
Squaddy says, ' Well I had that but I didn't get a medal.'

Sunday 8 July 1917

We have now moved into the St Jean Hospital proper though we are still taking in the Divisional sick.

The weather has been bright again, and not too hot. Recuperating patients enjoy having their beds brought out into the sunshine so that they can sit reading, writing letters home, playing cards, chess, draughts or, more secretively, crown and anchor for money.

We are tackling another dysentery problem and we have had a case of what looks like measles. Dysentery, as we are constantly warned, is the result of bad personal hygiene. It is more likely the result of bad water when thirsty soldiers will drink anything, especially with that thirst that comes from being under fire. I have seen men scooping water, with their tin hats, from pools where there is obviously decomposing material present, a horse or even a man. There is the problem of Jerry poisoning water in retreat. French civilians have also been known to contribute to the problem by refusing access to wells and pumps so forcing soldiers to drink bad water. The delivery of water in tanks by the Army can not always be relied upon.

Sunday 15 July 1917

We had news that American troops have at last arrived in France. A dispatch rider, a patient in dock for a broken ankle that went wrong, told of a trip that he'd made to Paris at the beginning of the month when he saw a parade of American soldiers in their 'Boy Scout Hats' marching down the Champs Elysee or some such boulevard in gay Paree. We look forward to their 'good deeds'.

We are still in the same billet. The food is good and we supplement our rations with fresh fruit from the market. My cigarette store is more useful than money as prices rise and I get a regular fifty to a hundred Woodbines sent from home to use in bartering. I can also visit one of the many canteens in the town and be guaranteed a good feed for ten fags. Plus we keep Mr Bun hard at work with supplies of flour, sugar and eggs.
This Sunday we played the 11th Field Ambulance at cricket, winning by a narrow margin. The locals who turned out to watch were intrigued by the game. One old French gentleman who spoke English fairly well, having done business in England, said that for the first time he understood the rules. Ever since seeing the game played when in England well before the war he had thought that the batsmen were on different sides in cricket and raced each other for runs between the wicket.

We are preparing for another Divisional sports meeting soon and hope to have even better success than last year. There will be a new category in the programme. Aquatic sports- swimming, diving and possibly water polo. For this new sport a few of us are already in training.

We are working hard as the dysentery outbreak is now of epidemic proportions and two of our Ambulance lads have gone down with it. We also have three more measles cases. The hope is that measles will not be as contageous.

During the week Fritzy reminded us that we are still within his range and began shelling the town just after a German plane passed over. The shelling did little damage to buildings but killed a French Gendarme, a civilian and a carter's horse. It is still really dangerous for refugees to return to their homes this close to the line but the temptations of easy money to be got by serving the Army's needs are too much to resist for some.

Sunday 22 July 1917

Lovely July weather with blue cloudless skies only marred by the occasional black cross marked German raider. There is rumour of a move but no evidence so far. What is interesting is that a leave rota has begun and it is steadily passing through the Division. I am beginning to hope. As a song popular here has it:

> 'I want to go home, I want to go home,
> I don't want the trenches and whizz bangs that soar,
> I don't want the Corporals and Sergeants that roar,
> Take me over the sea,
> Where the Alleymans can't get at me.
> Oh my, I don't want to die,
> I want to go home.'

German artillery is no respecter of Red Cross markings. Everything 'nailed down' and 'not nailed down' has our markings on it in bright red and white. In spite of this, in the early evening of today a shell pitched into the Officers' Mess of the 10th Field Ambulance and wounded everyone in there. If no-one else, Jerry is aware of the importance of the R.A.M.C. The destruction of the Mess and the injuries sustained by the Medical Officers in it was a disaster, not only for the men wounded but because of the fact that good M.O.s are as rare as 'maidens water', as we say.

Sunday 29 July 1917

We are still enjoying lovely summer weather in Arras. I get up very early and make tea for those of our patients who have had a bad night and then busy myself with a few cleaning tasks and then settle down with my tea and a quiet read. I am reading an English edition of 'Lés Miserables' which I got from a Y.M.C.A. book sale where I was assured that I could exchange it, 'for something a little lighter if I couldn't manage it'.

There has been a lull in German shelling. At least those many civilians of the Arras population who are returning to their homes, hope it is a lull. Many of them are pretty blanked off with the condition their houses and gardens are in, having left them open in panic or at least in a hurry when they fled the German guns. If they have not been damaged by shell fire they have been ransacked by the occupying soldiery in the search for souvenirs and home comforts to cheer up often subterranean billets. The strict orders in force forbidding looting and warning against breakage are not adhered to so there will be many applications for compensation.

Several times during the week I have been to the swimming baths while violent thunder storms have passed overhead. Swimming about as the rain pours down accompanied by Donner und Blitzen is an exhilarating experience. The noise of artillery rumbling in the distance is drowned in the great claps of thunder coming out of lowering black clouds that turned day into night.

Sunday 5 August 1917

As I have noted before I only get chance sometimes to write my diary up on Sundays and I am still concerned that my little notebooks with be confiscated and I'll be for the 'high jump'. If my leave does come I shall smuggle home the notebooks of what I have already written and leave them there. My anxiety comes from the fact that twice recently Officers and N.C.O.s have asked 'What are you writing there?' My excuse is usually that it is a letter home.

The war news is that a great offensive has been launched in the north, in Belgium, around Ypres. The offensive has been supported by a bombardment on this Front and the Germans have replied in kind. Shelling of the town has started again and so systematically that civilians so recently returned are reluctantly packing for a new exodus.

Another notable event in the Front Line is that Fritzy has been sending over some new and very poisonous gas shells. The casualties we have seen so far from this gas have burns that are similar to severe scalding, great superating blisters on exposed skin. Eye lids swell and close, causing what is hoped is only temporary blindness, and if the gas is inhaled, convulsive fits of coughing wrack the casualty. Our instructions are that we must wear gas respirators when carrying the victims and we have to be very careful when removing clothing as the gas is absorbed by cloth and can still injure some time after exposure.

Leave allocation is passing along the Line and I have good hopes to get mine soon, in which case I might leave for Folkestone and England next week.

CHAPTER 8 - HOME LEAVE

Friday 10 August 1917

I have just received my furlough warrant and I leave Arras this evening, as by tremendous good fortune there is an Ambulance Train en route for Boulogne that I can get a ride on if 'I work my passage', so to speak, and help as an Orderly on the train. I did not need asking twice, for straight through to Boulogne for an ordinary squaddy like me is always difficult as the line is reserved for emergency trains. Without this good fortune I might have had to have gone via Amiens and Abbeville with a long slow journey up the coast.

Saturday 11 August 1917

The journey was not as easy as I first thought it might be. I had to work well into the night with patients who needed care. There were a lot of boys who had not been out long and they were going back now, broken and disfigured. It was not like the aftermath of the Somme where amazingly many of the wounded I treated were uncomplaining. These lads took it very badly and they were like hurt children in their misery, crying for water, complaining of pain, and a number who could have got off their bunks to visit 'the slats' soiled themselves where they lay. I did not begrudge them the care. I was lucky, I was going on leave and in one piece.

Sunday 12 August 1917

After a slow journey that included being shunted into sidings to let a 'Staff Train' through, whose Officer passengers looked out from their comfortable compartments as they slowly passed our carriages. They were lit up, ignoring the blackout. We narrowly escaped an attack from the air just as we got within ten miles of Boulogne. As the train drew onto the quay I saw a queue of some two hundred yards long for the boat. To wait in that would have meant another lost day, or maybe two. I managed to 'jump it' by associating myself with the 'walking wounded' that were being taken off the train and led straight on board. But as I was assisting a young lad with a broken shoulder up the gang plank, I did not manage to escape the attention of the many Military Policemen who were checking warrants and permissions. They collared me. My ruse to avoid the queue, it seems, was often employed by unofficial leave takers and deserters. They simply put on a Red Cross armband that they had probably 'won' from an Aid Post and posed as R.A.M.C. Orderlies. My bona fides were checked and they told me to carry on.

145

Once on board I found myself a corner in the sick bay which was on the upper deck and settled down for what was really a short trip to Folkestone. My offer to help was declined as there were plenty of Orderlies for the wounded to call upon.

There was an alarm before we left port as it was thought that German aircraft had been spotted. But if there were any Jerries the squadron of R.N.A.S. planes that appeared, saw them off.

The crossing was smooth, but because of reports (I got the 'info' from a rating who cadged a fag from me) that a submarine had mined the channel it was slow and the Navy escort of two small war ships, that I saw when I went up on deck for a breather, seemed to be having trouble holding their course.

We arrived in Folkestone in time to catch the train to London that was waiting for us and being first off once more with the 'walking wounded' I was able to get a place in what became packed carriages. Unfortunately I wasn't able to wangle a place in the Ambulance Carriages. Volunteers on the platform went up and down the train proffering free tea and sandwiches and there was no shortage of takers. The good folk of Folkestone still appreciated our 'little bit' and have not yet grown too accustomed to soldiers to give us a cheery welcome and farewell.

Our train arrived in London very late because of delays on the line, so once more I was lucky enough to be able to play the R.A.M.C. 'card' again and I travelled in a Ford motor ambulance to King's Cross. That's where my lucky days ended. It was impossible to get on a train to the north. The last one to Leeds or York was full and bursting more with civilians than Forces Personnel. When I got there they had closed the gates. You would think that Service men and women (there were quite a few W.A.A.C.S., Navy and Flying Corps as disappointed as me) would have first chance at places on transport, time being so valuable when on leave. So I decided to stay the night at the Earl Roberts Club in King's Cross.

The club is cheap and cheerful and reserved for the Forces. The rooms are very small with a single bed and very cheap army canteen type meals, eggs and chips, etc., are served. I ate a supper of same and being dead beat after my journey, I went straight to bed and sleep.

Monday 13 August 1917

I was up betimes for the train north. After a good breakfast with 'all the trimmings' and the best mug of tea I've had for sometime, I made my way to King's Cross.

After being used as I have been over the last year or so, in spite of the war, to life in largely rural France, London streets were hectic and crowded. The khaki of the Army and the blue of the Navy are taken for granted. In my view the war has become 'normal'. London civilians make no concessions for the men who were once seen as the country's heroes off to crush the 'Barbaric Hun'. Tommy Atkins and Jack Tar seemed to be tolerated as necessary to earning a living. Judging from the well fed and well-dressed civilian passengers on bus, tram and train it was a good living.

Once again the train was loaded with civilians, not really making way as it chugged out of the station, for our 'brave lads'.

The journey was hot and uncomfortable and not made any better by the many stops that it took on its way to Doncaster.

I changed at Doncaster for Leeds and as the train travelled on I saw that I was once again back in the industrial north. Everywhere there was smoke from factory chimneys. The war effort is going 'full tilt' in the dirty towns we passed through and 'where there's muck, there's brass'.

The train to Leeds, when I caught it, was less full so the latter part of my journey was more comfortable and I was able to spend the time reading. I changed trains again and I rolled into Halifax and on to Mytholmroyd.

At the house there was Phyllis and Maud to greet me. Dad having spent some time looking for suitable work in the area had gone back to Hull, disappointed. There was rabbit stew on the hob in a big black saucepan and, showing how the family's attitudes had changed, a bottle of beer for me. I ate the stew, drank the beer and we sat and talked in the yellow light of the lamp. They asked me how things had been. Straightaway I could tell that I was going to meet the same old problem of them not understanding what it was really like. I like others found out that you could only talk of the war with those who really experienced it. So what you did was drop in to 'stock phrases' such as, 'oh it's all right, a bit hot sometimes, but not all the time'. You said this when really you wanted to tell whoever you were talking to of how really awful it was to see young men dying or blown to bits, or of your own terrors and fears. But, whenever you did talk this way to whom so ever you did, they seemed to lose interest and became a bit uneasy as if they were talking to a mad person, who might suddenly become hysterical.

I talked instead of going to see Tom's grave, of where it was and of how he had died quickly and peacefully in no pain. I did not know any of this for certain. What I did know was that he had taken a shell splinter in the stomach and so all this was likely to be quite untrue. But, it was what they wanted to hear. I was to repeat the same story to Dad and to Tilly when I saw her.

I washed in the bowl set for me on the wash stand in my bedroom and went to bed, but as I lay there I felt quite unlike the way in which I'd felt on any other leave I had taken. I was uncomfortable in the bed and inexplicably I found myself wishing that I was back in France with the lads. As Bert would have said, I'm sure, 'Some blanketty people don't know when they're blanketty well off'. Thankfully I soon fell into a deep dreamless sleep.

Tuesday 14 August 1917

I got up early and breakfasted alone Maud and Phyllis having gone to work an hour before as they were on at six. They had left me the makings of breakfast, eggs, bacon and black pudding on a shelf in the pantry. I cooked them in a pan over the fire which had been banked up the night before so all it took to get it into heat and flame was a good broddle with the poker. I made myself tea and cut thick slices of the fresh bread left in the bin. It was somebody's home made bread, but not Mother's.

Now it was morning, I felt more at ease. Having eaten I went out on to the back step and drank my tea. Looking up to the hills, green from early rain. The craggy outcrops of rock going up to the moors were of course unchanged from the last time that I had looked at them. All was peace. From below in the valley came the noise of a working town. The black smoke and white puffs of steam were not Jack Johnsons' or shrapnel bursts but the plumes of factory chimneys and the clouds from steam engines.

Tilly was working all day. Maud, who worked in the next shed to her had delivered that message to me, so I filled a bottle with water, put bread and butter in my emptied gaspirator bag and set out to visit Mother's grave in Luddenden Foot churchyard. It was well tended but with as yet no headstone. We couldn't afford one. I had brought a little bag of soil from Tom's grave and I sprinkled it over the little mound that was Mother's. I then went on a hike over the hills.

The walk on a gradually warming August day was exhilarating. Being under blue skies and trekking over green hills, quite simply made me glad to be alive. I came to realise something that before I had only vaguely felt: I loved the physical life. The life of the senses. I loved the pleasure of physical activity, whether I was swimming, cycling, walking on the hills or even demonstrating over there the strength and vigour needed to carry 'a case'. I did not want this physical life to end and there, high on the hills of Heptonstall moor, I vowed to the wind that I would come through the war in one piece.

That day I walked for a long time enjoying the changeable weather and watching the shadows of clouds move across the moors, and listening to what I thought were larks high in the sky. I didn't meet another soul. As I walked back down into the village and up to the house, I felt like a new man, ready for anything.

Back at the house I prepared to meet Tilly. I stood in a bowl in the scullery having filled it with hot water from the kettle on the fire, and had what Mam would have called 'a top and tail' wash. I shaved, brushed my hair, and then, after splashing some of Maud's or Phyllis's cologne over my uniform, which always had that distinctive khaki smell, I went to catch the train into town.

Halifax was thronged with 'hands' going to work or leaving work. The war still had the mills on three shifts or two shifts of twelve hours, seven days a week. Tilly was on days six to six. I saw her standing by the mill gate before she saw me. She had come out a bit early so as not to miss me in the crowd. She was casting her gaze around looking for me and from time to time exchanging banter with other mill lasses she knew who passed by. She was wearing the tam o'shanter in the photo she had sent me and her hair was in the same long thick plait. I also noticed that she was fuller in the figure.

I called to her and she looked up, saw me, and as she did her mouth opened in a happy smile. She ran across the road impulsively without looking almost in front of a passing brewer's dray. She dodged the plodding horses causing the drayman, high up on his seat, to shout: 'Watch out you silly little bugger'. When she reached the other side where I was waiting I wasn't disappointed. She was so pleased to see me.

For some time we simply strolled along the high street without saying anything to each other. She had both arms clinging to my right arm as we walked. We eventually stopped at a fish and chip shop where they served a sit down tea. We were served fish and chips, tea, and bread and butter at a table underneath a sign that said 'Customers are asked to refrain from eating their own food on these premises'. As we began to eat we both started to talk at the same time. I thought that I would have a great deal to talk to her about but really the pleasure was just in being with her. She gossiped about work and the girls there and I was content just to let her chatter on. Either by intuition or her own feelings she didn't ask me anything about the war in France. I was satisfied to leave it at that.

After eating we wondered into one of the many crowded pubs in Halifax town centre and stayed until time had been called. Tilly paid for the drinks with something of a sense of pride telling me of the high wages she was earning. Along with her drink she had a cigarette. I told her how disappointed I was that she had started smoking. She was surprised and asked me about all the cigarettes she had sent and she knew others sent to me. I told her what I used them for. In fact I had bartered cigarettes for the brooch I had bought her for her birthday.

The pub was crowded with civilians and only a few soldiers in khaki. Nobody seemed as interested in buying me a drink as at times before. I gauged a mood of indifference to the war except that it afforded opportunities for work and pay. The male civilians ranged along the bar, drinking up their pints quickly before the bell went, were certainly of military age, much older in fact than the drafts of boys that we seemed to be getting at the Front these days. They also looked very much fitter, if a little worse for drink.

We left the pub and before we had walked only a few paces Tilly coaxed me into a door way and gave me a kiss. There were times back there in France when I and others would have given anything for a cuddle and a kiss with a girl. Now all I could think of was the tobacco on Tilly's breath. I didn't betray this and held her close as we waited for the train to her Grandma's.

Grandma was already in bed when we reached her house. She still worked for Armitage's Mill although in her late seventies. She was an 'outworker' mending bolts of cloth that had flaws in them. But nonetheless she got up early to start her work. As we sat holding hands Tilly gave me a nice surprise. She told me she was going sick for a couple of days. Before the war that would have got her the sack but now the shortage of 'hands' guaranteed that her employers would ignore her 'twagging off'. She talked as if she was a truant missing school.

In the kitchen, both looking into the fire in silence, we sat on the battered chaise longue, it's horse hair stuffing poking out from numerous worn holes. Grandma shouted down to ask Tilly when she was coming to bed. Tilly shouted back that it would be in a bit and she added that she wasn't going in tomorrow. She began to speak and I knew straight away what she was going to say. She told me that she had been going out with someone else. I put my finger gently on her lips and told her that I didn't want to know and that as long as she could spend some time with me and still get her friend to write me letters I didn't care. I wasn't the 'jealous type' I said. What I didn't know would not hurt me. What I didn't want I said , was a letter telling me of it while I was over there . She then looked at me with tears in her eyes and said that it was me she really loved and that she would promise herself to me if I asked. I told her that I couldn't hold her to that, it wasn't fair. What if something happened to me and I didn't come back? At this she was silent. To cheer her up and to be less serious, what I asked her to promise me was to learn to read and write and I also said, wagging my finger as if to a naughty schoolgirl, was that she should stop smoking.

For some time she sat with her hands clasped in her lap looking into the fire then she turned to me, lifted her head, took off her little jacket. She was wearing a cotton and lace shirt, the buttons of which strained with her fuller bosom. She moved to embrace me. I had never been close to any girl as I was about to be with Tilly. I had of course played 'games' with girls as a boy, 'you show me yours and I'll show you mine'. But I had never made love or 'got warm' as we used to say. Tilly was to show me that she was a lot more experienced in such matters than me.

There was a bawdy song we often sang when altogether drinking plonkee. It was a parody of a music hall song of the day, 'I walked out with a soldier'. Our version went like this:

> I don't want to join the Army,
> I don't want to go to war.
> I'd rather hang around
> Piccadilly on the scrounge,
> Living off the earnings of a high born lady.

150

I don't want a bayonet up me blank blank
I don't want my blankers shot away.
I'd rather live in England, in merry, merry England,
And fornicate my blanking life away.

On Monday I touched her on the ankle,
On Tuesday I touched her on the knee,
And Wednesday, oh success,
I lifted up her dress,
Thursday I saw da da da da Cor Blimey.

As Tilly and I 'got warm' together, something I had longed for in those cold damp nights in dugouts, I forgot about the cigarettes on her breath, but what I could not forget as I did what the verses suggested was the same crude song going round and round in my head.

After fond goodbyes at four o-clock in the morning I walked into the darkness leaving Tilly standing at her back door sillouetted in the light of the lamp from the kitchen. We had known each other for such a short time. Before the war Tilly and I would probably have courted for months to get to this point, now it seemed to be a question of grabbing life while you could. We were to meet the next day for a trip to Leeds. I don't remember the long walk home. I could only think of Tilly's beautiful body and her willingness, if not generosity, in giving herself to me. In spite of her obvious experience she still seemed innocent. When I did get home I went straight to bed, forsaking the cold meats on the kitchen table the girls had left for me. I woke to a sunny August morning, happy to be home and alive.

Wednesday 15 August 1917

The trip to Leeds showed us a town full of shops selling all sorts of products in spite of rationing. There was also more evidence of the war in Leeds for I saw not a few obviously ex-soldiers, amputees with missing hands, arms and legs. We passed several 'basket cases' being wheeled along the pavement by wives, sisters or mothers. I said to Tilly, asking her to recall our conversation of the night before, 'And if I should come back like one of them?' Tilly became angry momentarily, and in a voice that was half of tears said 'You must not talk like that'. Home were the heroes.

We walked through arcades of shops whose entrances were festooned with 'the flags of all nations' and Tilly stopped to buy soaps and toiletries whose prices would at one time have been out of her reach. She was now an independent woman paying her own way. The prices of all sorts of things seemed to me have gone up three or four times since I'd seriously looked into shop windows.

For some time we sat on a bench in the city square by the town hall and ate sandwiches and fruit that we had bought from a shop we passed. We talked of what to do next and Tilly said she would like to go to the pictures. She knew where the nearest picture palace was and we walked down towards the station and found it on a corner across from a Hotel. In the darkness of the picture house we sat with our arms around each other, kissing and cuddling as many others were doing and not showing much interest in the picture. I was now well beyond the convention of just, 'feeling on top of the coat.'. Tilly unbuttoned her little jacket so that I could put my hand on her breast under her starched bodice. In the dark she coyly whispered, 'You don't think I'm a fast cat do you?' When we came out of the pictures we walked around the corner, found a pub that was not so crowded and sat for another hour enjoying each other's company.

By the time we came out it was time to get back as we wanted to catch the train. On the way to the station we had to cross the square. In the centre is a statue on horseback of the Black Prince and he is surrounded by bronze female figures. As we crossed the square Tilly whispered in my ear that a friend of hers had told her that it was good luck to touch the bronze breast of one of the female statues that circled the Prince. I felt that I needed all the luck that I could get so we ran to one of the figures and I jumped up and did what she suggested. We didn't get home too late and straight off the train had a last drink near the station. Grandma was once again in bed and once again the opportunity presented itself for Tilly to show me how much she loved me and how to love her.

I went home with the dawn but I got up when Phyllis and Maud went to work so that I could see them both. Maud told me over her breakfast cup of tea that she had a sweetheart. I had not met him but she revealed to me that they were planning marriage. Phyllis, the youngest, told me proudly that she was 'stepping out' with a young man who she had just met. Before they left they promised me that they would not tell Dad about my 'moonraking' but I really didn't care if they did or not.

Thursday 16 August 1917

Tilly came to the house after breakfast and although the weather didn't look too promising we decided to go for a ramble over the moors. We walked quite a distance before we rested. I was more used to walking than she was. Both of us sat side by side on rocks and looked down over cottages and farm houses nestling on the hills and valleys below. We moved on and found a pub where we ate bread, cheese and pickles. The war seemed very far away and I really would have liked our being together to go on for a long time.

We returned to Tilly's house as she had to go on an errand for her Grandma to pick up some cloth that had been mended by a lady who lived in Luddenden. We had to bring it back for Grandma's approval. It was late evening when we got to the house in Luddenden and we were put in the back kitchen to wait by her young daughter. There were 'guests' in the parlour. As we sat in the light of the kitchen range fire I heard knocks and scratches and what sounded like moans coming through the kitchen door.

Tilly seemed not to notice the noises and she sat, in spite of her promise to me, smoking a cigarette and saying nothing.

On the wall of the kitchen below a round wooden framed clock there was a large reproduction picture of a young British soldier boy, smiling, fresh faced, blue eyed with blond choir boy curls. He was standing 'Christ like' with arms outstretched, fully dressed in uniform and kit, ammunition pouches in a bandoleer over his shoulder and bayonet hanging from his belt. He had puttees and boots on and he was standing, his tin hat by his feet, in a small grove of red blossomed flowers. He had a halo round his head and the whole picture, although only a coloured print seemed to be lit from behind. He was obviously rising from the dead.

After about half an hour the lady we had come to visit came through the kitchen door with a length of cloth wrapped in brown paper and tied with string. 'I'm sorry, Tilly love, to have kept you waiting. Did you get a cup of tea? Do you want to stop for one? Tell your Grannie I'll do the rest by Sunday'. Tilly thanked her for the offer of the tea, took the parcel, and we walked out with the woman saying nothing to me.

As we walked back Tilly told me that the three guests were local women who had lost sons or husbands while serving with the West Yorks on the Somme. 'Grandma's friend' was not only a part-time out-worker for the mill, she was also the local medium and she held seances. The sounds I had heard were, I suppose, of her making occult mystic contact. I said, 'I should have listened more carefully and I might have heard the noise of silver crossing a palm'. Tilly dismissed this with a shrug and said that the three women had been taken out of the front door to avoid seeing me as they might have been upset by my uniform. On our way Tilly said that the woman had a lot of customers. 'That', I said, 'is no surprise to me, given the casualties I've seen'. Tilly went on the say that after the seances almost everybody had visions of their loved ones.

When we got back to Grandma's house she wanted to know if we had run her errand, and then as usual she went to bed. I stayed all night with Tilly and we talked. Tilly told me that she believed in the medium business and countered my sceptisism by pointing out that 'Jesus was born again'. Touché, as the French say. She said that all the girls at work believed it and that most of them or their mothers who had lost someone had been to a medium and had made contact. As the night wore on we both got less and less interested in the hereafter and more and more in the here and now.

I walked home early in the morning so that I could again catch Maud and Phyllis before they went to work and before Tilly's Grandma got up. As I put one foot in front of another I found my thoughts were very much on the many young men I had carried with my squad, some of course who later died, and I also thought of Tom and Mother. If only they could be resurrected.

The next day Tilly and I caught a train to Leeds and then changed for Hull. I wanted to see Dad who had moved back to Fern Avenue. We spent the day walking around Hull to Queen's Dock and then Riverside Quay. The docks were very busy. You could have walked across on the decks of moored ships. The streets were full of people and the town had an air about it that I didn't recognise. Hull had not had so much bustle about it when I went away. The traffic of trams, cars, lorries and motorbikes almost outdid the horse-drawn carts and other vehicles that had predominated pre-war. What I was also sensing, I think, in the foreignness of the town was an atmosphere of mourning for its men lost at the Battle of Oppy Wood, near Vimy, during the Battle of Arras. All four Hull Pals Battalions had fought and lost men in the action. I knew nothing of it when I was there in April/May and had learned of it from newspapers sent by post. The casualty list for Hull was what other towns who had sent Pals Battalions to the war had suffered at the Battle of the Somme.

We wondered around passing time until Dad came home from work and after tea in a tea shop in Whitefriargate we caught the tram from Victoria Square to Beverley Road. By the time we got to Fern Avenue it was six thirty and Dad was home in the scullery washing off the day's muck.

He was very pleased to see me in 'one piece', as he said, and he told Tilly how nice it was to meet her. But he, like everything else, was much changed. It did not take me long to notice that he didn't seem to have any heart in him. The solid, dependable, hard working, sober, no nonsense Father of the family was reduced almost to a shadow. The death of his wife and then his eldest son had knocked all the stuffing out of him. His reference to Oppy was that if Tom had not fallen in August 1916 he would have been taken in May 1917.

He made us a tea of bread, meat and cheese, although Tilly protested that she had already eaten. I ate mine, the scrappy, overpriced sandwich that I had eaten in the tea shop had not been enough for me.

We sat around the kitchen table for a long time and I told him about how I had visited Tom's grave and I re-counted the same story of Tom's painless death. I am sure he did not believe me.

Later he insisted that we went out. He said he would not be much company. We wanted to go out and Tilly particularly wanted to go to a Music Hall. We went to the Tivoli. There was a long queue outside and keeping it in order very effectively were two 'girls' in the uniform of the new women police. The theatre was packed and we only got seats in the Gods because I was, as the comissionaire in his brass buttoned red uniform said, 'One of our brave lads'. The highlight of the evening for me was a song sung that I'd not heard before:

> My girl's a Yorkshire girl,
> Yorkshire through and through

Tilly turned to me and said, squeezing my hand. 'Your girl's a Yorkshire girl'.

We arrived home late but Dad, though on early turn the next day, was not in bed. He wanted to say good night to me. Tilly went into my room and I made up a bed on the floor on the kitchen carpet. I don't really think that Dad would have minded if he'd known my plan was to share Tilly's bed. That's how much things had changed. Before the war it would have been unthinkable for me to be in a bed with a woman not my wife, under my Father's roof. The war had changed everything. As soon as I was sure that Dad was in bed and asleep I crept upstairs to where Tilly was to be sleeping. She was not yet in bed but standing waiting for me in her underclothes. She had on a short white pettycoat trimmed at the neck with lace interwoven with a blue ribbon. She had long white stockings on, tied at the top with the same blue ribbon. Her long blonde hair was undone and on her shoulders. We made love until the dawn when I crept downstairs to be there when Dad got up for work.

Saturday 17 August 1917

Dad got up very early, but then he always did in peace or war. Blacksmiths don't keep shop hours. I watched him make his usual breakfast of fried bacon on a fire of kindling, putting aside rashers that he would eat cold as his dinner at work. The tea we didn't drink went milk-less into a beer bottle that he stopped with a cork and he packed his things, tied his boots, put on his jacket and cap and we stood in the door and said goodbye to each other. Before he went I told him that I would leave my diaries in a tin box on the dresser and I asked him to see that they went into a safe place. As he walked down the terrace, he shouted over his shoulder that I should look after myself and that he would send cigarettes.

I made more tea and took a cup up to Tilly. She was still asleep as I slipped under the covers beside her. I suppose I should have arranged for us to be married on this leave in spite of what I thought and what she had said about seeing someone else. People these days got married on briefer acquaintance, and if I copped for it she would have a pension. But I hadn't thought of doing it really because I couldn't bring myself to think about it and I disliked myself for not having the thought. We both got up fairly late and had a breakfast of bread and eggs which I fried on the embers of the fire left by Dad. I asked Tilly to be quick about dressing as I thought we would get a train to Withernsea and spend a day by the seaside. I made sandwiches of bread and cheese, wrapped them in a parcel and put them in my bag. She thought it was a good idea and looked forward to it. As we left the house after I had locked the door and pushed the key through the letter box on it's string, we walked down the terrace and one or two curtains twitched. Some things, like nosy neighbours, don't change. The tram took us direct to the station and we boarded the local train just as it prepared to chug out at Stephney Lane. We had hoped for a compartment to ourselves but at Hedon a family of four on a day out got in.

As we left Hedon I pointed out to Tilly a little cottage just outside the station. 'There,' I said, once lived an old man I used to visit as a boy when I had my first bicycle, well before the war. I used to go there', I said, 'with a school friend who was a nephew of the old man. He was then in his seventies, it would be around 1909. He told us that he had begun his working life as a climbing boy of five years old, being pushed up chimneys to clean them of soot.'

At Withernsea we walked on the front. Although a seaside town there were lots of soldiers around as they were stationed in training camps, outside the town. We strolled back from the beach and ate our sandwiches outside a pub near the church. My leave was coming to an end. In a couple of days I would be back in France, back up the line, and back in the war.

We caught the train back to Hull and stayed in the station to catch one to Leeds. At Leeds we changed for Halifax. Both of us had slept most of the way back and it was twilight by the time we got to Tilly's Grandma's house. Grandma was out visiting somewhere and we sat together looking at the empty grate. There should have been a fire for it was cold in the house. Tomorrow was Sunday and my last day. Tilly seemed preoccupied. She was thinking of my imminent departure. She was also worried, she sai, that she might not see me again. 'And then where would she be?' I once again released her from any obligations she might feel and assured her that whatever, she would be in my thoughts over there. I told her again that if she found someone who could give her more security then she should take the opportunity. She cried and I comforted her. Grandma came in very late and went straight to bed without even a word to me. She didn't shout down for Tilly to come to bed as she usually did and I stayed with Tilly until the dawn broke, and I walked home.

Sunday 18 August 1917

Maud and Phyllis were still in bed when I got up. They were working, I wasn't. I busied myself packing my things, made a bit of breakfast and as always took my tea onto the back step where I could see a view down the valley. My thoughts were always the same no matter how rarely I took leave, would I come back and see this again? Over there life was much more day to day without much thought being given to the future.

I was to see Tilly later in the day and I told her to have a lie in so that she would be rested for the start of her work on the Monday.

I tidied myself up, giving myself a 'cat lick' and combing my hair. I went to church at Luddenden Foot but I didn't take Communion. What I did do, after the service, was to walk round looking at the various 'shrines' and temporary memorials with their photographs and fading flowers and their little notes such as 'to a loving son' and 'he died for King and Country'. I thought of the séance. Where was the difference here?

After a bit of a walk I went for my Sunday dinner at Tilly's but she was a bit out of sorts. Her Gran chided her, telling her not to be 'mardy' on my last day of leave. She saw that I was a bit disappointed with her mood and she had cheered up by the time that her Gran served the egg rich bread and butter pudding that I told Gran would make me think of home when I remembered it back in France. After that we walked back to our house to say farewell to Maud and Phyllis as I had to catch the train to London that evening to be sure to get back to France by the twentieth.

We hitched a lift part of the way on a cart and then we walked down into Halifax to go to the station and Tilly wore her Tam o'shanter even though it was warm. She knew I liked her in it. We waited in the station and I held Tilly close to me. She said a tearful goodbye and when it came in, shortly afterwards, I got on the train to Manchester to make my London connection. I told Tilly that because of her I had had a wonderful leave and that she was to keep writing to me and not forget what I had told her. As the train pulled out she waved and I watched her from the carriage window standing there on the platform until she was out of sight. As I sat back in my seat I was forced to reflect on my attitude to her. I had to face it, I was a snob. I couldn't accept her because she was illiterate. I was too immature to recognise the worth of this completely open, guileless young woman so capable of loving and giving love. I had never felt so un-Christian.

On the train to Manchester for my London connection I felt as if I was going down with something. I changed trains and when I arrived in London I went once again to the Earl Roberts club. I convinced myself that after a mug of cocoa, a bite to eat and an early night, I would be fit for the train to Southampton and the boat to Le Havre the next day. I went to bed thinking only on how groggy I felt.

CHAPTER 9 - I GO SICK

Monday 19 August 1917

I woke to a wet and miserable day and I felt no better than I had the night before. I couldn't even manage breakfast, a very bad sign. I dragged myself to Waterloo and I had to wait some time before I could get a train to Southampton. When I eventually arrived, after a very uncomfortable journey, I reported sick to an M.O. at the Port. He was sceptical at first, diagnosing 'end of leave Blighty blues' until he took my temperature and looked in my mouth and throat. I had trench fever. It caused him to ask if I had been staying with anyone 'cooty', that is lousy, in the frozen North. My concern was the possibility that I had left it with Tilly, Maud, Phyllis and Dad, particularly with Tilly who I was in most close contact with.

I didn't have much time for reflection on this for as soon as I was admitted to the sick bay on the ship on the orders of the M.O., I went into a deep sleep, induced I think by 'a powder' the M.O. had given me. I remember nothing from then to waking up on a stretcher in one of the bell tents of a hospital at Le Havre. My temperature was still high and for the next two days, isolated in the tent, I passed from sleeping to wakefulness so often that I could not tell dreaming from reality.

Wednesday 22 August 1917

I am still vomiting and feeling so incredibly weak that I have to be assisted with every function. I feel as if I am going to die. I am so low in spirits that I can't possibly recover.

Thursday 23 August 1917

Good God, I feel so much better and I don't know how I have come out of it. I am well enough now to be moved and I was transferred onto a hospital barge and I am now floating on a very pleasant slow journey up the river Seine to Rouen. The weather is fine and although I can't get up I have been carried onto the deck where I can watch the river traffic and talk to other patients and the orderlies, R.A.M.C. men like myself. How much things seem to be the luck of the draw. One of the orderlies has been out since 1914 and he has done nothing but cruise backwards and forwards from Rouen to Le Havre on Red Cross barges like this one. He had the educated voice of an officer and he thought he was entertaining me with stories of his V.A.D. conquests. I was reluctant to believe him at first as I had never exchanged so much as a word with one outside performing my duties. He was quite matter of fact in his insistence however and talked of times when the barge was empty apart from the two crew members, or when there were no officers or matrons on board during quiet periods. So much for the rain falling on the just as the unjust. The barge is full of men hideously or mortally wounded in the mud, blood and guts of the trenches having done their bit and 'caught a packet', and he is 'having if off' with a Nurse in the linen cupboard. I had to pull myself up short before I started to envy him. Some people have all the luck. One of the other orderlies said he was a 'bull blanker'. But I don't think he was.

Sunday 26 August 1917

I am now in hospital at Rouen and I have been here I think a couple of days, but I can't tell as the fever has reasserted itself so bad that I keep lapsing in delirium. Tilly's photo is beside my bed in the canvas marqee I am in and I think a nurse put it there after asking if the photo was of my sweetheart. I must be bad if V.A.D.s have started talking to me.

I am very sick and I am existing on a diet of milk dishes that all seem the same to me and anyway do not stay long with me, one way or another. I am past caring whether I live or die. In one of my more lucid moments an Army chaplain stopped by my bed to give me some sort of comfort, or even perhaps to read the last rites, but all I could think of was the story of the Sentry and Charlie Chaplin.

There is one consolation, as I get a bit better. I am occasionally treated to a glass of brandy with my hot milk. When I was asked by a V.A.D. nurse, if I wanted it in my milk, I tried to sound like a debonair man of the world by saying that I thought drinking it that way spoiled good milk and good brandy. The war still seems very far away. There are only the white blood stained dressings and amputee stumps of my fellow patients to remind me.

Sunday 9 September 1917

I have been a further week on the milk diet and my temperature has fluctuated alarmingly. I must have been incubating this from the time before my leave began. They say it comes from lice but I wasn't lousy, as far as I know, when I left France for England.

I am doing nothing except sleeping and trying to digest milk puddings and custards. I can't even get out of bed, though I have tried. I will not underestimate trench fever, or to give it it's real name, Typhus, again.

Thursday 11 September 1917

One day is still merging into the next. This week though I was able to get on my legs and start doing light work around the Hospital. I am making tea and waiting on other patients as they waited on me. I am also taking the opportunity to write up my diary, which is a great comfort to me, and I think it has prevented the worst effects of the disease as I have willed myself to keep it up to date.

Most of the lads in here are being treated so that they are fit enough to travel back home, but for so many of them that journey is not going to come.

They are from all over the British Line, from Ypres to Albert and quite a few have been here a long time and don't want to go back. As I have said before, the days have gone when stretcher cases would actually ask to be bandaged up so that they could get back in the Line and have another go at the 'Hun'. When you talk to casualties now it is about home, parents and sweethearts and I am frequently asked 'They won't send me back, will they?' As if I would know that. It did surprise me sometimes that some poor devils were sent back. 'As long as the trigger finger is working and he can still stand up' humourously summed up one definition of 'fit', but sometimes it wasn't a joke. I fetched and carried for a young lad in the Somerset Light Infantry who had been wounded on the Somme in late November 1916. A shell bursting within yards of him, tossed him into the air and when he landed he had a broken shoulder, a broken leg, his right arm was shattered and he was peppered with fragments. He had been shunted from A.D.S. to C.C.S. to hospitals all over the place. He had landed up here in Rouen in his third plaster cast, his bones having been reset. He expected to go home but by the time I left the cast was off and he was declared fit for duty.

Friday 14 September 1917

The weather is fine and warm and I can feel my strength returning. I can now make myself very useful. That is emphasized here because Rouen is a base for Staff Officers and there is a hospital for officers. That means that there are 'high ups' and 'brass hats' swanking about and inspecting this or observing that all the time. The whole place is kept spotlessly clean and I help.

Saturday 15 September 1917

I have not been sleeping well so better to see splendid moon lit nights. Singing 'Moonlight Bay' to myself, I long for the exhaustion that caused me once to be able to sleep anywhere. Bert used to say as I could get my head down anytime and anywhere, 'Ah think tha's got a button at the small of the back on thy blank. Thy art like one o' them dolls, Everytime tha sits dahn the eyes close'. I have begun perspiring as my temperature has gone up. I now have a red blotchy rash, which indicates a relapse.

Sunday 16 September 1917

I am back in bed again and feeling thoroughly fed up. The weather is lovely and I cannot get out. I can hear the 'walking wounded' chatting and laughing as they sit outside in the sunshine.
Letters from home have cheered me up a lot although they are worried that I am in

hospital. I have written right back to reassure everybody, Dad, Maud, Phyllis and Tilly, that I am not in Hospital and that I will recover completely in time. Thankfully nobody at home is ill so I didn't pass it on. Tilly's dictated letter said how much she had enjoyed seeing me on the last leave and she must have a very close relationship with the girl who writes it for her because she said some very intimate things. She thanked me as well for being so understanding and said it was one reason why she loved me. Encouragingly she said she was maintaining her resolve to stop smoking and that's nearly a month now. She wrote two whole lines in her own hand so I am really pleased that she is trying and these said that whatever happened and wherever I was and wherever she was, she would always be my sweetheart. I wrote a long loving letter back to her and ended with the German word I'd learned from off the mail I once found. Vergistmeinnicht 'Forget me not.' Tilly wrote back to me later and asked what the word was at the bottom of the letter that had a great black mark across it. The word had been censored.

Sunday 23 September 1917

The last week has seen my slow recovery and I have been moved to a 'tented ward' with other recovering patients. I am feeling satisfied with everything and everybody. I am glad that I have kept myself fit for I'm sure that this and refraining from smoking has contributed to my speedy return to good health. And I am young.

I share the marquee with South Africans, Scots, Irish, other English and Australians. This part of the British Empire at least gets on well together. We spend our time reading and I have never read so much English literature before in my life. I have discovered Dickens, Wells and even Bernard Shaw. I have also discovered gambling, that is playing cards, Vingt-et-un (twenty-one) or Pontoon for cigarettes. My fellow patients smoke them and sometimes fill the tent with such a blue fog that I have to seek the fresh air outside. I am reading Charles Dickens' 'Nicholas Nickleby', loaned to me by the South Africans. There are two of them from Cape Town . They had both suffered severe spinal injuries when a dug-out with metal girders collapsed in a bombardment at Delville Wood on the Somme. They have spent months in hospitals in France, then in England and now back to France from where they hope they will be sent back home. Their description of their 'home land' made South Africa sound like a beautiful place of sun, sea, mountains and fertile plains. Both with English origins they, had been farmers there, but I doubt if they would ever work again. One needed two sticks to move only a short distance and the other was fixed in a brace from his neck to his hips.

The Australians lived up to their reputation for being noisy and undisciplined but at the same time were generous and friendly comrades. One I remember was called Jim McDonald and he was from New South Wales. He proudly boasted that fifteen feet of his innards had been taken out after a shell splinter all but disembowelled him. It happened while he was with his Infantry near Ypres. He was often cheeky to the Nurses and he made suggestions that as he put it himself, in his Aussie accent, "Would make a blush come to the cheeks of a 'Pox Doctor's Clerk'. He would entertain us whether we liked it or not with renderings of various bawdy songs. One of them went like this:

> One night in gay Paree
> I paid five francs to see
> A lovely French Cheree
> Tattooed from head to knee.
> And on her jaw
> Was a British Man of War
> While down her back
> Ran the Union Jack,
> So I paid five francs more
> And up and down her spine
> Was the Mason Dixon Line.
> On her lily white bum
> Was the picture of the rising sun
> And right across her kidney
> Was a bird's eye view of Sydney

He was soon to be discharged home and was looking forward to showing his three children the network of scars across his stomach and abdomen.

Friday 12 October 1917

I have now been in hospital nearly six weeks and I expect to leave tomorrow. We all had a farewell party last night and I drank a lot of fizzy wine, eau de vie and plonkee that we had smuggled in via the good offices of a coloured French soldier who emptied the refuse bins around the hospital. He brought us a bin into the tent and with a great big smile opened it up to reveal our contraband. Once again the currency used was tins of bully beef. We were all a bit worse for wear the next morning.

I left today with everyone's address and promises 'to look up' if I was ever in Glasgow, Belfast, Cape Town or Sydney. Although I was in hospital I had a memorable time. Especially over the last fortnight when we'd had some very decent concerts and lectures on subjects ranging from English literature to German history. I had never realised before what a 'young' country Germany was.

CHAPTER 10 - YPRES

Tuesday 16 October 1917

I have now been some days at our Base Details Camp, passing various fitness tests, inspections, and being introduced to new gas weapons now being used. As before the gas tests were sometimes a bit hair-raising. The new gases were 'mustard' (Because of its yellow colour) and an 'improved' phosgene. Mustard gas was a terrible weapon and the phosgene gas was much more powerful than previous strengths. We were also warned that the Germans were exercising a new technique just prior to a gas attack. They had started sending over a relatively harmless gas that induced fits of sneezing just before a salvo of more powerful gas shells. This caused people caught in the cloud to take off their masks and so be vulnerable to the mustard or phosgene gas. We had to be on the look out for this tactic.

While at base I sent in a form applying for a transfer to the Royal Flying Corps but as yet I have received no reply.

Now we are standing by, with kit packed, ready to entrain for the 5th Division in the Ypres Salient. We are expecting orders any time to go to the train. Tonight we are going to a concert party.

Wednesday 17 October 1917

We were paraded early doors for the train to Belgium. The accommodation that waited for us on the line was the Horse Box. It was evident that the previous occupants had only just left. We all decided to assert ourselves and we refused to leave until we had swilled out the floors and brushed the horse muck out through the doors. Officers and N.C.O.s were a bit non-plussed at our near mutiny and they tried to single out ring leaders for disciplining, but as no individuals had stepped forward to complain and our protest was made by simply standing silently on the line they weren't able to make examples. In the end they saw the reasonableness of our complaint. There was no 'dining' car so we were handed out biscuit, bread and bully to eat on the way. I had a tin of butter and a tin of sardines which, as I didn't know anybody in the new squad, I thought I would keep to myself. At least we are not too crowded, there being only fifteen in our wagon. A large metal drum was handed up to us for our 'latrine'. I hope it won't be used too much as on journeys like this there is a tendency towards 'spillage'.

We set off but did not get far and spent the night in sidings at Etaples. We heard knocks on the door of the wagon and we opened it to cooks dispensing hot stew and dumplings followed by our favourite, rum flavoured tea. They were greeted with salutations. A further concession to comfort was that before we bedded down, dry straw was pitch forked from Service Corps wagons. The Waggoners said that if we looked carefully we might find a brace of land girls among it. With enough blankets to go round, a couple of candles lit, and the glowing of pipes and cigarettes, we sat round in the smoky gloom and jawed away and then someone produced a harmonica and old favourites were played and sung such as

> It's the same the whole world over
> It's the poor what gets the blame.
> It's the rich what gets the credit,
> Isn't it a blanking shame?

The incorrigibles stayed up playing cards until persuaded by calls 'to put a sock in it' and 'trim your lamps, wise virgins' to bed down like the rest of us. Eventually there was dark and only the sounds of sleeping. We were like creatures hibernating in a nest. We slept without a thought for where we were going, to the interminable mud of Ypres.

Thursday 18 October 1917

Reveille at five, and dixies of hot water were brought round for washing and tea. Thankfully this was not made in the same water as used for washing, though it has been known. There was a hot breakfast of bread, sausage and bacon that set us up for the day. We had had a very good night with few, if any, resorting to the 'bucket' during it. Those needing the shift of natural functions were able to use permanent latrines near to the train.

The train set off, though slowly, and we spent the day travelling to Calais, St Omer and finally to Hazebrouck where we stopped late at night. After pooling our rations we made a satisfying dinner but had to make do with cold tea and cold water.

When we de-trained we were marched past empty buildings, the populous having fled Fritz's long-range guns. We went into tents in a very muddy field instead of the obviously vacant barns. We were as unhappy about this as the meal that waited for us. It was what we used to call 'shadow stew'. We advised the cooks to be less lavish next time with the 'Aldershot stock'. The cooks turned away criticism with obscenities and told us they had been waiting all day for our slow train and that their kitchen had been raided by other 'birds of passage'. It was like it or lump it.

We would have preferred our cosy horse box to the damp mud that the tents barely covered. Sleep did not come easily as a steady drizzle throughout the night moistened the mud even more. In the far distance the grumbling guns could be heard and through the flap of the tent that I always placed myself close to for fresh air, I could see the arcs of star shells going up from the horizon into the black night.

Friday 19 October 1917

We got up to a better breakfast and supper. The cooks, though grudging, were intent on redeeming themselves. Perhaps the dryer weather put them in a better mood. There really can be few jobs more trying than trying to cook for scores of discontented men outside in the rain.

With several other squads we formed up and mounted onto lorry transport that was to take us a few miles to join 13th Field Ambulance at La Clytte south of Ypres where we were to camp at Chippawaa to wait a few days before going into action.

Sunday 21 October 1917

Our last few days here have been spent largely trying to keep warm and dry. We sit huddled round braziers for which thankfully there is no shortage of coke. If the tales we get from passing soldiery are to be believed, our discomforts are nothing to the privations being suffered by the men in the Line around 'Wipers'. We are told that there are no trenches to speak of as the ground is completely waterlogged. 'Carries' are almost impossible as progress is so much impeded by mud, and distances are measured in yards per hour rather than miles. We shall see for ourselves as we have been told to be ready to march from La Clytte through Dickiebusch, Café Belge, by the curiously named 'Dolls House' and then to enter Ypres by the Lille Gate.

Tuesday 23 October 1917

We marched, or rather trudged, through slippery greasy mud that swilled in eddies around our boots into the ruins of Ypres. The substantial 17th Century brick fortifications were shell scarred and broken but still standing. That could not be said for the town itself. No wall of the town's houses was more than waist high, and now the town streets' only addresses are corrugated iron 'arches' that lead to cellars and dugouts in the ruins. What was also striking, as our ranks marched through, was the mood of the place. There is not the usual banter from troops passing in the opposite direction. They are bedraggled, mud covered, down cast and hardly seem to be able to put one foot in front of the other. We are fresh and sprightly by comparison.

We carried on, wet, in spite of our gas capes, through ravines of brick piles to the sandbagged remains of what had been the Menin school and prepared to stay there for the night with orders to move up to the line at daybreak. We hadn't been long settled when there was an air raid warning. German aircraft began dropping bombs before we had time to evacuate to dugouts but they landed some hundreds of yards away and simply pounded more bricks into dust. We were all already dressed having bedded down in our boots. I had only removed my very damp jacket. What was more upsetting than the air-raid as we returned to our blankets and kit on the floor of what had once been a classroom, was the occasional shell burst near the Menin Gate not far away from a long range heavy gun accurately registered by Fritzy.

Wednesday 24 October

I had a very disturbed night so I got up at daybreak. I took a risk and walked up to the Menin Gate. As with the Lille Gate, the brick ramparts around are to a great extent still intact. There is a moat around the town and as the sun rose on what looked like being a bright day I saw a sight I shall remember for the rest of my life. In the early morning light I saw what I thought were white ghosts floating on the water of the moat. It was a pair of swans moving over the water as if pushed like small sailing boats by a light breeze.

With this image still in my head I walked back to our corrugated iron covered school room billet for breakfast. One of the squad in a scrounge in the wreckage of the school had found a damaged but recognizable panoramic photograph of Ypres as it was before the war. The Great Cloth Hall and the Cathedral stood splendidly above the decorated facades of the neat medieval terraced town houses. All this was now pounded into almost complete ruin. I remember that as a boy at school we had had a history class that told of a connection in ancient times between this part of Flanders and Hull. Ship loads of wool were once sent across the North Sea to this region to be processed into cloth. Cromwellian soldiers fought here because this trade had been interfered with. Here we were again but this time with more troops and bigger guns.

After daybreak we moved up the Support Line and had the reason for 'Hell Fire Corner's' name confirmed to us. We were exposed to fairly intense artillery fire. As we made our way cautiously along the Menin Road we were not much reassured by the very large and extensive hessian screen strung along the roadside. It was supposed to shield the road from the prying eyes of German artillery spotters. They might not have been able to see us but their shells sought us out. I think we would have been better moving at night. It was even more disconcerting to learn from one of our artillery men sheltering, as we were to be when we ducked into a dug-out covered by a substantial roof of what was called 'Elephant Tin' at White Chateau, that there was a strong possibility of the shells landing around being fired from guns now in German hands once supplied by us to the now dispossessed and defeated Russians.

When the 'storm' of screaming metal was over, we started again. On our right was Sanctuary Wood, with the positions Stirling Castle and Inverness Copse signalling by their names original occupation by Scottish troops. The destination of our squad was a concrete 'pill box' on the relatively high ground that had once been the village of Gheluvelt. It was now just a mound of rubble. The position had already changed hands a number of times. As we made our way over the five mile or so route to it we dropped off other squads in locations along the road. Over the last months advances had been made and the battle we were all about to take part in was a thrust to shift the Germans off all the high ground in the Salient, particularly north of where we were, Passchendale Ridge.

By the time my squad got to our destination and settled in it was dark. We felt safe in our concrete billet. Things for us were quiet in the night but Fritz was shelling heavily further back.

Thursday 25 October 1917

First light showed us that we were in fact in an old German 'pill box'. The entrance tunnel was facing the wrong way. After a cold breakfast on our rations we had a look round at the conditions we were going to have to work in.

The sight outside was depressing but then what else should we have expected. Around the 'pill box' in a radius of yards there were many unburied German dead. Their bodies had been plundered for they had no belts, helmets or boots on and their pockets were all turned inside out. Their looters had left unwanted personal possessions strewn about so the mud was littered with the sodden remains of paper, photographs and identification material. The outside of our concrete hut was blackened in a way that suggested it had been taken by fire. Then to our intense surprise and alarm we were attacked from the air. Two German fighter planes began to fire on us from a very low level, diving down so close that the fire from the muzzles of their machine guns could be seen flashing as they straffed us. We were back in the 'pill box' like rats up a drain and did not emerge again until informed by a Sergeant in our lot who rattled on the aperture of our pill-box billet to inform us that we would be needed in the attack that the Division was going to make on Friday morning.

Feeling it safe enough to go outside we went further back to the Support Line to get more rations and for new stretchers as we found the two we had carried up had been destroyed in the straffing.

Going back was more difficult than coming up as we had to go over a terrain churned up into a morass from the impact of thousands of shells. It was a veritable sea of mud. Shell holes that are full of liquid mud blend into the ground so that their surface is almost indistinguishable from surrounding, and just a little more solid, mud. One false step usually means a drowning in a mud bath. The mud sucks on the wellington boots we have been issued with and from time to time in trying to walk a boot is left behind. It has to be pulled out but the suction and resistance of the cloying mud needs great effort to overcome it. The last time I was in the Salient the conditions were bad, but not as bad as this. We reflect on the difficulties that face us in bringing wounded back to Dressing Stations.

We returned to our concrete shelter late that same night. The trek of a few miles is taking us hours. The tramping, squelching journey and the effort needed to make it has completely exhausted us. It is also numbingly cold. We are so cold and soaked that we risk making a small fire in the 'pill box'. With boots off and a mess tin on the fire to make hot tea, our billet warmed up, we thank Heaven for small mercies and turn in.

Friday 26 October 1917

We 'stood to' early doors and as we did the bombardment began. The rain was falling in torrents. We were kept back for the first part of the day and treated the wounded we were called to where they were, while they were carried back by other squads. Conditions were impossible. Moving about in the mud under fire was so difficult. We could not do our job. We had to watch lightly wounded men crawl into new shell holes where they might drown as water flowed into them from the downpour. When we started carrying we could only make very slow progress back to the old German Line where we rested at Hooge and our carries were taken further back.. I treated one old sweat who had the 'Blighty one' in the leg he had been looking for since 1914. He was one of the old brigade that we usually called 'out since Mons'. While enjoying the smoke I gave him he told me that the Chateau that once stood here at Hooge had been an H.Q. at the beginning. He told me that he had 'waited on' once at a dinner where champagne and caviar were served to the top brass. I left him to be collected and hoped he managed to get shifted before his wound went off, as it was taking hours to get lads to the rear.

Saturday 27 October 1917

We slept where we sat last night, luckily the night was dry. Having no rations of our own we got nothing to eat until seven o-clock in the morning when we had a bit of biscuit, cold water and rum given to us by a Regimental M.O. The whole of our Division the 5th attacked on Friday morning, eighteen to twenty thousand men, but they have advanced only a few yards. Casualties have been high and we have had a hot time but a very slow one getting them back. Apart from 'Out since Mons' our carries have been young lads who seemed to be in their teens. For many of them it is the first time they have seen action.

Our work in the night took us to the north and we had to shift some Canadians who had been caught by shell fire. They were a Lewis Gun Team and were badly shot up. Their lot had been hit so much their own bearers had their own work cut out to move their casualties so we stepped in. During this work I had a nasty incident with gas. I looked into what were the remains of an entrance to a tunnel to see if any wounded had crawled in. There was a small pocket of gas in it and I wasn't wearing my mask. I only took a mouthful but it was enough to give me a coughing fit that lasted fifteen minutes. I could not get any air into my lungs and thought I had 'bought it'. God knows what it must have been like to be in a cloud and get your lungs full.

Sunday 28 October 1917

We are miles back along the Menin Road at our Aid Post, which is called Clapham Junction. I had a whiff of oxygen which took the last of the gas that I'd gulped out of my system. We spent what was left of the night here. It was a night wherein we had blundered about in what had once been a wood north of the Menin Road looking for wounded who we discovered had already been moved. Once again we came across a lot of unburied German dead. In the dark we trod on the backs and bellies of the poor souls who are now part of the muddy, almost liquid, clay that surrounds us. The wood was shelled all the time we were in it but few went off. The ground was so soft they didn't detonate or they were duds. The ones that did explode made more of a splash of mud than an explosion as they went so deep.

At the Aid Post we were rushed towards the small hours and our mouths became blue from the indelible pencils we licked when marking a big 'M' on the foreheads of casualties who had been given morphia. Unlike at the Somme there were plenty of medical supplies, disinfectant, antiseptic, lock jaw serum and anaesthetic. But what really made the difference as always for those who could take it, were the hot cups of tea laced with rum. We needed it just as much.

Monday 29 October 1917

Early this morning we were ordered to a position called Polygon Wood. We were sent there to give a hand to the regimental bearers of a Company of Sherwood Foresters. Although we had had very little sleep we were set to work straight away with a 'carry'.

In training we were taught a regulation step so that with a man at each corner and the stretcher hanging by leather straps 'the pendulum effect' of the stretcher swaying from side to side would not be set up. As with a great deal of the stuff we learned in training, the practice did not survive reality, especially the reality of the Ypres Salient.

Fighting in the Ypres Salient was even more hell on earth than anywhere else on the Western Front. A more unsuitable place on the planet for a battle could not have been chosen. When it was dry there was no cover and the Germans having got there first, as usual, had what little high ground there was, fortified with concrete bunkers. When it rained the whole landscape became a sea of porridge-like mud. To move at all was very difficult. For us to carry a wounded, groaning, full grown man out of it was almost the height of impossibility. But, we did it, not once but over and again and that sometimes for up to five miles.

We couldn't tramp down trenches. They were either crowded, destroyed, water-logged, too shallow or all four. So the only alternative was for us with super human effort to slowly slosh, squelch and slog on top. Sometimes we hoisted the case on our shoulders, sometimes we hung the 'carry' from the straps on each corner, with the weight of the stretcher, causing the leather to bite into our shoulders. We trudged a few yards then rested.

Often we had men die on us during our slow progress. When this happened the poor soul would be tipped off, arranged by the side of the road, duck boards or 'corduroy' track if in evidence. If not then simply plonked in the mud. Identification discs and personal effects would be removed and a note taken of the location and the unit he belonged to. We would rest for a bit and then set off for another one. While all this was going on there were machine gun bullets flying about and artillery shells splashing into the mud. What was most terrifying during these ordeals, was to be caught at night in the open by a flare. It felt like being naked in the fires of hell.

On the occasion of the 29 October as we set off once again from our pillbox for Clapham Junction Aid Post with a carry, our left-hand bearer at the stretcher head stopped a bullet. It lodged in the fleshy part of his upper shoulder and, lucky for him, it did not hit bone, for he could still articulate it. When we had all picked ourselves up I saw that there was little blood and he asked me to disinfect it and dress it. He said he didn't want to leave us in the lurch so he would try and carry on, and carry on he did, with little complaint, right to the Aid Post where he and the patient were treated.

The other three of us found an officer and immediately reported his courage and 'conduct above and beyond the call of duty'. We all thought he deserved a medal. Nothing came of it. I suppose there was so much confusion and so many other things to do. If it did get to 'the top' I'll bet it was dismissed as something that four 'chancing rankers' had dreamed up to earn a few bob. Money was sometimes offered as an alternative to medals. It was unjust, but then who looks for justice in war? We had all seen medals handed out left, right and centre, when the staff thought they might give encouragement. Then they 'came up with the rations' as we used to say. But when one was really deserved, as with our mate's conduct, it was not forthcoming.

Thursday 1 November 1917

I have spent the last few days in the Aid Post at Clapham Junction so I have been able to grab some sleep and some grub. On Tuesday night I was excused duties so I walked into Ypres and tucked into chips and bread and butter and tea in a canteen. As I scoffed them down I could hear a barrage of guns and see flashes on the horizon to the north as the battle for the ridge went on. Here I was, sitting on a bench, drinking tea, and that was happening a few miles up. It was as if I was in another room waiting to be called.

Another 'comfort' I associate with my Ypres visit was the convenience of visiting a latrine that wasn't under observation or even under fire. As it was a sit down job there were even visitors reading newspapers as they communed with nature.

I hitched a lift back to the Aid Post with a dispatch rider on the back of a motorbike that I thought I would like to ride if I ever got back to 'civvy street'. It was a three fifty 'Douglas' and it coped at speed with the holes and bumps of what was left of the Menin road until finally impeded by mud.

Back at the Aid Post we are kept busy with casualties coming from the slopes up to

Passchendaele Ridge and from the action down the road to Ghelevelt. Most of them are bullet wounds but there are not a few suffering from the new gas. The worse cases are impossible to treat, even with the whiff of oxygen that is now available. They cough incessantly and spit blood. Unbelievably they are still offered, and they take, cigarettes.

Sunday 3 November 1917

I became a casualty myself today. I was hit in the foot and calf by shell splinters as we were carrying a patient who had been brought down by regimental stretcher bearers out of an area of blasted trees that has once been a wood. They had brought him a long way down from just north of Ghelevelt and put him down by some duck boards. He was only a young lad, very slight and not looking his age. We had no great difficulty in picking him up. He had a awful stomach wound.

As we picked him up he screamed with pain and we hesitated about moving him. Just then a shell burst in the air just above the ground about a hundred yards away. We hardly heard its explosion. But nonetheless, splinters shot behind my right leg and cut through the top of my boot. That morning, because I knew we would be walking on 'corduroy', I had taken off my rubber boots and put on my leather hob-nails. My feet, like everybody else's in wellingtons, went white and wrinkly and in spite of socks were always chafed. I think if I'd kept wellingtons on instead of the leather boots I was wearing, the splinters might have taken my foot off. As it was I had a deep cut underneath the sliced leather, almost from my toes up to the bottom on my leg. Another splinter had cut through my puttees and into my calf before continuing on its way. Both wounds were bleeding profusely and though not in much pain I could not walk.

We laid our lad down and my mates looked at my foot, disinfected it with iodine and dressed it, binding the dressing round the boot. I asked them not to take the boot off as at the time I was convinced that my foot was held on by it.

As we wondered what to do about getting me and the 'carry' to the Aid Post we saw a group of surrendered Jerries being escorted to the rear and we cadged four to lift the 'carry' and two of my mates helped me to hobble along. The fourth member of our team picked up a discarded rifle and bayonet from the side of the road to 'encourage' our prisoners. There was no need for any of that, they were relieved to be taken. It was obvious.

With the help of my mates I limped or was carried into the Aid Post and by the time I got there I wished that they had taken off my boot as my foot had swollen to the size of a football and the pressure of the split leather was agonising. In seconds I was on the table, having jumped the queue. The M.O.s orderly cut off my boot and immediately blood spurted out but stopped after a short time. The M.O. warned me that he had almost run out of anaesthetic but new supplies would be here within the hour. He said he needed what was left for more serious cases and gave me the alternative of waiting or being stitched up without it. I decided to have it done. I had to bite the bullet as the long curved needle was stabbed first into the skin on the top of my foot and then into the lesser wound at the bottom on my calf. When he had finished the top of my foot looked like the lace holes of a rugby ball. The treatment and stitching up had been excruciating but now I had to worry about getting further treatment as quickly as possible. I knew all too well of the dangers in treatment being delayed. My worse fears were that gangrene might set in and then it would be, first a foot off, then a leg below the knee, and then the rest off at the thigh. I knew it went like that - I had seen it happen all too often. My other thoughts were that I had possibly got myself 'a Blighty one'.

Sunday 4 November 1917

No such luck. I am down at Headquarters Base Hospital and I have been here since last night. I hopped an ambulance driven by an A.S.C. driver, who had been trained in Bradford, only too pleased to give a hand to another 'Yorkie'. He went first to Ypres and then straight through by the Lille gate. My troubles aren't over because last night, as soon as I had been admitted into the hospital and slipped between nice clean sheets after a bath and a shave in my clean pyjamas, I was hoisted out again because there was an air raid. I didn't go back in the ward I had been first admitted to because it had been smashed to pieces by German bombers. Fortunately there were no casualties in the raid and I had had the presence of mind to collect my 'ditty' bag on evacuation so my possessions, my fag store and my precious diaries were safe. I was re-accommodated in a marquee in the hospital grounds and I slept like a baby for the rest of the night.

Wednesday 7 November 1917

I must have spent the last few days doing nothing but sleeping, eating and having my leg and foot looked at. The last few weeks have really taken it out of me and I am whacked. While on duty I never gave exhaustion a thought. We just carried on. Now I don't feel I can lift my knife and fork, never mind a heavily laden stretcher on my shoulders, and then set off for a four mile, six hour trudge through the mud, blood and the unspeakable mess that the war has made of the Ypres sector.

Saturday 10 November 1917

I have just eaten a curry for the first time in my life. It was made of some sort of meat, I didn't ask what, and I ate it with vegetables and boiled rice. It was delicious.

I am now one of the walking wounded. My foot is healing a treat and I am already limping around the ward. The stitches are coming out tomorrow or the next day. I feel quite light headed with relief that the wound did not turn bad. Although the dressing has been changed frequently and inspected for infection, I was always on the Q.V. for that unmistakable cheesy smell of gangrene and the change of colour that went with it.

Certainly I have to accept that it wasn't 'a Blighty one' for I will be back on duty in a few days, but it wasn't, thank God, a leg off job.

Monday 12 November 1917

We who can get out of bed, sit around the stove playing cards, reading, or we help the orderlies serving meals or making tea. The talk is, as we rest, always of course of the war and home. Gossip and rumour fly back and forth. 'The Russians have completely packed in and their Army has walked back home'. 'There is going to be a general strike in England'. 'The French Army have shot all its Officers'. 'The Americans have gone back, because no-one has seen them'. There was a rumour that concerned me and that was that we were to be sent to Italy. The only confirmed piece of information was that Jerry had been pushed off the ridge and Passchendaele village had at last been taken.

Tuesday 13 November 1917

Still in dock and a little bit worried because two of the stitch holes have gone septic. I took the dressing off to let the wounds breath and because I was itching like mad. I got a right dressing down from a Q.A. Sister. She was intent in putting me in my place and said that my business was 'carrying' and it was her business 'curing'.

Saturday 17 November 1917

All the stitches were taken out today. The wound at the back of my leg was no problem but taking the stitches from out of my foot was more painful than when they went in. Each knot was snipped and then the thread pulled through, but not one of the sixteen stitches came out cleanly. In every case the skin had grown over the cat gut and it had to be tugged out with sharp pulls. I was in a sweat when the treatment had finished and the lecture the Nurse gave me on the pain my Mother would have had giving me birth didn't' help. Nor the Nurse's comment, 'It's a good thing men don't have babies'.

But all's well that ends well. The foot obviously is not as good as new and I shall carry a reminder of the battle of Ypres until I die, but I have lost no articulation and there were no tendons severed and no bones broken, so I thank my lucky stars and count my blessing,s etc., etc.

Sunday 18 November 1917

I am now out of hospital and well away from Ypres. We have left Dosinghem, Bandaghem and Mendinghem and are now back out of it at Lottinghem, a village of a small cluster of houses. The three aforementioned names are Aid Stations that were christened by adding the letters 'em' to the healing functions of the R.A.M.C. 'em' is a common ending in the names of towns in Flanders. Lottinghem is a few miles from Boulogne. Hilly and picturesque, untouched by war, it is a nice quiet place to rest and recuperate. However, after a month at Ypres we would have preferred somewhere a bit more lively.

Thursday 22 November 1917

We are still resting now, about twelve miles from St Omer, and I am with a few other bearers who like me are recovering from light wounds. They have given us the job of marking for the Infantry at firing practice. An old Sergeant from the Regular Army is showing us what to do and at the same time lamenting the quality of marksmanship amongst new recruits. In his day, 'the Infantry could loose off as many as twenty aimed shots a minute'. He then pointed to the crossed rifles of a badge sewn onto his sleeve: 'That's the insignia of a first class marksman. I get one and six a day extra for wearing that'. He then indicated the line of new recruits standing ready with their rifles: 'This lot could not hit a bedroom door with a piss pot'.

On Tuesday I had a riotous evening with two bearers from 'A Section' of our Field Ambulance. We went to Devons, a town declared out of bounds, but we managed to find an estaminet that catered for the 'wanton soldiery'. There was a piano installed and someone was found to play it. Another produced a mouth organ and a further comrade accompanied the music by playing on the spoons. We had stimulated by rounds of plonkay a right old sing song. The talent there is for entertainment never ceases to amaze me. The lad on the spoons whose name I think was Albert said he had earned a 'nice penny' busking the queues outside music halls and picture palaces in London's West End before the war. A number of songs were got through, quite a few that were new to me. One I recall was a parody of the popular song 'I wore a tulip'.

> You wore a tunic, a dirty khaki tunic,
> I wore no underclothes.
> You weren't in the trenches
> But off with hot wenches,
> You were out blanking
> While we were all ducking
> Out on the Menin road, etc., etc.

In spite of the fact that the town was out of bounds the place was thronged and the beer and the plonkay flowed like water. I am mildly surprised at the change in me. If authority said 'jump' I would be 'first on the shovel' and I would never had got drunk or sang coarse songs. Here I was disobeying orders and doing both.

The weather is dry but cold and dull.

Sunday 25 November 1917

We are at Lottinghem again. At church parade this morning instead of a sermon we got a 'dressing down' because of the 'out of bounds' visit. Our Sergeant had a 'strip torn off him'. So after the parade he had a go at us. 'Little fleas have smaller fleas upon their backs to bite 'em, smaller fleas have smaller fleas and so ad infinitum'. We were also told that the Division is moving again. There were no details so rumour as usual was rife - the Somme, Flanders, Italy, The Moon?

On Thursday last I had a very pleasant quiet evening in Lumbres, the nearest village to the firing ranges. An old lady had opened up her front room as a small restaurant and at a table for two I had a fine meal of soup, followed by sardines, cold boiled potatoes and mayonaise, followed by roast chicken accompanied by garlic flavoured french green beans. After that she brought fresh bread, Camembert cheese and apple tart for dessert. 'The apples, beans and chicken came from my garden', she said as I drank an excellent cup of coffee to round off the meal....................if they come steady. It cost five francs including wine. That's nearly a week's pay but well worth it. I felt quite the cosmopolitan traveller as I indulged in a cognac with my coffee. I heard later that officers had discovered her and annexed her little restaurant. 'Why should the devil have all the best tunes?' I must have been one of her first customers.

I've had no letters from England or France for some time. Maybe it was because I was at Ypres. I have sent one or two Army postcards and only written a long letter to Tilly. I have had no reply.

Monday 26 November 1917

Back to Lottinghem again to mark at the ranges. Although it was against regulations I had a go myself, five rounds rapid fire. I had played with the Lee-Enfield before and even handled a Lewis gun. I wasn't a bad shot in spite of my bad eye. 'A lot better than some of these fingers', as the Sergeant said, who had looked the other way when I had a go.

In the afternoon before the practice had finished and while we were having a welcome tea break we got the order of recall. The Division is definitely moving to give the 'It-ies' a hand against the Austrians, who are attacking in the north of Italy along a river called the Piave. There are five Divisions going and we are to travel there by train in the next few days. We have never been so well informed.

Tuesday 27 November 1917

We got up early to leave Lottinghem for St Paul. We were much cheered by the news that we were to travel to our destination by lorry and not by shanks' pony. We seemed to go everywhere by motor transport these days, if not by Ford ambulances then great multi-wheeled Albion or Maudsley lorries. I am informed that French troops have travelled like this since 1914.

The journey, however, got more and more uncomfortable and some wished that we could go back on the march, at least that kept the feet warm. Several of the lorries broke down on the road and as the serviceable lorries had to have the other lorry cargoes transferred, some of us were packed tight towards the end of the long cold journey. It is however an 'ill wind' for small quantities of said cargoes were won from their boxes, in particular tins of sardines, cheese slices, pork and beans and, very unusually, bottles of picked eggs. Our luck continued to be in for we were not searched on arrival.

Thursday 29 November 1917

We were told not to get settled in but to be ready for an imminent move. I took the opportunity with the three others in my squad to go into St Paul. There was however a misunderstanding for each of us thought the other had the funds for a night out. We had about two francs between us. Only enough because of still rising prices for three drinks. I had no fags to exchange or to sell but showing how we could sing 'the Bells of hell' in harmony and give a tenor solo of 'Keep the home fires burning', an Australian on his 'tod sloan' in the estaminet joined in with versions of 'Waltzing Matilda', 'The Wild Colonial Boy', and knowing the words from other Aussie acquaintances we were able to accompany him. From then on the drinks flowed free.

We had a very good night and only just made it back to our billet, leaving our new found Australian friend maudlin as he mourned for his lost 'outback' and sheep station. Like most Australians that we met, generous to a fault.

Friday 30 November 1917

This morning we were issued with fur coats and gloves and we are standing by, with kit packed and rations ready, for what we have been told is a five day journey to Italy.

The fur coats pong a bit and there is some speculation as to the origins of the fur. The goat seems the likeliest owner but, as some wag commented, 'I only wish they had wiped its blank before they made it into a coat'.

CHAPTER 11 - ITALY

Saturday 1 December 1917

We are definitely going today so I was up at six to get to the ablutions first for a good strip down wash, shave, and visit to the 'slats'. The prospect of a long train journey without the 'usual offices' made preparation essential. I had a leisurely breakfast at an Infantry Field Kitchen where the cook gave me a bacon sandwich and a mug of tea in return for a favour he said he owed the R.A.M.C. 'Four of your lot carried me for five miles when I was wounded on the Somme in 1916'. 'It might have been me, I was there,' I said. He was a big man and knowing the task he described it was worth quite a lot of bacon sandwiches.

After breakfast we were marched to Wavian, St Paul, where with full kit and two blankets each we entrained in clean wagons with straw filled paliasses covering their floors and we settled down with a mixture of apprehension and anticipation to our long trans-continental train journey.

Our anticipation was short lived for we spent most of the night in a siding and did not set off until the early hours. The night was fine but cold, so we all settled to sleep except for the inveterate smokers and card players who thumbed the boards by candle light until the break of dawn.

Sunday 2 December 1917

The weather was fine as we trundled slowly through a northern and central France that was completely untouched by war. Villages, hamlets, isolated farmsteads and towns were roofed and walled and the fields around, though brown and cropless, were not pock-marked with shell holes, nor were they dug up with trench lines or strung with thick hedges of barbed wire. Rather, there were hedges that curved across the countryside to dense copses, woods and even the edges of forests. Farm workers out with cattle or sheep held onto forks or rakes and waved their berets as we made our slow way across their 'campagne'.

Early this morning we passed Paris. I was asleep at the time for in spite of the never ceasing rattle and jolt of our passage I managed to have good sleep, warm in my two blankets and comfortable on my straw mattress. I asked to be woken up in the half light in order not to miss our travel through the city. It was difficult to see clearly, but I could make out the Eiffel Tower on one side of the great panorama and the Church of Sacre Coeur on the other. In between, dots of street lights 'curved across the bridges and down the boulevards of legend and literature'. I think I read that once in a book about Paris.

At nine or ten we stopped in a siding to attend to calls of nature and to have a shave and wash and brush up. There was hot water from the engine for that and to make tea to drink with the bully and biscuits we drew to combine with our contraband stores.

When I went to the engine to get hot water I found that the driver was English, from Sheffield. His name was Tom Elsey. We chatted for a while as he knew Hull from trips he had made to Paragon Station with passenger trains. He described an awful event he had witnessed when driving an ammunition train to the Somme Front during the battle. The gas shells some of the trucks contained were being unloaded near Albert by coolies from the Chinese Labour Battalion. One of the shells went off when dropped and the whole train load went up. He managed to be out of it as he was presenting chitties to a Transport Officer down the line. When the gas cleared the line on either side of the train was carpeted with the bodies of Chinamen. Hundreds, he said. The Army sent in other coolies to clear the dead onto lorries and carts and he heard nothing more about it. Nothing more was said, no enquiry, no investigation, nothing. He thought this was most unusual because generally whenever an accident happened or material was pinched from a train they never stopped asking questions.

We got back on the train and it began to move off. As it did we heard shouts and running on the track. A few chancers had popped in to a local farmhouse to get extras and they nearly missed the train. As they ran alongside, their mates hauled them up into the trucks. Lucky for them that the train was going slowly, for if they'd missed it they would have been technically deserters. Their luck wasn't completely in for they were spotted by an Officer and would certainly be on a 'fizzer' at the next stop.

We have just passed Roumillon-sur-Seine and we are rattling on to Troyes. We are making good time. The rail system in this part of France is free from the congestion and disruption caused by war. There are no delays from crews repairing the damage done by shells or air raids. There is no waiting in sidings for ambulance or ammunition trains to pass on priority. Our train is chugging along leaving only a wide plume of smoke and white steam in its wake. It is only slightly tinged with black. An ex- railway man, now a Medical Orderly, standing at my shoulder as I look out of the truck at the rest of the train curving along the track, tells me that that is a sign of efficient combustion in the engine. As my old school teacher used to say, 'a day without learning, is a day wasted'.

In the afternoon we halted for a short time at St-Germain-au-Mont-d'Or. The scenery is splendidly beautiful. I had seen France on maps but had really no idea of the grandeur and beauty of its landscape. It is such a big country compared with our little island. We have been travelling for over two days and we have still not traversed France. We have crossed so many regions, each with its own individual style of building. I have seen roofs change from slate to tile to Roman clay and back to tile again, with house construction changing from brick to grey, white or honey-coloured stone.

The view up the valley that we rattled through towards Lyons is one I shall always remember. I saw hills and streams with villages nestling in the shadow of the slopes and well kept fields and gardens. I want to see it in the seasons of spring and summer, when it must be even more beautiful.

Monday 3 December 1917

Once again I enjoyed a good, comfortable, undisturbed sleep. Before I got my head down I played cards using a borrowed stake of five cigarettes. I won twenty, so now I have some currency.

We had breakfast on the move, boiling water for tea and shaving on a stove improvised from a large empty paint tin. The fuel was a gift of coal from the engine driver 'but don't say where you got it, no names, no pack-drill'. The stove gave off a lot of smoke at first but the fire soon served its purpose. The weather is fine but cold. By mid-day we passed Lyon and were on our way to Marseilles. We stopped again at Le Tick for tea and grub. I exchanged a pair of good leather gloves I had bought with cigarettes for some French bread, chocolate and more cigarettes. I got the best of the bargain.

I don't think I have had such a comfortable trip all my time in the Army. Not only are the facilities good but the company is excellent in our truck. We share and share alike and so far there have been no upsets. I spend my time sleeping, chatting, looking out of the door or as I am doing at the moment, writing my journal. I also read a great deal. I am reading, at this time The Three Musketeers. It is a book I borrowed from a Y.M.C.A. library in the hospital and 'forgot to take back'. I don't feel so bad as it was obviously donated in the first place. It has the initials B.B. of Monpelier Square stamped on the frontispiece.

Tuesday 4 December 1917

The weather is still very cold but it is fine. Yesterday we sighted snow-covered mountains and travelled for miles alongside vinyards that bordered the river which is called the Rhone. This is the great Burgundy wine region of France. We have just gone through a long tunnel and are now in sight of the Mediterranean Sea. It is of a blue I did not think existed outside painting. The air is so clear here, it seems that you can see in details for miles. We shall soon enter Marseille.

As we were going through the tunnel our improvised brazier was upset and it nearly set fire to the truck. We had an exciting five minutes putting out the blaze. Some French grape farmer is going to be puzzled by a charred British Army straw mattress amongst his vines, and we shall have to 'win' one from another truck to make up the numbers.

From the vantage of the railway Marseille seemed at first a crowded, noisy city, very poor and dirty in places. But, perhaps this is only in contrast with the clean villages through which we have passed, and anyway all big cities are the same, especially when viewed from the railway. Then as the train moved on I got a better view that set Marseille on high, with its russet red Roman tiled rooftops, in surroundings of hills, washed by sunshine from a blue sky that was mirrored by the Mediterranean sea. The whole of the Port had come into view and my impression of the city changed completely.

Wednesday 5 December 1917

It is early morning. We have halted at the seaside station of Cannes. Real hot coffee, freshly baked French bread with butter and real jam was ready for us. We sat and ate it bathed in bright sunshine from a clear blue sky. I have wanted to repeat that breakfast ever since, and have only ever managed a pale imitation.

We were told that it would be some time before we set off again so I took a risk and with a mate went for a walk on the sand by the sea to enjoy the beauty of the morning. The sun was above the horizon and in spite of the season there was already some warmth in it. We took off our boots and socks then kicked the fine sand about like children and even dared to put our toes in the cold sea. My mate, seeing the scar on my foot, asked me how I had done it. In telling him that I got it just outside Ypres made me feel quite the war hero.

Back at the station we bought bread and some onions from an old man selling them on the forecourt. He was, as I saw it, typically dressed as a Frenchman with a beret and a striped jersey and we returned to him his 'Bonjour'. Before climbing back into our truck we bought bottles of beer on the platform and then our train moved off along the coast between hills and sun-lit blue sea.

It seemed strange to me that most of our chaps can spend their time playing cards and dozing while we journey through such novel and beautiful scenery. I hardly ever move from my position in the door-way and I feel that I should never tire of enjoying such countryside. All along the coast there are the prettiest of fishing villages, already busy with their people stringing nets along the quayside and working at boats in harbours or starting out on the sea for the day's fishing. The larger towns such as Nice and Monte-Carlo look elegant and prosperous, their streets moving with modern motor cars and horse drawn carriages. Everything seems so clean and fresh, especially to someone like me brought up in the industrial north of England. Villas, churches and houses are washed white with coloured shutters that contrast with the dark green shrubs, trees and bushes whose shapes and leaves I do not recognise.

After Menton we crossed the Franco-Italian frontier at Ventimiglia. French colonial soldiers gave us waves as we passed and brilliant white smiles. On the other side were Italian soldiers but they seemed less cheerful in their tattered and patched uniforms. Our first view of the fields of Italy saw us looking at olive trees in the groves that skirted the lines, and on railway stations large cactus plants were growing in great terracotta pots. In many places along the line there is only a low stone wall between the railway and the sea and we pass through many tunnels, cut through spurs of hills which project into the sea. The changes in light and sound as the train rattles and echoes in the dark, then chugs its steam into the bright sunlight, makes the trip into something of an exaggerated fairground ride.

We made a short stop at San Remo and ladies with young and older children came to the station with gifts of flowers and fruit. The ladies were beautiful with dark, almost black, hair and pale complexions. The older girls were very pretty and like a drink of fresh water to us who had not seen women for a long time. Oh, what dreams and fantasies they stirred in our empty hearts.

All too soon we were on our way across a terrain that had obviously not seen rain for weeks. The river beds we traversed over viaducts were covered by dry shingle with only a trickling stream running in their deepest part. Yet the grandeur and massiveness of the bridges over which we crossed told of the strength of the torrents which would rush down in the wet season.

Our journey took us through Onegila, Diano Marina, Savano and Savoygea. The names seemed like a song as we rattled and swayed through their little stations as the line brought us on to Genoa. When we reached Genoa we were greeted with flowers, bread, sausages and even postcards and cigarettes. The greatest of treats were the kisses of welcome from the ladies waiting for us on the platform, though I don't suppose they got much of a thrill from kissing the stubbled, unwashed cheeks of our smelly crew. After the greetings the Mayor with the officials of Genoa, who were professionally dressed in uniforms crossed with the red, white and green sash of Italy, delivered an address of welcome. We were all given embellished printed copies of his speech, in English, one side and Italian the other.

This day has to me been the best of the journey so far. After such a variety of new and beautiful sights, I feel excited, almost intoxicated.

For the rest of the day we bumped and rhythmically clicked and clacketty-clacked along with the sea on our right, and on our left steep hills dotted with red roofed white cottages and farmhouses.

We ate our supper in the wagon. We brewed the tea on our stove more cautiously as we supplemented our standard rations with the last of the purloined pickled eggs, pork and beans, sardines and cheese. All this was further augmented by the gifts of sausage and bread from the populace of Genoa. It would not be the last time that we ate pork and beans for in Italy it replaced largely our rations of bully beef.. We bedded down and I had a last look at the sky which was now like purple velvet, with more stars on it than I had ever seen in my life, twinkling and glittering in the clear air. The weather had been splendid and the warm sun had shone all day. 'God was in His Heaven and all was right

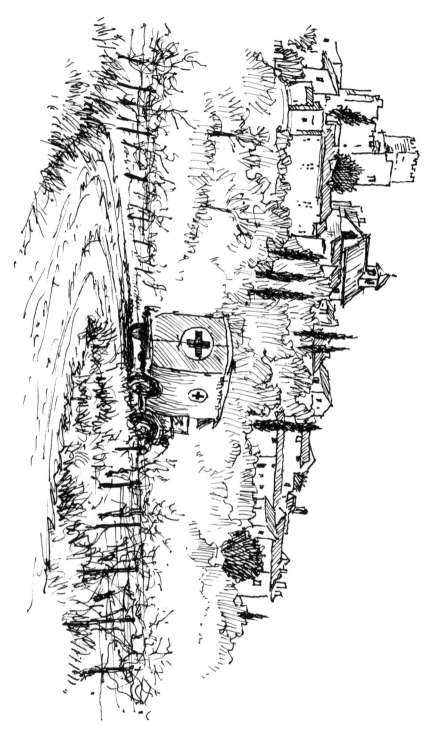

with the world'. At least in our little world of a railway truck that could carry forty men or eight horses, it was.

Thursday 6 December 1917

As if to remind us that there was a world of violence and death behind us and that we were still going to war, there was the most awful tragedy this morning. Before most of us were awake and the night was still dark we stopped on a bridge over a river bed. The line on the very narrow viaduct, we saw later, was single track. We were there some time when just as the dawn was breaking we heard someone shoving a wagon door open. There was silence and then a yell. After that was a general commotion. A chap from another wagon in front of us banged on our door and told us that someone in a wagon behind had got up to relieve himself and, thinking we had stopped on the track, jumped out and fell over the bridge. We crowded round the door and in the pale light of the early dawn we looked out. It wasn't a high viaduct that we were on but the trucks had stopped in the middle and he had fallen from the highest point. We piled out of the wagons ignoring orders to do the contrary and stood in a line along the low wall of the bridge. As the sun rose we could see his crooked arms and legs and his broken head, bleeding on the rounded stones and pebbles below. The banks of the dry river bed were steep so it was difficult to get down and he died before anyone could help him. He was a young Jewish boy from Manchester and had only been conscripted into the Army a few months before. A party of bearers eventually got down to his body and it was wrapped in a blanket, hauled back up, and stowed in the equipment truck. What an irony. There he was, travelling away from the Western Front and its dangers, going to what was, we found, one of the quietest theatres of the War, and he gets himself killed in such a stupid accident.

With much subdued and mumbling references to the fact that we should have been warned, and generally in the Army manner, shifting blame, we scrambled back into the wagons and were once again soon on our way.

We are just preparing to de-train at Montagnana. The weather keeps fine and most of day is spent coming from Genoa to Bologna and then to this station. The country we have passed over in the latter part of the journey was the flat planes of Lombardy and they are covered with groves of olive trees. At the stations we pass through we were cheered but the ride has been much marred by the tragic accident we witnessed so we are not in the mood of previous days.

The body of our young comrade was taken off the train and buried in the local cemetery. It was done without much ceremony as there was no Rabbi to officiate, I suppose. There were a number of chaplains about but they, of course, are Christian.

Friday 7 December 1917

We are now billeted at Pojgani Maggiore to which village we marched this morning; no lorries in evidence. After sleeping in the train at Montagnana we had a 'mad hour's' work getting our transport wagons on to the road again. I just had time to locate our C.C.S. and a large dump of stores at the railhead.

The weather here is splendid, very cold, but the air is so dry you hardly feel it. There is dust everywhere for the drought continues.

The billet we are in at Pojgani Maggiore is a well-built stone farmhouse which has some fine painted ceilings in its interior, statues in the formal garden and a grand covered courtyard. It is more a Roman villa than a farmhouse, or as one of our comrades has it, a high class brothel. I looked at a map at the part of Italy we are in and it seems that it is also the land of Shakespeare's plays. On our journey we have passed Mantua, Verona, Padua and Venice is to the south.

Saturday 8 December 1917

One of our comrades insisted on continuing the impression that we were billeted in a high class brothel, for this morning he rushed in to where we were sleeping, like a madam, and shouted 'Get up, get up, you lazy bitches, it is eight o clock, there isn't a po emptied, a whore painted, and the Italians are in the parlour'. It was just what we needed to cheer us up, for we have had to put our marching feet back on again. Today we marched to Castgnero. It was however a very pleasant and easy march, over a good surface, that is to say, flat and dry. On the way we passed through an ancient walled town whose architecture is typical of the region, St George's Imborco. The walls completely encircled the town and were as high as the roof tops.

Entering one gate we marched through the cobbled streets, the sound of our hob-nailed boots ringing round the shops and houses whose upper stories projected over the pavement. These floors are supported by pillars so forming a canopy that protects the inhabitants from rain and gives shade from the sun. We did not stop but marched straight through and out of the far gates on the other side of the wall.

We arrived at Castgnero in clear and fine weather and made our billet once again in a well built farmhouse that had a large garden.

Sunday 16 December 1917

We have been here a week now with little to do so we all feel really rested. We have had time to socialise with some of the inhabitants and so we have met Italians for the first time. With the aid of a dictionary and their smattering of English our Italian counterparts have told us of the extreme difficulties they have had against the Austrians and they described the disaster of Caparetto. They seem extremely grateful for the assistance we and the French are giving them.

I was just getting used to Castagnaro and our new found friends, who over a drink and a bite to eat have tried to teach us some Italian, when we were ordered to move again, this time to Guisicano.

Tuesday 18 December 1917

During the march, which started early after breakfast, it began to snow. That slowed us down. We were slowed down even more when we had to pick up an Italian machine gunner who, while carrying the heavy and clumsy mounting of the gun, had fallen and broken his leg. My squad fell out and carried him for a while until our Sergeant stopped a staff car with one officer in it and the M.O. persuaded the Italian Officer to take the injured machine gunner on.

We arrived at Guisicano and found a very small village with a water mill turned by a swiftly running stream. One of the first things I noticed was the regular slap as the water hit the paddles. In this pretty small village there was an albergo, a bake house, a post office and a butcher's shop . Myself and a bearer I had not met before were billeted above the post office in a nice comfortable room with a stove that was already burning. No sooner had we unpacked and arranged our kit and blankets over the two metal cots in the bare but cheerful room than we were told that the next day everyone else would be on the move. We, however, the two of us, would be left to guard a dump of petrol and blankets. Much to our consternation, and in spite of protests to our Sergeant that it wasn't quite our job, we were even issued with a rifle and a side-arm, very much against regulations. We were told that a lorry would be along in a day or two to collect us and the stores. Our protests were countered by our Sergeant telling us that ours, 'was not to reason why'.

Thursday 20 December 1917

We have been here now two days and have run out of rations and money. My partner and I have had an almighty row over the question of using the W.D. petrol as currency to provide for us. Apart from this he is not good company and something of the kill-joy. In the end, persuaded by pangs of hunger and his desire for cigarettes, he agreed to using one or two tins to see us through. I jumped on his offer straight away and with four blankets and three cans of petrol I did a private deal with the patron of the albergo and we moved in, and for another two days we were promised full board, drinks included, and even cigarettes for my addicted comrade. The patron also wanted to throw in the services of a lady of his acquaintance. She was, however of doubtful age, so I drew the line on that and just had her as a dance partner when we shoved the tables back in the dining room and Mine Host put records on his wind-up gramophone for us and the other clientele to dance to.

By the end of the first day in our new lodging my Army companion had lost all reservations regarding my terms of barter as he was having as good a time as I was. I should mention the food but all I really recall is my first taste of polenta. It was fried and delicious with the steak it accompanied.

Sunday 23 December 1917

The big Fiat lorry for our transport did not arrive until late in the day and when it did I decided to come clean with the A.S.C. Sergeant in charge of the party loading the stores. I wanted to get in first because I was sure that my 'mate' would shoot his mouth off about our filching the stores and blame it all on me. To my mild surprise the A.S.C. Sergeant was completely understanding. It was he who had been charged with collecting us and the stores in the first place and he said that as long as I didn't make too much of a fuss about him arriving late, it would be 'least said, soonest mended'. I did warn him about my 'mouthy friend' but he said that I could leave that to him. I learned later that he had blamed the delay on the lorry for breaking, down when in fact he had been a little worse for wear after a 'vino rossi' party with some very accommodating Italian girls and he had forgotten to collect us and the stores. That might have been true because no-one yet had become accustomed to Italian red wine. It was much heavier and stronger than the old French 'le plonkay' that we were all used to.

But the story was not over yet. Our adventures had only just begun. Once the lorry had been loaded we got in, ready to set off. I jumped in the front and left my mate to travel as comfortably as he could in the back. The Sergeant sat on the other side of the driver for the steering wheel was almost in the middle of the cab. Either the driver was not used to handling these great Fiat juggernauts or he wasn't used to Italian roads, or he was still recovering from the party that he had been to. Take your pick, for he drove inexpertly, to say the least.

As we left Guisicano long columns of Italian Infantry marching to the Front could be seen moving in our direction. The road was wide enough for the lorry and the soldiers marching four-abreast, but only just. Our driver, as I have said, was new to the vehicle and he was trying very hard to keep his speed under control, so we were not driving too fast. I was sitting in the cab at the front and I could see, as we arrived parallel with the first rank, the nervousness on the faces of the marching men as the lorry got close to them, and I could hear, but not understand, the curses and see the hand and arm gestures they were using to indicate their uneasiness about our proximity.

But, in the end, as the driver wrestled with the large spoked steering wheel, causing the lorry to lurch first to the left and then to the right, the great mudguard of the lorry got too close to the marching soldiers, and what must have been a whole company of men intuitively swayed as one to avoid the enormous solid tyres of the Fiat's front wheels. The Italian soldiers collapsed in a heap of boots, helmets, caps, blanket rolls and rifles into the ditch at the side of the road. Luckily for them all their bayonets weren't fixed.

Italian rifles had a very clever bayonet fitting that was hinged under the barrel. One very unlucky 'soldati' however was too close and didn't get out of the way quickly enough. The lorry struck him and he went down, but not under the wheels. We stopped and I was out of the cab like a shot and diagnosed very quickly that he had broken his left leg. He was in a lot of pain but I had nothing to give him. At that moment an Officer arrived on the scene on his horse, looking very smart, in polished boots and very well cut uniform. The first thing he saw was his Company of men now recovered from their fall in the ditch, squatting and standing, having already got the fags out. He thought they had stopped his war for a smoke until he heard the moans of the soldier with the broken leg.

He quickly summoned his own stretcher bearers and they put a splint on the leg of the unfortunately Italian squaddy. Then they loaded him into a horse-drawn ambulance wagon. I suggested that it would be quicker if we took him but I quickly gathered that that would be tantamount to delivering the evidence of the driver's and the Sergeant's incompetence so I withdrew the suggestion.

We piled back in and set off again only to collide with another lorry at a busy corner. This accident buckled our steering gear so that the rest of our journey, as the driver wrestled once again with the wheel, was a series of escapes from the ditch on one side and oncoming traffic on the other. I was very glad in the end that I got to rejoin our Ambulance at Fontaniva where I was greeted with shouts of 'Where the blank have you been, Corky. We thought you'd eloped with an Itie bint'

Monday 24 December 1917

This Christmas Eve was the happiest I have enjoyed for many a year. A crowd of us went into near by Cittadella and in an albergo that was candle lit and seasonally decorated, we settled down to an evening of Christmas Carols and bawdy soldier songs accompanied by an Italian accordionist who was clever enough to pick out the English tunes.

We ate pieces of chicken and hard boiled eggs in flat Italian bread and the vino rosso flowed. We were also offered 'grappa', a very strong spirit. It was served from a many spouted vessel called 'the cup of friendship' and as it was brought out one of our number from another squad stood up and sang 'Silent Night' in German. I thought there would be ructions but nobody batted an eyelid. In fact the general reaction was very emotional, and as the applause died down our irreverent lot gave a few chorus's of 'Christmas Day in the Workhouse'. We went out of the albergo into streets that had had enough of a sprinkling of snow to make it a 'White Christmas'. I went on by myself to Midnight Mass in an adjacent local Church where there were lots of candles and a service that, though it was in Italian and Roman Catholic, I basically understood. What I can say is, and I suppose it was because of my uniform, I was made very welcome, with lots of smiles and a place being made vacant for me in the pew.

Tuesday 25 December 1917 (Christmas Day)

It being Christmas Day I decided to attend Holy Communion, the first time for some weeks. After Communion, as the weather was dry and cold but very sunny, I went for a walk alone. As I passed house, cottage and farm I shouted to bemused residents "Buon Natale', the Italian for Happy Christmas' and I got a happy wave and the reply of the same 'Buon Natale' from all I met. By the time I returned from my walk it was nearly dinner time.

A fine dinner had been prepared for us and we were served by the Officers. There was fresh pork, chicken, potatoes, onions and cabbage, followed by cake and Christmas puddings sent from England. When asked what they wanted to drink most had opted for a bottle of beer, but I preferred red wine.

After dinner there was a general desire for a rest and so we returned to our respective billets and smoked, chatted and dozed until tea time. We had a Christmas tea with sandwiches, mince pies and fruit, apples and pears, followed by a very nice Christmas cake. My Christmas then became clouded because as I began to talk about the cakes our old mate 'Mr. Bun the Baker' used to make, a regimental stretcher bearer from another section interrupted and said that he had known someone who fitted the description, collapsible oven and all. He, he said, baked for a group of officers and would not listen to advice on the smoke his cooker produced and somewhere near Bethune a shell hit him and blew him, oven and contents to pieces. I wondered if it was our 'Mr. Bun', I can't think that anyone else would fit the description.

After tea, though somewhat depressed by the news about Mr. Bun, I went with a party of others once again to the fine old walled city of Cittadella. The medieval atmosphere of the town and its narrow cobbled, arcaded streets gave a special quality to our Christmas outing, and we found a place where we were given a very hospitable welcome by the Italian Padrone. We had a very good, if somewhat drunken, supper as we were liberally plied with grappa and once again the cup of friendship was brought out for toasts to unity. We toasted the allies, wished for the defeat of the Austrians, and in loud voices shouted at the wooden beamed ceiling 'Viva Italia, Viva Inghilterra'. Our eating place was aptly named the Trattoria Roma.

Sunday 30 December 1917

I am nearing the end of the old year. It is truly the most eventful one I have ever lived.

We are still at Fontaniva and for some reason, only known to the military mind we are drilling and doing fatigues, latrine and cookhouse duty, not fortunately at the same time. We do have as well the occasional game of football. I have been several times to Cittadella, not for meals or drinks, but just to walk around, fascinated by its walls, washed on one side by a fast flowing stream, its imposing gateways, cobbled and pillared streets, with quaint and ancient shops and houses. What must it be like to live your life in such a place? How different from a life in an industrial town living in rows of terraced houses that have no character at all.

Tuesday 1 January 1918 (New Year's Day)

There were no New Year's Eve celebrations because of a stand-to as a result of artillery fire. In the night we heard bombs bursting and guns replying but as yet nothing has dropped near here. The civilians get up and flutter about at the first boom and they seem very nervous and highly strung. Of course veterans like us can't see what the fuss is about and take the skeptical view that the stand-to was to guarantee no New Year's Eve shenanigins. Our skepticism was confirmed by news of a riotous party in the Officers' Mess. As usual one law for one.....

Sunday 6 January 1918

The weather is cold but fine. For the last week we have been working hard assisting No 38 Casualty Station Fontaniva in preparing their hospital. We have being doing lots of work appropriate to the qualifications of the experienced R.A.M.C. Orderly, such as pitching marquees, putting beds together, unloading stores, making paths, organising latrines and W.H.Y. When we asked the N.C.O.s who were in charge of us where the Pioneers and Service Corps, who were sometimes known to work in such a manner, when they can be found, were, the reply was: 'Do what you're blanking told.'

Sunday 13 January 1918

We are still at Fontaniva and continue a programme of drills and guard duties. We are also path building. To build our paths we fetch gravel in lorries from the River Brenta a few miles away. The river-bed is dry except for a stream in the middle so we can barrow it out. It is up towards the line so there are thick masses of barbed wire spread from bank to bank.

We have had some time off and have arranged visits to a canteen and a rather scruffy albergo where we eat fried eggs on fried polenta . There is always the sing-song which we never tire of. One of our number, a quite acceptable tenor, has learned 'Santal Lucia', which he sings in unintelligible Italian, but the locals know the tune so they join in with the real words.

We hear all kinds of rumours: peace, transfer to Palestine and even a return to France. The one rumour that persists is home leave; highly unlikely at this distance.

Sunday 20 January 1918

After a breakfast of hot pork and beans, bread and tea we were told to spend the day packing in preparations for a move from Fontaniva. Our squads set to and did this in record time because we wanted to pinch a bit of time to go to our favourite albergo, the Trattoria Roma in Cittadella, to say 'good bye'. We rushed so much to get there that we were almost knocked down by a convoy of lorries that passed as we ran down the road. The last one stopped and we hopped in the back and hitched a lift for the rest of the way. When we got there the Padrone, his wife and their two daughters came out of the kitchen to welcome us. We couldn't stay long as we had been told that roll call and lights out would be earlier than usual so there was little time for drinks, but there was enough for lots of 'Arrivederci's' 'Tornate's' and they insisted on bringing out the cup of friendship. We left vowing to return after the war with the wives and the children the Padrone's wife assured us we would have by then.

Monday 21 January 1918

I think most of us thought, or rather hoped, that lorries would be arranged for our journey, but we were mistaken. It was to be a day's slog in the cold and melting snow. So we set off on what we thought at first might be a miserable trek but we soon cheered and warmed up as we got into step. It did however take us most of the day to arrive at the village at Camposampo because it turned out to be a rough march over muddy, broken, roads that had suffered the wheels of war, that is, convoys of lorries, tractors, artillery and many men had already tested the Italian road builder's craft.

At Camposano we were marched into a system of barns whose floors were already laid with fresh straw. There were also wood burning braziers that the Service Corps had prepared. The heat they generated was making the place steam. Pots and kettles were soon bubbling and we ate hot food, albeit the by now ever available pork and beans. We drank hot mugs of tea and rested our weary feet for the night.

Tuesday 22 January 1918

Came the dawn and we set off again but this time we had a much better day and the march was made easy by good roads and long halts for dinner and tea.

Wednesday 23 January 1918

We are now billeted in a commandeered farmhouse having arrived here last night, late. We are to be here for two or three days in order to rest before carrying on to just behind the line on the River Piave. The country is flat and well cultivated with an air of prosperity that is signalled by its neat and well built villages and well dressed peasantry. We needed the rest and we have spent the time sleeping or dozing, getting up only for meals and calls of nature.

Saturday 26 January 1918

We moved up to Povegliano which is six kilometres behind what is a very quiet part of the Line so far. But hardly had we unlaced a boot than my Section were ordered to Arcade. Just a little too close to the Line for our comfort.

We are to take over an Advanced Dressing Station from the Italians. It is a fine big house called the Villa Elana. The village has been evacuated because of its closeness to the Line.

The Italians left in a hurry, leaving behind a lot of mess, but on the positive side they also left some useful stores, wound dressings, antiseptics, stretchers and so on. There are also some tins of what looked like food, but as they are unlabelled we will have to 'suck it and see'. We have plenty of room to billet in and two nice beds with mattresses intact. It was a toss up as to who should claim them and I was one who shouted 'heads'. Oh, the sleep of the just. My head can't wait to touch the pillows that go with them,

Sunday 27 January 1918

We got up early, as there is a lot of work to do. They don't tell us much but by now we know that if we have been given the job of fixing up an A.D.S. of this size so close, there is the likelihood of an attack or even an offensive.

So we make the best of it and are settling down and enjoying the quiet, even though it might be the calm before the storm. What we do see is a lot of air fighting and later in the afternoon a great black German bomber we have seen before, the Gotha, came over, either looking for a target or on photographic reconnaissance.

The attention we seem to be getting from the air has made us a little more cautious about our cooking and heating fires. We did light one in the kitchen, with its great green range, and I think the smoke from the chimney that it produced attracted the attention of intrepid German or Austrian airmen. We still have more than a week's work to do and don't want it interfered with by Fritzy or the Austrians.

Sunday 3 February 1918

We were right in anticipating trouble. Since last week the village has been air bombed twice and shelled once. The bombs were of medium size, from fighter aircraft, but the shells were twelve inchers. When fired they seem to be coming from behind the mountain peak that you can see beyond the river, and even though you can't see the gun and gunners you can hear the shells as they rush through the air as if they are tearing it. As one burst in the village it demolished a whole row of houses. They disappeared in a great cloud of dust, debris and smoke. Windows and doors, floorboards and ceilings, roofs and tiles collapsing into heaps of rubble as if what had held them together had only been waiting to be blown apart.

In part of the week we left off our A.D.S. preparations and once more took up a task usually organised by another branch of this man's Army. Because our artillery has 'got up' we have been sandbagging the house as if it were a gun emplacement. Things are getting warm and once again I am in the thick of it.

The leave rota has begun and there are rumours of a peace treaty, 'Pigs might fly'.

Thursday 12 February 1918

This last week we have had to keep our heads down at Arcade. Hardly a day went by when we weren't shelled and bombed. What was once a beautiful village in the pretty setting of meadows, rivers and streams, with magnificent mountains in the background, now is a heap of rubble to rival villages on the Somme. When war comes to the countryside there is complete devastation. We have moved up from the A.D.S. that we had so lovingly transformed into a place of sanctuary. Two squads of us have just been transferred to an Aid Post about half a mile from the river which is also our present Front Line. We are sharing the Aid Post, a huge house called the Rotunda with Infantry Headquarters so we have to watch our 'P's and 'Q's as there is a lot of brass about. To regular Army Officers, and even 'hostilities only', we in the R.A.M.C. are, as the song has it, 'Less than the dust beneath their chariot wheels', 'Poultice Wallahs'.

The Rotunda stands at the crossroads and is four storeys high. It has a fine balcony along its front and two wings which shelter the large courtyard. All the furniture has been removed except what remains of a grand piano. Whoever moved it, the residents I suppose, took the outside wooden cabinet but had obviously no time to manhandle the heaviest bit. This, the gold painted iron harp, its wires, pedals and keys, stands forlorn at the top of the staircase, like a golden skeleton. Starved of music it has died. Even the white and black keys at the front lend credibility to the image. Apart from this the house is undamaged, for the moment that is.

The Italians dug an underground shelter in the courtyard that is an extension of the cellar of the house, but under present conditions we don't see the need to use it as a billet so we have taken a suite on the first floor. There is no room service but we will manage, as our new accommodation has been described variously as 'better than a poke in the eye with a pointed stick or a slap in the belly with a wet cod fish or a lucky gypsy kick on the knee'. That is to say, better than nothing.

Infantry observers use the very top floor as a look-out point but the enemy have got cover in foothills and mountains. Our position is on a flat treeless plane, very exposed. It is like the Western Front in that respect. The Germans there won the high ground first; they got there before the French and the British. Here the Austrians have the high ground.

195

Sunday 17 February 1918

We are still at the Rotunda Aid Post, having busied ourselves over the last few days in making the preparations we are competent to do. Comparing my experience with those of the other squad members, I see why we have been chosen. We have more or less seen the same service – Ypres , Arras, and the Somme. We gently cursed the fact that we 'Joe Soaps' have been chosen but secretly nurse a sense of pride that we are considered to be reliable and efficient enough to do the job. However, when this view is discretely and modestly aired, the phrase 'butters no parsnips' is the reply. Because none of us have had any promotion. We decide together that the reason for this is because we are too 'lippy'. As an N.C.O. once said to me, touching with his left index finger, in turn, his ears, his lips then the stripes on his sleeve, 'a little more of that (ears), a little less of that (lips) and you might get some of that (stripes)'. 'Yes Sergeant, No Sergeant, Three bags full Sergeant'.

Things are, by comparison, very quiet. We have only had a few large shells over and four stretcher cases up to now. They were all what we might have at one time called 'Blighty ones' but I have been told that all our wounded are being treated in modern, well-equipped Italian Hospitals far in the rear and the 'Blighty one' as a ticket out no longer applies. Blighty is for the time being, too far.

Owing to the enemy's precise observation we are not allowed out during the day so we pass our time reading, card playing, dozing or, as always, smoking. Italian cigarettes, the only ones available at the moment, are strong and produce a thick blue mist. Their tobacco, I think, is home grown. I haven't any cigarette currency, as I am waiting for a parcel from home. I am reading my favourite Dickens, 'Great Expectations', and getting down to learning a few words of Italian from a book that cost me five Woodbines when I had any.

My other activity is Cucina Italiano. Yesterday for tea we had steak and polenta, which I am getting good at making. The steaks were large and thick and bought from a farmhouse some way back. I tried to tenderize them by wrapping them in a sandbag, laying them on the window ledge and beating them with a stick. I did not describe this process to my dinner guests - 'what the eye does not see' - and the results, though chewy, were palatable.

Sunday 24 February 1918

My forays into my new hobby of Cucina have been suspended for the time being. I was in the middle of making polenta, which was to be wrapped round some thick pieces of pork, accompanied by our cheese slices that melt very easily. I got the polenta (maize flour) and the pork from a pedlar who risks his life and that of his donkey coming up to the Line to turn a coin. A shell landed nearby, shook the house, and fine grains of plaster dust settled on the surface of the boiling polenta. I thought I had better postpone the completion of the dish until the 'strafe' was over.

Three times during the week light shells have burst on the sandbag roof and we have had some wild panic-stricken rushes to the courtyard dug-out. Down the stairs we rush, past the bones of the golden piano, its strings giving off a strange hum as they vibrate in the concussion. If you happen to be dressed it is a lark watching others trying to put legs into the coat sleeves of jackets, or both legs down the same trouser leg. They hop along the floor and are only saved from falling by the balustrades that run along each storey. All this as the white ceiling plaster falls down in flakes, its showers getting lighter as we descend from above.

Sunday 3 March 1918

We are still at our Aid Post and expecting some work shortly. There has been a very heavy bombardment, Western Front style, and we are expecting to cross the river behind a mass attack by the Infantry. We have been watching from our vantage point, as pioneers and engineers, sometimes under fire, make piers and bridges ready for the assault. They swing baulks of timber, using pulleys and A-frames, then hammer piles into the river bed by hauling, team-handed, a great block of concrete on ropes up the frame, then they let it fall as a pile-driver. The methodical thud of the concrete block hitting the pile can be heard all day. They seem to have found three times during the day when they can carry out their work. Breakfast time, dinner time and tea time. The Austrians don't seem to want to make war at meal times. Outside those schedules, however, any movement observed comes in for shot and shell. The piers were all in and our bridges were ready to take the fight across the river but almost as if the Austrians knew something we didn't, the rains have come. It has been raining for three days and that shallow stream flowing in narrow shingle banks, with plants and weeds growing in between rocks and stones, that could so easily have been jumped by the most heavily laden Infantryman, is now rising into a river that will need boats to cross it.

Sunday 10 March 1918

We are now having fair and fine weather again after a week of thunder storms and torrential rain. I have never seen rain come down as it did. At times it was like being behind a waterfall. The rain poured curtains of water down on us as lightning flashed and thunder clapped louder than the guns. The gutters of the house having been smashed, and the shell holes in the roof opening the house to the skies, has resulted in great gouts of water entering on every floor. This grand house is well on the way to being completely ruined.

In the courtyard dug-out, water flowed down the steps in a cascade, filling the cellar to calf height, and in the near by trenches, once so dry, there is only mud, collapsed sandbags and revetments. The troops are wet through with nowhere to go to dry out.

After a week of waiting and 'stand to's the attack has been indefinitely postponed. The flooded river has filled its channel with a bucking, curling avalanche of water which carries the trunks of great trees, logs, branches, planks and waterlogged military equipment and stores. The patiently built bridges and piers have been smashed to matchwood. Even in the shelter of the house we are like miserable drowned rats with water entering at every fold of our uniform in spite of our waterproof capes. The only casualty we have had to fetch in was during one of the storms. He was thought to have drowned in a flooded dug-out. We got him out in a state of unconsciousness and we gave him artificial respiration for twenty minutes before he began to cough the muddy water from his lungs. His mates thought he was a 'gonner'.

We made him as comfortable and dry as we could in a sheltered corner on the ground floor of the Post and he began to recover. I went down to him to take a hot drink of tea and also, I must admit, to accept his gratitude. But when I said we thought we had lost him but managed to revive him, he took the tea without a 'thank you' and with a dismissive wave of his hand: 'So what? What do you want, a blanking medal?' Justifiably miffed, I said: 'Right, you know what you can do next time'. His reply was: 'There won't be a blanking next time'.

When I was giving him artificial respiration after nearly drowning and he came back to life, so to speak, I had felt the strangest sense of having been redeemed of all my sins. I had performed the one good act. I had saved a man's life. Here he was, reviling me and denying that I was his saviour. It made me feel really bad. I felt even worse later when I discovered that in 1917 he had joined the Army as the result of accepting an amnesty on the condition that he was conscripted. He had been serving a sentence in prison for assaulting his wife. I didn't want to believe the story and thought it had been cruelly and mischievously concocted just to make me feel worse. I felt much better when he was taken away to recuperate in another station. Good riddance.

Monday 11 March 1918

A rider on a motorcycle and sidecar came to fetch me today to take me to Ambulance H.Q. I was called as a witness in a Court Martial case. I had been present when a chap in another squad was involved in an incident with a Junior Medical Officer. When picking up a stretcher with a patient on it the carrying handle had knocked the Officer under the chin as he bent to examine the label on the patient's tunic. The Officer went flying and was almost K.O.'d. He accused the Bearer of doing it on purpose, that is to say, according to King's Regulations, he had 'struck a senior Officer', a very serious offence. In fact, in some circumstances, a 'shooting offence'. It had not helped that there were quite a few squaddies around to laugh at the Officer's misfortune and I think pride had been hurt more than chin. I was by the side with another 'carry' and I stuck my neck out, against the advice of my Sergeant, and said I would testify to it having been an accident. I didn't think that my testimony would carry much weight and I hadn't expected to be called.

We chugged and spluttered down the roads and tracks to the rear and as the Army never misses a trick when I arrived I was put on duties while I waited, and that meant parades, drills and fatigues. After my time at Rotunda when I had more or less been my own boss it was very distasteful.

Sunday 17 March 1918

I am still waiting to be called but the Court has not even been convened yet. I tried to see the accused yesterday, more to find out what was happening than to express sympathy, but I was not allowed.

During the week I got out of H.Q. duties by volunteering along with some other Bearers to take a course of lessons on the gentle art of managing mules. As I know something about horses I thought that I could apply that know-how. I found them to be much less responsive than horses and I don't think that the same relationship you can achieve with a horse, is possible with a mule. But as the training is about how to use them simply as beasts of burden I think I will be able to handle them. They will be used to carry stretchers and supplies by means of a special cradle fixed to their backs and as they have smaller feet than horses they can negotiate mountain paths more nimbly.

I had just completed the 'mule skinning' course when I found out that I wouldn't be needed for the Court Martial as the charge has been reduced to one of insubordination. I did not see my 'comrade in arms' to congratulate him. He must feel very relieved. They nailed him for something, of course, but not the major crime. I rounded off my visit to H.Q. by having a riotous booze-up with some Irish Bearers who invited me to their St. Patrick's Day celebrations.

Monday 18 March 1918

I am now at Istrana. It is a small clean town with a C.C.S. but, more to the point, a B.E.F. canteen. The same motorcyclist who took me to H.Q. brought me back to join my section. My rides on motorbikes encouraged me to think about getting one if I come out of all this and get back into civvy street. The Douglas 350 is so far the favourite. I joined the section at Istrana because we have quitted the part of the Line we were in and the newly confident Italians have relieved our Infantry. My motorcycle transport saved me the day's march my other squad members had to make to get here. 'Corky, you are a jammy blank', was the greeting when I sat down to a mug of tea in our new billet. I do miss the Rotunda though, it was a cushy number.

Friday 22 March 1918

We are having a nice quiet time in the comfortable sheds that serve as our billets here at Istrana and we are having an un-looked-for rest. The rest might have been welcome if the proposed attack had gone ahead but we are resting now not really having done any 'carrying' for some time. But the Army says rest, so we are resting.

The canteen proved too expensive for us. Even a little tin of sardines costs three lire that's about one and six. I prefer to buy the fresh hand pulled milk that is for sale. The eggs that are plentiful and cheap and maize flour for polenta. All this is sold by the Italian peasants who walk from billet to billet, with little donkeys carrying packs of provisions. I even managed to buy a small piece of smoked ham that is a bit like cured bacon but can be eaten raw. With this and cheese slices I can knock up a substantial meal. Tins of pork and beans are in plentiful supply but I haven't won the competition yet on who is first to find a piece of pork. Polenta, which I am becoming quite expert in preparing, is very filling. I fry it in the olive oil that I also buy from the peasants and top it with fried eggs. After four days at Istrana we are again preparing for a move.

Saturday 23 March 1918

After a day's march over good roads and in fine weather we are billeted in a school at Vigore Deseres, near the river Brenta. There is a stream, across some fields near our billet. It is a tributary of the Brenta and a few of us are going down to see about a swim.

The water here, as it did up the Line, comes down from the mountains, and so is very cold. Our 'swim' consists of stripping down to our 'birthday suits', diving in off the bank, striking out for a minute and then climbing out again for a run up and down the fields until we get warm. This is repeated for a time or two then we get dressed and feeling fit and hungry we set out to scrounge eggs for supper. They are for sale at two and a half pence the dozen. The first farmhouse we arrived at was run by quite a young woman whose husband, she told us, was in the Italian Army. We hadn't realised just how close the farmhouse was to where we had been running and jumping in our nakedness. 'She wouldn't have seen much', volunteered one of our group, 'considering how cold the blanketty water was'.

When we knocked at the door she had come to it with a small child at her skirts, a little girl. She offered not only to sell us the eggs but also to fry them. So we sat in her cosy kitchen while she cooked a dozen eggs in a big black frying pan over charcoal, set in holes in the top off a big stone stove. She served us sitting at her table and she gave each one of us a big flat cake of Italian bread and for a few lire more we got a big jug of fresh milk straight from her cow. Her little girl, at first shy of these foreign strangers, was soon sitting on our respective knees, being fed morsels of egg and bread. Her mother was quite a pretty woman but prematurely aged-by hard work I suppose. Although my newly learned Italian was faltering and faulty I got a strong impression that she enjoyed having five young men at her table. She must have been quite lonely but she was not in the least bit nervous of us and, of course, she had no reason to be.

Monday 25 March 1918

There was a bit of a rush this morning to get up and packed and breakfasted and paraded before we were collected by lorries to be driven from Istrana to Rubano, which is about five kilometres from Padova. We expect to be here for a few days. Unfortunately as we have got a taste for swimming, there are no convenient streams nearby.

Wednesday 27 March 1918

The same lorries that took us to Rubano collected us again and after a bumpy and uncomfortable drive deposited us in billets in a farmhouse at Pojana. It is almost midway between Padova and Vicenza.

Not far from the farmhouse we found a deep clear stream with firm banks on either side so we shall be out for a dip first thing tomorrow.

The weather keeps dry but it is cold, with a frost at night. A log fire in a great open chimney in the main room of our billet keeps 'Jack Frost' at bay and we sleep well wrapped up warm in our blankets on a bed of thick clean straw on the farmhouse floor.

Thursday 28 March 1918

As we were attending to our ablutions and boiling water for those and our breakfast tea and preparing for our morning swim a Corporal came trotting in from another section. He was out of breath, not only from his run but also from the excitement of the message he was carrying. What he told us knocked all thoughts of swimming out of our heads and everything else for that matter. The news he brought was that the Germans had attacked in France and pushed the allies back on a very wide Front. It is a disaster. They might still win the war after all we have gone through.

For the rest of the day, in between various duties and chores, the rumours and counter-rumours flew backwards and forwards. Separating fact from fiction was difficult but it seems that the Jerry big push came with reinforcements and equipment from the Eastern Front, where the war has stopped as the Russians have signed a peace treaty. Stories of the British having been over-run do not seem to be exaggerated. Rumour has it that we, the 5th Division, are going back to France to hold the Line. I should 'cocoa'!

Saturday 30 March 1918

Today was a day off so we visited Guisicano, the scene of my adventures with the blankets and the petrol dump. We were there to watch our Divisional Ambulance beat the Divisional Royal Engineers in the semi-final of the divisional rugby competition. The match was played on a polo ground, level and tree sheltered with deep green turf. It was a fine ground, set in lovely scenery. The weather was fine and warm and everyone involved was jolly and high spirited and seemed to have forgotten completely that France was falling apart.

As I was at Guisicano I took myself off with a couple of mates and went to the albergo where I had stayed a couple of nights. The people there remembered me and treated us splendidly. I felt like a returning long lost son.

Sunday 31 March 1918

It is Easter Sunday and for the first time in weeks I attended Holy Communion after a Church parade in a field outside the village at Pojana. When it was over I went straight out on to the road and hitched a lift to Guisicano again.

The journey wasn't far but it seemed to pass in minutes for the driver and his mate, both in the Royal Engineers, did not stop talking about their imminent departure for France. They dropped me off, their curses at having to go back into the kind of action all three of us knew awaited in France, ringing in my ears. I went back to the albergo expecting it to be open but it was closed. However, when I peered in through the front window I saw that the family was sitting around a table. They saw me and rushed to the door to invite me in. I felt privileged to sit down with all the family at their Easter dinner. Most young men of my age were away in the Army so they placed me between two very pretty young girls with black hair. As the dinner progressed through red wine to fizzy white and then the powerful grappa my Italian seemed to improve as my French had before by 'piccole salto et grande salto'. I said a very fond and emotional 'good-bye' to my hosts and I left, vowing to return one day. The increase in traffic that the new circumstances had created made it easy to get back to my billet.

Tuesday 2 April 1918

Here in Pojana it is raining but the weather cleared up in time for us to have a swim in what is now a swollen stream. We have been cautious because the current is swift and we could soon be away with it even though the five of us are strong swimmers. We will not be swimming in our Italian stream anymore, the orders are that the whole Division is to return to France.

Wednesday 3 April 1918

Last night before going to bed I went out to look at the stars. The clouds had cleared, leaving a fine night, the frosty air emphasizing the thousands of twinkling points in the Heavens. This morning I got up early to watch the sunrise of my last dawn in Italy.

By late morning our kit and bits and bats have been packed and we entrained at Pojana on the first leg of our return to France. We are going back to stem the Teutonic Hordes, but not all the Expeditionary Force is leaving. There are some Divisions staying so that the Austrians can be held and then, hopefully, defeated. Unless, of course, they have the same success as the Germans in France.

I have many regrets at leaving this country. All the people I have met have been as hospitable as a family to me and to others of my acquaintance. The country, towns and villages that I have visited were, without exception, attractive and welcoming and I was just getting fairly proficient in the language. As we moved slowly away from the railhead at Pojana, a few voices struck up with the chorus of the song 'Good byee' and soon the whole train was singing:

> Good byee, don't sighee
> Wipe the tear, baby dear from your eyee.
> Though its hard to part I know
> I'll be tickled to death to go.
>
> Good byee, don't sighee
> There's a silver lining in the skyee
> Bonsoir, old thing, cheerio, chin chin,
> Napoo, toodle oo, good byee.

CHAPTER 12 - BACK TO FRANCE

Thursday 4 April 1918

We slept very well and very comfortably in our roomy carriage. No horses had been there before us and the doors and windows were in good condition. As before, when we stopped, there was water from the engine for washing and tea. The driver and fireman were Italian. We rattle on past Monselice and Rovigo. On we go, leaving behind Voghiera, Pontedecimo, Genoa, San Remo. The names of towns I shall never forget. Even the weather runs parallel to my mood, dull and cold. There are four of us in the compartment. Ordinarily such luxury would bring me out of the deepest slough of despond but all I do, as the others play interminable games of cards, suck on strong and blue fug making Italian cigarettes, is sit by the window as more and more of Italy disappears down the track. I later console myself reading a little book of poems I bought from a Y.M.C.A. canteen or I open and read H.G. Wells' 'Time machine'. It passes the time.

The other activity that is indulged in is the rather more dangerous one my mates perform of climbing out through the doors and clambering on to other carriages on the wooden foot board that runs their length. One intrepid traveller passed our window on his way to win a bet that he could visit all the carriages in the train. But he forgot that he had to pass the Officers in their first class carriages. He had to hold on to door handles grimly as the train went into a tunnel. When he was hauled in his hair was all over the place and full of soot and his eyes full of grit. His experience stopped that particular activity for a while at least.

I have provided myself with plenty to read and I either do that, sleep or write my diary. The advice I get when doing this is to chuck it out of the window before somebody sees it and puts me on a 'charge' so fast 'my feet won't touch the ground'.

Sunday 5 April 1918

We seem to have passed into France without even noticing it although we are travelling very slowly and avoiding large towns. We are not returning by the same route as we came.

We went through Nice and I saw the Med under a lowering grey sky. Just outside Aix-en-Provence the train had to be stopped because a section in one carriage panicked when they smelled smoke. They all got out of their carriage as the train was moving and shuffled along to the next compartment. Sure enough smoke was coming from the wheels under the carriage next to us. Because I had some Italian I volunteered to get to the engine to warn the driver. I clung on, one foot sliding along after the other, just as the joker had done before but this time with a serious purpose. We were only going slowly but we were on a double track and occasionally a train came from the opposite direction, whistling and blowing off steam. I had to flatten myself against the carriage body to avoid being swept off the foot board. I managed to get to the engine and in my pigeon Italian told him what was happening and he put on the brakes.

When the train stopped we all got out on the track and for a time caused the Officers to almost have babies. We were milling about on the other line, stretching our legs, and they could see us all mowed down by an express. When we were all off the track and well back from it the fireman came along and knocked a brake shoe off which had not released and so become red hot. I did not get a 'thank you' or even a 'kiss my blank' for my 'Perils of Pauline' train rescue. I had already written the headlines, 'Man in dare devil train rescue'. Percy Cawkwell, young debonair, veteran R.A.M.C. man in a daring.......

What I did get as we waited to get back on the train, after the necessary repair was finished, was a bit of curious information from a lad in a carriage three compartments along. He said he had been looking for me since before we set off because he had heard I was from Hull. He told me that he knew in the usual way that rumour travelled about a soldier in the East Yorks from Hull who'd been shot for desertion just before Christmas, somewhere in Belgium or Northern France. He had no other details so it left me a bit in the dark. I vowed to find out more when we got back up north.

Saturday 6 April 1918

Yesterday our train, now the one we had changed into and so French rolling stock with French drivers, passed through Avignon of Sur le Pont fame. The weather was brighter so it was possible to see what a beautiful town it was. This morning we stopped for breakfast at Paray-le-Mourail and had fresh French bread, locally produced butter, orange jam and the best coffee I have ever tasted. Will I ever be able to reproduce that authentic French taste? The cry from the others 'Can't stand coffee, give me tea every time'. Yes, I like tea too, but coffee and fresh French bread, that is something else.

The weather has brightened up again and once more I am stunned by the beautiful Rhone valley.

Sunday 7 April 1918

We sleep long in our sleeping car and as we don't breakfast until we stop, then that is late. We are on the rail-road to Paris but I can't remember the towns we went through-Corbeil, Essone, Javisy, Gisors. There was no-one waiting for us with flowers and kisses. We had to make our own breakfast and even the engine driver, now changed

205

to a Welshman, grudged us hot water. Can you believe it? 'Not too convenient for me to be doing this for so many. It lowers the pressure'. The glares and obvious irritation of the more aggressive of us persuaded him that perhaps some hot water should be forthcoming. This was especially the case when a great big lumbering Lancashireman said in a voice loud enough for him to hear 'How do you think the blank would burn if we put him in the blanketty fire box?'

So no jubilant welcomes, no pretty girls, no Mayors in sashes with printed addresses. The train picks up speed after Paris and it is Doullens and Petit Houvin before we know it. We have arrived, but not as the returning heroes. The French we see are very sullen. 'Non bon alleyman' as been replaced with 'Non bon anglais'. But can you blame them? Firm reports say that the Line held by the French, did just that, it held. In the British sector up to Ypres and down south to the Somme the German offensive has pushed us back over the ground we paid so dearly to take. Even if I just think of the work I put in. Every slogging footstep we took, we paid for it in blood. All that has been taken back by the Germans in days. It took us months to gain it.

I, of course, don't know the full story. In no way is a 'buck shee' stretcher bearer like me going to get the full picture. But the French must be heartbroken. Once again they feel the alien boot on territory they thought had been taken from him. This isn't our country, we aren't defending or losing our homeland. What would I feel like if, say, I was in somewhere like Preston in Lancashire and I knew that thousands of foreign troops were tramping all over Yorkshire, smashing cities, towns and villages with artillery, annexing farm land, looting possessions, killing our countrymen and raping our women and taking them as hostages? (That image usually resulted in a few pricked up ears). I am of course reporting the results of arguments and discussions as we settle down in our first billet since arriving back in France.

Tuesday 9 April 1918

We are in a barn at Bonnières near Frévent. I know the area, having been here before. I am wondering if the canteen that was open then is still open now. The weather is very dull and overcast.

The rumbling guns in the distance do not help the lifting of the gloom that has settled on our party. There is no chit chat, gibes or joking. We can hardly look at each other. The suggestion that we should go and find some plonkay is met with little enthusiasm. We thought we were out of it, or at least it would be over before we were brought back in and so survived the business, but now the renewed uncertainty is testing our courage. We are back where we started, is the only way of summing it up.

Thursday 11 April 1918

We have a quiet time at Bonnières and one reason it was quiet was because we were warned by a visiting 'Red Cap'. It turned out that it was not because we might be assaulted by the French townspeople but because their attitude to us might provoke disturbance. We were not ordered to stay in so we did visit the still open canteen at Frevént. There wasn't much on offer and what there was, was too dear so we went into an estaminet and tried to get up a 'sing song'. It was as successful, as someone put it, as chatting up the widow at a funeral.

Friday 12 April 1918

We have moved from Bonnièrers and are on the road again to Grouches-Lucheul, near Doullens, and we are waiting at the railhead to entrain for the Front Line again.

Saturday 13 April 1918

We spent a fairly comfortable night in the train, made nicely endurable by the visit of a Field Kitchen just before we settled down. We had a hot supper and said hello again to Maconochie's Irish Stew. It was very welcome, along with the tea, into which more than a dash of rum was added from a big earthenware jar brought round, by of all things, a tee-total Sergeant. That is what we need, a Company of T.T's to dispense the rum.

> If the Sergeant steals your rum – never mind.
> Repeat
> He is such a blanking sot
> That he'll drink the blanking lot,
> If the Sergeant steals your rum – never mind

Tee-total rum dispensing Sergeants aside, I heard once a report from a D.L.I. man of a Captain who was T.T. and would not allow his men rum. On one occasion just before going into action he ordered his company paraded to watch him pour their allowance into the mud of the trench bottom. One of his Corporals was so incensed he threatened to kill him. The Corporal got a year in the 'glass house'. The Officer's name was Captain Jolly. 'Jolly by name ……….'

When we woke the train was at Thiennes, a station near the Forest of Nieppe. We got down out of the train and 'formed up'. As we did a column of civilians appeared on the road alongside the railway. They were fleeing before the advancing enemy. There is no more saddening sight than to see whole families hurrying in panic, from aged Grandma, or even Great Grandma, down to the smallest babe in arms. Along the tree-lined road, carrying what possessions they had salvaged, they were pushing carts or were on farmwagons pulled by horses with a cow roped to the back. As they trudged along in silence all that could be heard was the creak of furniture tied down to their wagons and the turn of iron wheels on the road. What more heartbreaking sight than a little girl of around six, lost, standing by the roadside, ignored in the passage of a population, and crying in between sobs 'Maman, Maman'? Another unforgettable face of war and an experience we have not had in England in hundreds of years.

The Germans are reported to be in the Forest, and as we move off the road our Officers are uncertain whether to advance or retire as only machine gunners are up with us. The Infantry, for some reason, have de-trained at Aire some way back. We couldn't get back on the train for it went off towards Armentières and we don't know if it will be captured or not. As we, the Ambulance stretcher bearers, stood around waiting for someone to tell us what to do, there was the distinct sound of small arms fire coming from the Forest. To put it politely there was also a distinct sense of nervousness among us. Less politely we all had the bloody wind up. As it is sometimes described a part of our anatomy went alternatively from the size of a half a crown to the size of a threepenny bit. Our wind up went into a different key when a Machine Gun Corporal came round with a hand cart piled with rifles and mills bombs and said that if Jerry came through we were ordered to take up arms. Our barrack room lawyer piped up with the question, 'Isn't that against the rules?' 'Blank the rules' was the only reply he got. Our Officers weren't around to ask.

The weather that night was fine and a good thing, for we bivouaced where we stood. We did not get much sleep as we were afraid we would wake to the sound of 'Hande Hoch' accompanying our breakfast. Just before dawn our Infantry came up in force and cleared the enemy out of the Forest so we weren't called upon to bear arms and the hand cart was trundled away. We did though help one Infantry Platoon 'dig-in' between the Forest and Merville, which the Germans hold. For that favour we shared a breakfast of looted bread and milk. Our Ambulance then fixed up very hastily constructed Aid Posts and cleared about a hundred lightly wounded casualties, mostly small arms and wood splinters from stick bombs thrown in the trees, serious enough though. One of our M.O.s became a casualty when he followed our squad into the woods and he caught a bullet when he didn't duck fast enough at our shout of 'Enemy troops ahead'. They were about two hundred yards away in the trees and you could see the muzzle flashes of their rifles in the undergrowth.

The Germans have advanced so fast that they have had to leave their artillery behind to catch up. Ours is not yet active either so it is rifle against rifle, bomb against bomb and even bayonet against bayonet. There have been one or two charges with fixed bayonets and it is terrifying even seeing it from behind. The yells of the Infantrymen curdle the blood and they have the same effect on Jerry because he soon hops it. We picked up a young Jerry lad who didn't move fast enough and he had got a bayonet thrust in his upper thigh. It must have caught an artery for the blood was coming out in spurts and only a tourniquet stopped it. He was very young. I wouldn't have said seventeen. We got him back to the Post and our M.O. plugged the hole and stopped the bleeding and he was out of it.

Tuesday 16 April 1918

On Monday 15 Fritzy attacked again, this time he had brought up trench mortars but still no light or heavy artillery. Our Line, which is now a kilometre north of St Vernant, held firm, although a bit further north we have heard of a possible break through. We have been told to hold steady. There is all sorts of frantic activity, infantry marching at the double or lucky ones carried by lines of lorries, and when our artillery comes up it's noticeable that guns and limbers are pulled by four horses rather than the normal six. Not surprisingly, given the dead horses I've seen, there's a shortage of horse flesh.

We spent yesterday and most of the night 'digging in' and establishing Aid Posts. The Ambulance M.D.S. is at Thiennes, a few kilometres back. Our Aid Posts are in abandoned houses scattered over the forty square miles of this Forest. These houses have no cellars so they are not shell and splinter proof, but that hardly matters at present because we are not subject to artillery bombardment.

Had we ever had such comfort and such supplies? In their hurried flight the local population have left almost everything. Their furniture and clothes, the contents of their larders and their livestock. This has so far included pigs, chickens, calves, rabbits and their dogs and cats. The dogs have been tied up and the cats behave as if their owners are coming back soon. The only animals not in evidence are horses and oxen. Opportunists as we are we are cooking chickens and rabbits and accompanying these dishes with the contents of tins and jars we find on shelves in kitchen cupboards. They contain such goodies as bottled green beans and peas, with tins of pears and apples for afters.

At night we bed down in clean linen sheets on down mattresses and pillows. We know this comfort will be short lived. When Fritzy brings his big guns up these houses will be blasted into rubble, as we have seen so often. We are making hay while the sun shines and our disgraceful plundering is watched with disapproval by the faces in the portrait photographs of dispossessed owners still hanging on the walls of our commandeered billets.

West of the Forest in which our defence Line is fixed is the Nieppe canal and that runs into the wider Aire canal. This gives us an efficient waterway for the evacuation of our wounded by barge and boat.

Sunday 21 April 1918

On rising this morning we had in our billet, a full English breakfast of eggs, bacon, pork and beans with fried bread, followed by tea and bread and jam. The only way to start the day. We were a bit worried about the eggs but they seemed to have been preserved in something. Anyway they were palatable. We sat down round the kitchen table and breakfast was cooked on the stove by my own fair hands. We ate it off plates with knives and forks. We are 'living like Lords bastards'. Add to all this the fact that our Line is

fairly safe up here and that neither side have attacked for a week, and we have paradise enough.

In this last week we have had news of Douglas Haig's 'backs to the wall' speech and the report that the Virgin of Albert has been knocked off her tower. This last communique caused more consternation than Haig's ultimatum. Given the average soldier's superstitious mind the fallen Virgin is much more of an ill-omen than descriptions of the speed of the German advance. For the legend is that the side that knocked if off would lose the war. To the horror of those who believe in such things we have heard that a British gunner did it.

Although there have been no major attacks there are still casualties to deal with. These are from sorties and raids that are being carried out in the Forest.

In the daytime the Forest is, without putting too fine a point on it, a pleasant place to work in. As yet there are no snipers – thank God. There is thick undergrowth and thick cover for the tracks we have made through it that we carry along. At night it can be a place of sheer horror. The artillery has come up and Fritzy's shelling has explosions bursting high in the trees, lighting up our work with ghastly flashes and showering us with branches, twigs, shrapnel and splinters. Often as we are tramping back, gas masked, goggle eyed in the gloom, with some groaning soldier boy, bleeding and twitching with the agony of his wounds, a blasted tree comes crashing across our path and the branches throw us all in a heap, Bearers, stretcher and wounded. Adding to his pain, a knock to the ground. The shell bursts echo and re-echo under the trees and from time to time a flare shows everything in bright white light, including the thick clouds of gas that hang about the damp ground for days. When we first entered the Forest it sheltered deer, wild pigs, songbirds and all kinds of small game. Now all are gone and the place is a death trap.

We have been able though in spite of the troubles and fears of the day to return to our cheerful billet which is not yet devastated. We take off our boots and put our feet up, make tea that is just more than wet and warm as we are used to, and scoff a hot tasty meal that has us groaning with satisfaction as we push our greasy plates back. It can't last.

Wednesday 24 April 1918

It didn't. After a very busy week our Section of Bearers were relieved and we had to give our little house over to replacements, telling them to look after it for we had kept it really quite tidy. We returned to Thiennes and after a bath in the canal we were given new uniforms and underwear. There seems to be plenty of everything these days. I remember when I first joined and getting my first uniform the Quartermaster telling us that we should think ourselves lucky that we were *getting* a uniform when somebody complained about the size of his being too big. There were units in France, he said, who were still wearing their own suit trousers. Those days have gone. We have been completely kitted out new and our old stuff is going to be de-loused. We didn't consider ourselves lousy. The little beggars have not troubled us since we came back from Italy and they didn't trouble us much when we were there. The benefits of clean living cannot be over estimated. Our new billet, which is an old workshop, is not a patch on the Hansel and Gretel cottage in the Forest that we had to vacate. The weather continues fine.

Friday 26 April 1918

Our troops attacked last night and we 'stood to' as it looked as if we might be needed, but by 3 a.m. we were stood down again and got back into our straw nests to sleep for the time that was left before reveille.

The attack, though not on a broad front, was successful and a few German positions were taken. In the morning, as we were being paraded to march down to our M.D.S., we saw Jerry prisoners being brought up in some numbers. They were a mixture of the very young and those past middle age. They are scraping the barrel like us. I heard in a letter from home, that they are raising the conscription age to fifty for the British Army.

Sunday 28 April 1918

We are still at Thiennes but we have found a better billet. It is on an old canal barge that has rudimentary living quarters on board. Somebody has made a crude attempt at conversion.

We have spent the last few days helping the R.E.s to build a new splinter and bomb-proof M.D.S. in the Forest. There are plenty of trees for support and roof timbers from off the canal banks and out of the Forest. Looking at the substantial progress being made and the scale of operations I wouldn't mind working in it when it is finished. I would feel safe.

Thirteen new men joined us today to make up for casualties. Two of these casualties were from my squad. They got a touch of gas in the woods as we were making our way back with a carry. My mate and I, though we coughed and spat a bit, were more or less unaffected. We had taken our gas tablets, they hadn't. We had to leave them both sitting against a tree while two handed we struggled back with the casualty. Then we went back for them with six others to carry them both back. Typically when we got back we found them cheerfully sitting in the sunlight having a smoke, then all the way back they almost coughed their lungs up.

The mail caught up with us at last. It had followed us from Italy. I got letters from home including a parcel of cigarettes. According to Dad's letter the news of the German advance has not been kept from the public. The newspapers are full of it. He was even able to note that from what the papers say, the advance has run out of steam. I said

to those around who would listen that we should be popping over to tell this to the Germans in their trenches in the Front Line who keep up a lively machine gun, bombing and shelling programme. It's obvious they don't know.

Tilly wrote me a long letter or that is had it written for her. It was chatty and affectionate, with kisses. She wants to know when I am coming home. So do I. She did not seem to have had my cards from Italy. It was nice to hear from home though.

Sunday 5 May 1918

I have just returned from a very busy and tiring four days in the Forest. The weather has been changeable and has contributed to my feelings of exhaustion. It has varied from light rain and drizzle to downpours to very welcome periods of sunshine. These intervals made the Forest a magical place as wide rays of sunshine come down and light up clearings, green with plant growth and the beginnings of wild forest flowers. A great deal of our forest in England has disappeared. France still has the forests that must have covered the counties of England in Robin Hood's time. Of course it's not long before Fritzy spoils my 'sylvan reverie' with the plop of gas shells and a sprinkling of bombs and whizz- bangs. We, as a squad, hurry through the undergrowth, the stretcher we are carrying swaying on its straps. We are caught in our progress and dappled by flashes of sunlight and could be 'fairy people', 'Denizens of the Forest'. I am brought to earth by the obscene curses of one of my fellows as he trips on a root and is responded to by the chatter of a machine gun from deep within the Forest bowers.

Our work has been made much easier and more efficient, for the R.E.s have laid a light railway line from end to end of the Forest and small motor tractors take up troops and ammunition, bringing wounded, and sometimes the dead, on their return. Such developments contrast sharply with the reports on German transport. People say that they have seen Jerry using an extraordinary range of improvisation for this purpose. The Germans have had to use, in their rapid advance, from ox drawn wagons to dog carts. More indications, so our war correspondents say, of 'Germany's imminent collapse.' If they had spent the night as we had, bringing out wounded under intense bombardment, they would be less optimistic.

Thursday 9 May 1918

After four days' work at Thiennes and a bit of a rest I moved with my squad up into the Forest again for another spell at our Aid Post. The weather is fine. The Aid Post is now a very well constructed shelter of logs, earth and sandbags and certainly proof against shrapnel and direct hits from light shells.

While we were there early one morning, having a minute for breakfast after a 'mad hour', Jerry artillery sought us out. It was more by luck than judgement on the part of the Jerry gunners because we were very well camouflaged. We are protected from air observation by the leaf cover and no-one can see us through the thick standing of the forest. However, they kept our heads down for a lively ten minutes as they bracketted us with the explosions of heavy shells. Trees crashed down, thick branches whirled and thumped into the structure but by the end of the 'strafe' all that had been brought down inside the Aid Post were little trickles of earth from in between the joints. We patted the thick baulks of timber, confidently pleased with the strength of their support. We then dusted the little dots of soil off our bread and jam, blew the top off our mugs of tea, compliments of a 'dixie-full' delivered before Jerry opened up, and settled down to breakfast.

> There is a happy land far far away
> Where they eat bread and jam
> Three times a day.
> Oh! How they laugh and grin
> When the blanking jam comes in....

Sunday 12 May 1918

Return to M.D.S. after a relatively quiet time in the Line apart from occasional artillery attention. The weather is fine and like early summer, as it should be. During our stay in the Forest we only 'carried' a few lightly wounded casualties and we were able to treat and shift them quickly. They were all boys new to the war. You could tell this as bandaged at head, leg or arm, they cringed when they heard the crump of a shell outside that we knew was far from hitting us. 'Don't worry' was the reassuring comment that we made with a smile, 'You never hear the one that hits you'. How much comfort that was to already wounded boys I'm not sure. We wanted them to know that we knew what it was like to be afraid. We had all been through it. We had been in it for nearly four years.

As we are near to the canal, myself and a companion have dared to swim in its cool clear waters. We have to strip off in the cellar of a nearby canal building and then keep as much as possible under cover or risk drawing a few shrapnel shells. So there we are, white, freckled, naked (or bollock same, as our coarser comrades would have it), dodging from whatever cover on the canal wharf we think will protect us. Hiding behind a broken wagon then moving on, to a pile of rubble, military paraphanalia, wire, petrol cans, ration boxes, gingerly we place our feet away from broken glass and brick fragments, then dive in off the worked stones on the edge.

After swimming up and down and across the canal's width for ten minutes or so we climb out dripping wet and repeat the antic-hopping journey back to our cellar. How vulnerable we feel, but we risk it. Imagining what would happen to us if a shrapnel shell popped off above us does not bear thinking about. We have seen the effect of shrapnel balls on tin-hatted uniformed bodies. Hit while naked we would look like shredded pork

Sunday 19 May 1918

There has been a lot of work to do at Thiennes as things hotted up, up the Line in the Forest. A great deal of gas shells have been dropped. The Forest seems to magnify the effect of the gas as it takes so long to disperse. We have though managed to clear the backlog of casualties by swift and effective use of barge traffic. It does not matter that the barges are slow as long as they keep coming. I myself got a touch of gas again when I lifted a stretcher that had held a gas casualty. The residue held in the canvas folds caused me to have red eyes and to lose my voice for a day. I recovered quickly and did not have to go off duty.

Work for this last week has been routine, accepting cases, cataloguing them and receiving stores. This last work was very welcome because supplies were running down. Much material was lost in the German advance as there was not time to remove it before hospitals were over-run, patients and all. Now we are being re-equipped.

In the middle of the week we returned to one of the Forest Aid Posts that we haven't visited before. It is in an old sawmill and its brick construction has been reinforced with timber, sandbags and earth. For an A.D.S. it is very roomy so patients can be laid out in two rows. The weather is now warm and we are being plagued by mosquitoes. They are a nuisance to us but to some poor chap already, to put it mildly, uncomfortable because of a bad wound, they are a blanking menace.

Thursday 23 May 1918

My birthday. My twenty-second. Fritzy very generously tried to give me a special present. I was travelling back up the Line on the light railway, pushing an empty trolley after having delivered a patient to the A.D.S. We were almost back at the Line when a five-point-nine landed a yard away from the rails. It buried itself in the soft ground and threw up earth, roots and forest floor litter from quite a big hole. The impact had enough force in it to throw us and the trolley off the Line, but it did not go off. It was a dud. It was one of the closest shaves I have had up to now and my mate shared the view, but as they say, a miss is as good as a mile. To calm our nerves we spent a little time well away from the railway in case they sent another one over. Then our nerve recovered, we set the trolley back on the Line and continued our passage. All the time I have been out here I have never ceased to marvel at the skill of the gunners from both sides. With good observation they can drop their shells right on the spot. We must have been seen. It wasn't a chance shot, they were after us.

Friday 24 May 1918

We have been relieved by the 15th Ambulance and have been attached to that unit. The weather is splendid. During the night we marched the relatively short distance to Steenbecque. It is a village on the old Roman road south east of the Nieppe canal and it

216

is where the 15th Ambulance have their H.Q.

They treated us very well and immediately organised a hot bath with a de-lousing, a change of underwear and uniform. The uniforms they issued are brand new and of a softer material than the khaki serge we are used to. Being brand new there are no patches or stitched up holes that suggest the fate of the previous wearer. They then sat us down to a hot meal of pork and beans, fresh bread and tea made from fresh water.

Saturday 25 May 1918

I slept a little and then got up to go out and explore the village. There is English and Portuguese Infantry here. The Portuguese soldiers I met told me in surprisingly good English that they were in the forefront of a German attack in April at Neuve Chapelle, just north of where we were, and they lost many of their comrades, killed, wounded and captured.

Over the village there is a great sausage shaped observation balloon with the observer's basket under it .

Monday 27 May 1918

I was ordered to return today to our 13th Field Ambulance H.Q. at Thiennes. A motor ambulance came for me with two patients in it who had had blood transfusions. When I was called for I was told by the driver that he had been instructed to ask for me as I knew something about blood transfusions. My sudden qualification in the treatment had come about I am sure because I had described to an M.O. the transfusion I had witnessed in a Canadian hospital some time ago. I hadn't exaggerated my knowledge but merely recounted the experience. Now I was an expert.

Luckily I wasn't called upon to treat the patients, just to sit with them as the ambulance, trying to avoid the shell holes, rattled down the Roman road to Thiennes. When I got to Thiennes I found that H.Q. had shifted its position to a corner of the Forest near to the railway station so that it was handier for Ambulance Trains. My patients went straight on into the hands of two very pretty Nurses.

Sunday 2 June 1918

I'm still at Thiennes H.Q. and have been here for the last few days. I think I have been forgotten. Nobody asks me to do anything here. No parades, no drills and no 'carrying'. I have kept out of the way and I have not been asked any questions. I even changed my mind about going to church parade in case somebody asked me who I was. Occasionally I swan about with a handful of dockets looking busy but most of the time I am having the life of 'Riley'. I sleep in a corner of an old ruined canal building and as the weather is splendidly warm I have only need of the blanket I have cadged from a Ward Orderly.

Rations and tea are provided by the occasional exchange of cigarettes but there is never any shortage of food around the hospital. I have even had my favourite, curry, once or twice. I swim every day, usually before breakfast.

Sunday 9 June 1918

Somebody somewhere looked up and said, 'Where's Cawkwell?' I have been put on ward duty until they need me back at Steenbeque.

Enemy artillery has been shelling the surrounding villages. The gossip is that the Germans are preparing another offensive so there is a bit of a flap on. Certainly the remaining civilians are leaving and their sad and slowly moving columns of carts, barrows, bicycles and prams can be seen trekking West. Opportunistic looters have already been braving an intermittent heavy bombardment to see what they can pick up from the deserted cottages, houses and farms on what is rapidly becoming a wasteland.

South of the Aire canal is an area of heavy industry with more English-type terraced houses where workers lived. This quarter is now receiving special attention, particularly a large steel works whose chimneys have already collapsed into dust, after very accurately direct hits. I think the chimneys had been used by artillery spotters. Let's hope they got out before precisely aimed German shells began to punch holes in the brickwork of the chimneys.

The weather is un-seasonal with squalls of rain and cold winds, only occasionally is there bright sunshine. I am still near Thiennes and Fritzy has been livening things up in this corner of the Forest, dropping several high explosive shells in and around the camp. Our somewhat uninformed view is that he wants us to shift further back. We didn't expect him to drop such big ones so close and the thirty patients we have here in this part of the camp are under canvas with no shelter. It needs no imagination to picture the effects of shell splinters from H.E. tearing through fragile canvas, even if falling a hundred yards away. Nobody seems to respond to the 'Gypsy warning' and we are still here.

Three times last week the balloon above Steenbeque was brought down, twice by aeroplanes and once by shrapnel, and three times another balloon has floated back up. On a trip into Steenbeque to collect stretchers I witnessed one of the attacks by a German aeroplane just after a new balloon had been lifted for a second time. Its black cross marking clearly seen, it swooped down, made a couple of passes and then came in for the kill, its machine guns shooting the tracer bullets that could be seen entering the fabric of the balloon before it exploded into white and yellow flames and black smoke. It then began to descend, with the observer scrambling out of the basket hanging below to escape by parachute. Our anti-aircraft artillery and machine guns mounted on the backs of trucks for mobility were assisted by a machine gun firing from a motorcycle and sidecar, did not score any hits on the German plane, and if I had been the observer in my light weight wicker basket I might have been as much afraid of being hit by them as by Jerry.

Sunday 16 June 1918

I'm still down at Headquarters and I have been put on night duty at the hospital proper. We are busily occupied with an outbreak of influenza. Either we are not getting any casualties from up the Line or the wounded are being diverted because of the outbreak. The majority of patients here are quite seriously ill with the malady and exhibit extreme symptoms, high temperatures, shivering, depression, vomiting and diarrhoea. There is little we can do apart from the light diet, tonics and Epsom salts. The worst hit are from recent drafts. They hadn't got the resistance of the veterans and two young men in their late teens have caught pneumonia and succumbed. It takes all the heroism and glory out of war (if there is any in it in the first place) being ill or even dying from a disease like influenza.

I have had a hectic week when I have not really been able to tell the difference between night and day. I eat, sleep, go on duty. Then the work starts. We have so many patients it looks as if what was an outbreak of one or two cases is now an epidemic.

Sunday 23 June 1918

I have been relieved of night duty at last and I am glad. There has been no respite. I am now looking forward to a welcome rest. After a couple of days wherein I mostly slept, I got up, bathed, shaved and changed and visited the nearby town of Aire. I hitched a lift on a horse-drawn artillery limber and after a bumpy ride that took me through ruined and deserted villages I got off at the village crossroads of Pecqeue and I walked the rest of the way. The town of Aire-sur-la-Lys has been shelled and heavily bombed from the air, and near it we have several hospitals, Aid Posts and C.C.S.s. The 39th Stationary Hospital and the 54th have both settled there. Nearby, in fact too close, there are military emplacements, stores and troops. I suppose these are what Fritzy is really after.

CHAPTER 13 - THE GERMAN RETREAT

Friday 28 June 1918

'Stand to' this morning, nap-sack packed with new supplies and carrying new stretchers with new webbing rigging. We were quickly got up into lorries and they took us only about a mile up the Line where we were in place when our Division attacked in force over a relatively wide Front. They met surprisingly little resistance and took all their objectives by the beginning of the afternoon. They were so successful the biggest problem was handling prisoners. A group of them, numbering easily fifty, approached us as we were coming back from a 'carry'. They were not guarded and the one leading them, a young German in his twenties, asked me in excellent English which way was the best to go to get to the rear. Within minutes a Sergeant M.P. came puffing his way towards us, quite out of breath and menacing the group quite unnecessarily with his drawn pistol. I thought that he smelled strongly of rum. The Sergeant wanted to know what was going on. The young German tried to explain, again in good English, but got a slap in the mouth for his pains. It was obvious that the Sergeant and the escort he commanded, who also came up at the run, had lost their prisoners in the confusion. The confusion being, I'll bet, whose turn it was to swig at the rum jar.

As this incident passed I began to feel decidedly unwell. I took my own temperature and saw it was over one hundred. There was no way that I could go sick for we suddenly got very busy again, fetching and carrying. I had to wait until the rush was over and by that time I was nearly dropping with whatever it was I had.

Sunday 30 June 1918

I remember little of being taken first to an Aid Post and then to hospital. After I was undressed and placed between clean white sheets and given a hot drink I was diagnosed as having a mild bout of 'flu. So began a week of high temperatures, feverish sweating, loss of appetite, and the most excruciating aches and pains in joints. I coughed a lot of course but I did not get the chronic bronchitis that the inveterate smokers did. The fact that I didn't smoke contributed, along with my fit and well fed condition, to my speedy recovery.

One thing that needs to be said is that I was lodged in very comfortable conditions and very well looked after by skilled and caring nurses. This wasn't 1916. But in spite of plentiful resources with their experienced compliment the virulence of the influenza strain that infected us struck down an Army more effectively than bomb or bullet.

Within a few days I was up on fairly shaky pins, doing what I could to help in the ward. I made tea, served meals and assisted those who could not get out of bed with their bottles and bed pans. Another job I got when I was strong enough was carrying the increasing numbers of poor soldier boys who went down with the 'plague' to their last resting place.

Sunday 7 July 1918

I am now discharged from the hospital and dodging about doing a variety of camp duties. The Line is quiet apart from news of sporadic trench raids that keep the poor bloody Infantry on their toes, and are not much use for anything else.

The weather is summer perfect and we, the recovering sick, are having a good time. We visit the neighbouring villages of Thiennes, Steenbeque and Boesingham in the hope of discovering treats such as chocolate, cigarettes and le plonkay, which we have not tasted for some time.

As we walk the streets with their demolished houses it makes me wonder whether it will ever be possible to repair such comprehensive destruction. Everything has been reduced to rubble, either by artillery or air raids.

Back in our billet I read another Dumas novel, The Count of Monte Christo, or a tattered and torn little book of late Victorian poetry. I have acquired the reputation of being something of a student, the reason for this is that I don't read 'Comic Cuts'.

Apart from my reading keeping me out of mischief there is walking along and swimming in the broad, deep, tree lined Aire canal. It is very popular as a venue for swimmers. They can be seen in the water or enjoying the summer sunshine on the banks in quite un-self-conscious nakedness. I reflect on how I have seen so many of them broken and bleeding, and I wonder on the point of it all.

Sunday 14 July 1918

I have just crossed the canal after a very good breakfast of bacon and cheese omelette and bread with, for a change, real coffee. I bought it in a packet from a Portuguese. We are going to Steenbeque in preparation for another trip up the Line. I am feeling fit, clean and ready for hard work.

I have been transferred to another squad of bearers and we are now eight altogether. I have not worked with them before, but they seem decent chaps. I am the one with most service but I have no seniority. It is obvious why I am with them, I shall be able to tell them how it's done. There's no extra pay and no stripe.

Tuesday 16 July 1918

It has taken us two days to get up to this part of the Line. On Sunday and Monday night we were billeted in a little cabin at the edge of the Forest, living on basic rations and cold water. We daren't make a fire to heat our water in case our smoke was spotted. We were so cramped that on Monday night I slept outside. It did not rain so I was fairly comfortable except that I woke covered in dew. Eventually I arrived with my seven companions at Casa Duss, one of our relay posts in the Forest. The Line is quiet apart from the activity of snipers who are hidden in the tops of trees. Nobody likes snipers, even our own are not all that popular. One reason being that they get more than twice as much pay. German snipers, if caught, get short shrift. I suppose if that happens to ours they get the same.

We are having a comfortable time at this station apart from the rations being basic and so poor. We supplement them by harvesting new potatoes, peas, beans and cabbage and onions from the large garden planted by the one time civilian residents before they fled the German advance. We cook at night to avoid our smoke being spotted.

Sunday 21 July 1918.

We are still enjoying fine weather and have had an uneventful week here at 'Casa Duss'.
Casualties are few even from snipers, the result of a sweep that bagged a couple and these two have not been replaced.
Except for a few shells of light calibre which fell on Friday night, just as we were cooking our supper of harvested vegetables served with bully and accompanied by red wine, the gift of a grateful patient, we have not been troubled by Fritz.
One patient who had been with the Division in the Ypres Salient brought news of the East Yorks lad who was shot for desertion at Christmas in a prison in Ypres. He said he got the information, and it was 'the gospel truth' from a corporal in the EY's who had been there when they read the lad's name out at a special parade. The name of the soldier they shot was McColl. It was right, he was from Hull. There was no point in writing home to find out more, the letter would have been censored.

Wednesday 24 July 1918

After a breakfast of the cold left-overs from last night's supper, three squads of Bearers came up to relieve us. We left our little post of Casa Duss with regret. Although the job had been easy we had done it well together. We got on well as a team. The first thing the Army did of course, when we got back to Steenbeque, was split us up.

Friday 26 July 1918

The last couple of days have been spent polishing the paintwork and brass of our equipment and vehicles in preparation for the Divisional Horse Show. The Divisional Horse Show !! The scrappy bit of news we get from England is that the country is in turmoil from strikes and the population is on low rations. In the towns and cities there is an anti-German hysteria verging on madness. Not even we are that anti-German and they are shooting at us. We are told that our fathers are being called to the 'Colours' and here the Germans have taken back large chunks of France and Belgium that it took the lives of a generation of young men to hold- and we are having a blanking Horse Show.

The weather was of course fine, and the show with games, competitions, and jumping by the Cavalry, was very enjoyable, reminding me of a good County show during an English summer. I was just about to note that the only thing that was missing was the cake and jam stall when a mate corrected me and pointed to the work of a Field Kitchen that had won a prize for its cakes and jam. 'Oh, to be in England ………..'

Sunday 28 July 1918

A motor ambulance came this morning for me and the new squad that I had been drafted to. We got all our stuff together out of the bell tent billet that we had spent our nights in and we piled into the Ambulance. I sat in the front with the Lance Corporal driver and he said that we would get our breakfast up the Line. But I knew such chauffeurs of old. He wanted shut of us as quickly as possible so that he could nip in and nip out of artillery range. Because of that and because he was only a Lance Jack we rebelled and caused him to stop at the Field Kitchen run by the Portuguese, where we had our breakfast. The Portuguese welcomed us and gave us bread, sausage and their coffee. The Portuguese wont eat bully, they know that in Brazil, where it comes from, they call it cat meat. We then set off, the inner man satisfied but with the driver in sullen silence.

His caution was vindicated for as soon as we got close up Fritzy started dropping them. He could hardly wait for us to close the doors before he was off down the road 'like a rat up a drain'.

We had to wait all day in a communication trench before we could make our way up to the Front. The perilous nature of our position was highlighted by the charred splintered ruins of a Salvation Army canteen wagon that covered the entrance to the trench. It had been hit by a Jerry shell. We were well within the range of Jerry's guns. You had to hand it to the Sally Army, sometimes they came very close to the Line to offer their very welcome service of a cup of tea and a wad (sandwich).

In the end we had to go forward and we had a very warm fifteen minutes as we moved into the left sector to our Aid Post, which was an enormous shell hole made by one of Frity's big ones. It had been covered with sheets of elephant tin, sandbags and thick tree trunk logs. We settled in, stowed our gear and waited for requests to 'carry'. As this post is clear of the trees of the Forest and close to the Front Line we can see the wire in sillouette as the usual Brock's benefit of flares lights up everything in relief. We will

226

have to sit out the day time and carry casualties in the dark.

Wednesday 31 July 1918

Heavy rain for the last few days has made things mildly unpleasant but at least the Line is a bit quieter. We've only had about ten 'carries', so far mostly from trench mortars and bombs. One lad we brought back was screaming and shouting so much we had to strap him to the stretcher and gag him to keep him quiet as he was attracting the unwelcome intentions of a machine gunner. A mortar had demolished a dug-out with him inside and it had taken his mates an hour to dig him out.

Sunday 4 August 1918

We were relieved from our Post on Saturday morning but the relief came during broad daylight that it attracted a lot of attention from Jerry. What that meant was that we had to wait until dark, so they got another day's work out of us 'buck shee', treating wounded in the Aid Post and carrying them out to the railway line, which the R.E.s were often called to repair. When we got back to H.Q. we were sent, the four of us, to a village away from the Line, Quistede. It was to be for a well earned rest. We went there by open Staff Car. It was going out empty to fetch some Officers from the next village, Ecques. I felt very grand speeding down the roads passed marching troops, going up to the Front and overtaking lorries and other traffic on its way to the rear. I sat, my arm on the back over the folded hood and thought, 'this is the life'.

At Quistede we were billeted in a little school abandoned by its pupils, but still with pictures on the walls and exercise books scattered on the dirty floor. We fixed ourselves up in a room that had perhaps once been the Principal's office and after having sorted out our sleeping arrangements, we searched around for a kitchen. We soon found a stove and with sticks from already broken chairs we soon had a fire boiling up a mess tin for a brew. We were the first of a whole contingent to occupy the place and thought we might get winkled out of our comfortable little room by N.C.O.s or Officers, but they occupied what I suppose was the caretaker's or head teacher's house.

Tuesday 6 August 1918

Our rest was short lived. We spent a couple of days with our feet up then we were paraded today having been warned of a full kit inspection. After that we embarked upon a programme of training drills and route marches. There were two things positive, the weather and the countryside. The weather was fine and the countryside a picture of peacetime, successful agriculture with acres of fine ripe crops untouched by the bane of war.

There has been no exodus from this region only that the young men have gone to war. The old men who are left, the women and children, are busily engaged with bringing in the harvest and it seems a pity that we are not allowed to help instead of dancing about on the roads, forming fours and doing right turns. We know all this business is to keep us occupied. Working in the fields would do just the same and be a lot more blanking useful.

Sunday 11 August 1918

We are having French summer weather. Our billet is very comfortable and rations are now supplemented by goods bought from the inhabitants of local farms. The bit of French I have picked up is useful in this because I know what to ask for and how to ask for it. I have discovered that local farmsteads while having, in war time, a ready market for all their produce, keep back a fair larderful for their own use and that they are willing to sell, not cheaply I hasten to add, something of their surplus. I negotiate for Officers and N.C.O.s and arrive at prices and quantities of eggs and sausages, etc., and cuts of meat. I get a commission for 'going'. I find that my 'profits' enable me and my mates to visit one or two selected addresses to partake of veritable feasts of egg and chips and occasionally, when we really want to splash out, at some farmhouse kitchen table we eat soup, steak, fried potatoes, salad, cheese and the local apple tart. All this with Vin Rouge and Calvados thrown in for five francs a head. We are also offered from time to time, bottles of the local beer, which it is the tradition around here to brew at home. It is better than any English bottled beer I have tasted, even speaking as a converted non-drinker. The French who brew it call it bier du garde. I sent Tilly a card and a letter for her birthday.

Tuesday 13 August 1918

This morning we got orders even before we had breakfasted, to pack our kit and be ready for a march to St. Omer where a train would be waiting for us, destination unknown. Perhaps it was going to Boulogne and the boat home: some hope.

The march was short but a bit nerve-wracking because as we marched through shell and bomb torn villages, over crudely repaired roads, we were followed all be it at very high level for the last part of the journey by a Squadron of Jerry aircraft. They were seen off by our Fly-boys and we watched them diving and turning and looping the loop in the blue sky but Jerry, like so many black flies, came back again. When we arrived at the station, marching right past the brewery, our train was waiting for us, its engine gently steaming and giving that chug and rattle that steam engines do when at rest. Just as we were opening the doors to get in, a single plane detached itself from the group and came over fairly low. With machine guns rattling it dropped four bombs. We ran in every direction, to every point of the compass. I dived under the train and as I lay on the sleepers I thought in horror that the train might move out to escape the raider. It didn't, thank God, and the Jerry plane flew off.

When we were sure it had gone we finished entraining.

Wednesday 14 August 1918

The journey from St. Omer was slow with halts and diversions, and the worry about air attack did not disappear especially when it was decided that we should stop for the night. Doors opened and made a line of candlelit trucks whose light must have shown a chain of illumination from the air. There was much shouting of 'Put that blanketty light out'. Realising the dangers we closed doors or blew out candles and once more there was darkness. 'And God said let there be light' and there was light, and you could see it for blanking miles.'

When we arrived at our rail destination, Bouquemaison, we were immediately formed up to march to Sericourt, a village near Frévent. I was back on my old stomping ground.

Saturday 17 August 1918

We are billeted in barns. The attached farmhouse has been nabbed by the Officers and N.C.O's. It doesn't make too much difference for the weather is fine and dry. A young Officer Chaplain came round and told us that we should expect to stay here for some time and he suggested that we form a committee with the object of arranging a Divisional Sports meeting. 'Does he know that there is a war on?'

Sunday 18 August 1918

The beautiful summer weather holds and this takes the edge off the rigours of drills and route marches. As we have had to learn to march again we have also remembered to sing some of the old favourites, 'Pack up your troubles ', 'Tipperary', 'Wash me in the water', 'Bells of hell' and some new ones, 'Keep the home fires burning' and 'Keep right on to the end of the road'.

As there is no swimming in the vicinity we pay visits to neighbouring villages and as a special excursion, St. Omer, where there is a brewery that sells its beer at the gate. I'm not a beer drinker but round here it is very good, thirst quenching in this weather and with a very satisfying after-taste that indicates its strength.

Back at Quisted in my spare time I write letters or get my diary up to date or read. I am onto H.G. Wells 'Kips' and I am re-reading my Victorian poetry book along with a translation of 'Omar Khyam'. I have to put up with a lot of light hearted ribbing because I am a bit of a queer cove, I read books and I don't smoke.

On Monday as we were resting our weary 'plates of meat' after tramping miles of French country roads we heard the drone of aircraft outside. This neighbourhood does not escape the attention of enemy aircraft and sure enough a lone German flyer was scouting about above, below the clouds. While we were on one of our interminable route marches the anti-aircraft wallahs had mounted machine guns in two nearby trees and thankfully their accurate and long-ranged fire kept the raider high and at a distance. I wondered though what might have happened had he chanced across us in the open country in columns of four, shoulder to shoulder, as we marched along oblivious to everything except our brotherhood and the bright sunshine.

Monday 19 August 1918

As for the Chaplain and his Divisional sports meeting suggestion, he needn't have bothered for we suddenly got the word of a move. I was in Frévent with some pals on the way to a canteen for supper when the order came through to shift. We had to 'leg it' back to the billet to sort things out P.D.Q. We nearly missed the departure of our Ambulance. The totally unexpected night march we made was to Haute Visée and we arrived very hot and bothered. My section couldn't sleep so we spent most of the night chatting and playing cards until in the early hours at last sleep overcame us.

Tuesday 20 August 1918

We moved again yesterday and are now in a hurriedly erected bivouac near the village of Coigneux, on the Somme. It is familiar to me as I was around here in 1917 and a bit further east in 1916. In those days we talked of the 'Big Push'. Things are different today. There is a great deal of confidence as the war seems to be moving East on all fronts and, dare I say it, the Germans seem to be on the run.

Wednesday 21 August 1918

Having abandoned the bivouac camp we followed our Division this morning as it attacked on a wide front. German artillery was desultory and mainly gas. Resistance from the forces that opposed us was slight. There was a thick mist as we went in and very quickly into the day we had gained five kilometres. We are not 'carrying' but treating wounded where they are fallen, leaving them to be picked up by those following behind.

We are now in an old British trench that the Germans with their usual thoroughness consolidated. We have been told to await orders.

Thursday 22 August 1918

As a squad of four we spent the night in the trench and nobody came near us. We could hear the noise of battle as the night went on but we weren't called upon and I advised my less experienced mates not to go looking for work. If there was any I assured them it would find us quickly enough. Because we had moved so quickly we began to get uneasy about the possibility of a counter attack. I decided to mount a watch during the night. It wasn't difficult to make ourselves comfortable as there was an enlarged dug-out in the wall of the trench with plenty of room for three. A two hour watch for each one of us in turn was sorted out. Half-way through the night a Medical Officer came to us and told us to take the wounded we had left in the rear back to Bucquoy.

The poor lads we had been told to leave had lain in the open for almost a day and part of the night. We dealt with them as quickly as we could and we were much helped by the dry conditions and the arrival of two motor ambulances with crews who must have got the message to move them after we did.

Friday 23 August 1918

We came back to our dug-out and settled down to a few hours sleep with now no need for a watch.

This morning after a wash, shave and a drink of cold water to wash our biscuit and bully rations down, we moved up again through Souastre and Gommecourt. The Infantry are still striding on and it is a lovely sight to see them in their thousands on top, their lines reaching almost to the horizon.

Sunday 25 August 1918

We are now somewhere north east of Bapaume and very busy. The last few days we have been called upon to do a variety of jobs in the confusion of the advance. I have been Stretcher Bearer, Pioneer and Guide. Sometimes I have been so close-up with the Infantry that I have been side by side with them.

In improvising a Dressing Station I took on the mantle of M.O., arranging the reception of casualties, prescribing treatment and filling in their casualty details before dispatching them to the rear. I returned to the Ambulance in order to direct them to where the Division's Infantry were resting in preparation for another attack. The Infantry are on the attack every day and each time Fritzy gives way with little resistance. His artillery is active but not very effective as at the moment they have no observation, not even from the air. Our lads are in very high spirits and have to be warned about the over optimism that is making them incautious. The weather is very good and everything seems to be going very well.

Sunday 1 September 1918

After a very busy week moving backwards and forwards, resting when we could, sleeping where we finished up, we are now billeted with a Company of Warwicks. We are very comfortable in buildings recently vacated by Jerry who obviously left in a hurry for he abandoned some of his wounded. They have been treated and sent to the rear. The poor buggers were terrified when we found them. They thought we were going to shoot them.

Being up with the Infantry and performing the duties, really of regimental stretcher bearers, has it's advantages, not least as far as rations are concerned. They have Field Kitchens that follow them wherever they go or they are waiting for them with hot grub and tea when they arrive for billeting. Rations are also good because we have come across food dumps that were originally British but looted by Jerry during his advance. There are still stocks left of tinned bacon, butter, jam and sardines. He was in too much of a hurry to take them with him.

Everyone is in a good mood and it's not from rum; we haven't had a ration doled out yet for days. It is because there is a strong sense that we are pursuing a demoralised if not a defeated Army. In some other sections there are reports of prisoners surrendering in droves. We have seen some who were ill-kempt, their boots broken, uniforms patched and with obviously no stomach for the fight. When we looked like this a couple of years ago we had a song about it that went to the tune of 'The Church's one foundation'.

> We are Fred Karno's Army,
> The Rag-time Infantry,
> We cannot fight, we cannot shoot-
> What blanking use are we.
>
> And when we get to Berlin
> The Kaiser he will say:
> 'Hoch hoch, mein Gott,
> What a blanking rotten lot
> Are the Rag-time Infantry.'

I heard last night half a dozen Warwicks talking about the German advance in March. They told how our lads had held on in the face of the German onslaught, sometimes to the last man, before they were over-run. Apart from reported minor counter attacks in the north there is little evidence of that happening here on the German side.

We attack again tomorrow in the morning and instead of the usual worries the prospect is being looked forward to.

Monday 2 September 1918

We spent all day and afternoon pushing on from one objective to the next. It is not artillery harassing us but their planes. They come over bombing and machine gunning day and night. Last night attacking German low level bombing planes were responsible for what was for me the most dreadful and tragic event of the war so far.

I was with a Medical Officer and a number of other squads, on a short night march towards Cambrai along the main road which is very straight and, I think, built on an old Roman way. It was a warm night, so the hundred or so men in the company of Warwicks we were marching with were not wearing their tin hats and to relax they had broken step and they were smoking and lighting each others fag's.

Because we were not on the Q.V. we failed to hear to drone of planes above. They must have been attracted in the very dark night by the pin points of glowing cigarettes and the flashes of struck matches and lighters. We had been told before that such lights can be seen from hundreds of feet above. We were certainly being allowed to get careless and we paid for it.

Suddenly the length of the road we were marching on and the fields and buildings on either side were lit by the phenomenally bright, white, light of a parachute flare. As it slowly descended over us it swayed from side to side in the blackness of the night. For a second we all looked up, a hundred or so faces up-turned to a glowing light in the night. Before the majority of the ranks of men could think to scatter for cover, bombs began to fall and explode in amongst them.

Being in the rear of the column we managed to dive into a culvert by the side of the road and I was protected by the smashed remains of an artillery limber. I watched in horror as men were blown high in the air or bombs blew the men in all directions on the ground. I don't know how many bombs fell but the road seem to be carpeted by explosions. They became so concentrated the whole scene disappeared in a great expanding cloud of multi-coloured flame and thick grey and yellow smoke, out of which flew great red sparks. All this was lit by the still gently floating falling flare.

I can't say how long it went on. It seemed that the awfulness of it would never end, but I don't suppose it was more than twenty or thirty seconds, or maybe a minute before the flare fizzled out in a nearby field, spluttering and spitting its last flashes of light. The black night then cloaked everything again and for a fraction of a second there was an awful silence. Then the cries, screams, groans and shouts of the wounded filled the air.

Pulling ourselves together, out of the shock that the terrible events had put us into, we went in amongst the jumble of broken, shattered and disintegrated bodies and slipped and slid on blood that was flowing on the road as if a short shower had washed it. By the time ten minutes were up we counted seventy six casualties, out of a hundred, most of them fatal. Those few men who were not hurt were shocked into immobility and some became hysterical.

We had enough to deal with as we knelt amongst the bodies and parts of bodies and tried as best we could to treat those wounded first who we thought might have a chance. I don't know how many died by the side of the road for some were so badly torn up that the life ran out of them as we squatted by them and attempted to help.

It took us what was left of the night and into the morning to get the casualties there was hope for carried back, the walking wounded following behind in a daze. Some Pioneers came up and lay the dead and the parts of the dead by the side of the road and covered them with gas capes. What we saw then as dawn broke and when the horrible scene was cleared of men, tin hats, kit, rifles and Lewis guns, was that there were no craters in the road. The bombs that had been dropped were for the express purpose of killing men. We heard survivors back at the Aid Post, most of them splashed with the blood of their comrades, vowing vengeance for what they saw as an atrocity.

We spent the rest of the day moving up to Cambrai. I was offered hot rations but it would be some time before I thought I could eat and expunge from my mind the awful sights I had witnessed. For days and days afterwards I could not close my eyes to sleep without the terrifying business rolling round my head like a cinematograph.

Thursday 5 September 1918

With an understanding in my experience rare in the Army, although it was obvious we were needed for work and not due for a rest, we were left alone. I suppose it was for us to recover from our ordeal. I would have preferred to have gone on and continued working to take my mind off it. So we are back with the Ambulance, billeted in an old but capacious and well fitted German dug-out. We are in the side of a railway cutting at Achiet-le-Grand. To keep ourselves busy we are cleaning our kit so that we will be ready when called upon. I spend my time writing up my diary.

Sunday 8 September 1918

We are still at Achiet-le-Grand and generally feeling a bit better. For diversion we are exploring old German trenches and dug-outs. There is all sorts of abandoned equipment and we are holding shooting competitions with German rifles and ammunition that can be found in abundance. It is dangerous but entertaining.

Monday 9 September 1918

I have just returned from an adventurous trip to Doullens by motor. It rained all day, we had five punctures and on the return trip I had to get up in front to tell the driver how to find the right road.

The purpose of my visit to Doullens was to have a tooth out by the Army dentist there. Unlike many of my fellow soldiers I opted to keep my teeth as I looked after them and rarely had any trouble with them up to now. So many I knew had them all out at the first opportunity, either 'because they were too much trouble' or unbelievably having them all out and a false set put in meant 'excused duties' for a while.

I found the dentist easily and I didn't have to wait. Before long I was in the hands of someone who did not seem all that sympathetic and whose gruff chair side manner indicated that he wanted to get it over with as quick as he could. Before he gave me a jab and without waiting to ask me which tooth hurt he tapped my teeth until he knew he had found the right one when I nearly leapt out of the chair. Quite unnecessarily he said, 'Yes that's the one', and then he literally 'bayonetted' my gum with an enormous hypodermic. There did not seem to be anything coming through but he ignored my protests and began to grasp the tooth with his pincers. Pushing the gum down with them he began rocking the tooth back and forth. I felt everything and heard the cracking as the offending molar was wrenched out of its socket. I can only say he was quick, but during the short time he was in there the pain in my mouth was excruciating.

He told me to rinse but I was still bleeding copiously and dripping over the form he asked me to sign. He plugged the hole with cotton wool and fortunately the pain began to subside. I left his surgery and to compensate for my discomfort I decided to try to enjoy the few hours I could spend in Doullens. The first thing I treated myself to was a jug of the local Calvados and what pain was left was dulled by a good swig.

Saturday 14 September 1918

We have been moved to Barastre for another spell in the Line. We Bearers are going up tomorrow while the 10th Sub Division, whose responsibility it is to erect provisional Aid Stations, set about running a Divisional Rest Station.

Sunday 15 September 1918

I am now at a Relay Post near Havrincourt Wood. The generally held view was that the Germans were collapsing. To the consternation of the plans of High Command, there is evidence that resistance is stiffening. One way in which they are making their presence felt is by their searching around with big shells and gas.

Our billet, which is a tunnel cut into a bank at the roadside, is always in a turmoil. Just across the road is a battery of six-inch howitzers, and every time they fire they send a blast through which puts out our folding candle lanterns. If nap or vingt-et-un are being played this interrupts the games. As I am reading or writing it is very inconvenient. We are thinking of sending someone over to tell them 'to go away'.

Sunday 22 September 1918

The weather is fine and a few days ago we left our tunnel and moved a little way along to a ruined village, Metz. We are in a cellar that has a reinforced ceiling and it has been enlarged so that we can accommodate twenty stretchers in comfort. So far we are having a quiet time there and we don't have any customers as no Infantry action has taken place in our vicinity. A squad of Bearers with us drew the short straw and was ordered to go south east to Gouzeaucourt where fighting was said to be bloody.

The leave rota has started again and I have been told to expect a furlough shortly. That is, unless I am caught by one of the 'booby traps' which Fritz has left around in ration boxes, old German kit, attached to bottles and boxes of cigarettes and tobacco. We have had no patients who have been victims but visitors say that hands have been lost and blokes have been blinded. The souvenir hunter should beware.

Tuesday 24 September 1918

We have just been relieved and we are now at Ytres, another ruined village that the Germans at one time made into a strong point. It is now a busy camp, railhead and dump. Our Ambulance is running a hospital in the camp that is plastered with red crosses. It has still attracted attention from enemy aircraft. I shall be charitable and say that what they are really after is the military emplacement. However, I am being generous because I have heard the news that some weeks ago Jerry torpedoed two red cross marked hospital ships and a great many wounded drowned. It pained me to think that some of them might have been lads that we had taken out of battle who then thought they were going to comfort and safety.

Wednesday 25 September 1918

The hospital has a comprehensive system of baths with hot and cold water. I have availed myself of the service as I was getting very scruffy and unhygienic.

The weather is fine with the ground very dry and hard, just right for 'stunts'. Reassuringly our aircraft patrol regularly and keep Jerry at bay.

Thursday 26 September 1918

We moved up the Line this morning and I am raring to go. I feel fresh and scrubbed having had another bath early before breakfast. Yesterday's soak only got the thick off. Oh, the luxury of being clean. I also scrounged a new shirt and a set of combination long john underwear from the hospital laundry plus nice clean socks. I am fit and ready for another stunt.

Friday 27 September 1918

Our Division attacked again this morning, took their objective, a position in front of the old Hindenburg Line, then repelled a counter attack from out of the old fortifications and through the thick tangled belts of murderous German wire. We had a busy time stretcher-bearing as casualties from German bombs and machine guns were rather heavy. We had to carry them about four kilometres across country. A good job it was not mud. We felt quite safe carrying them on open ground as Jerry was not tooled up for spotting us. The only things we had to keep an eye out for were planes.

Sunday 29 September 1918

Thankfully for us the fine weather continues. Our part in the war is best done in the sunshine.

We are now with the Infantry near Villers Plutch. Our attack was, after repulsing the counter attack, well followed up. The Hindenburg is breached and Fritzy is on the run. The predictions were that the Hindenburg Line would hold us up. It hasn't been a walk over by any means but a damn sight easier than it was in 1917. In other parts of the Line, according to reports, the breach had not been achieved without loss. Talking of loss, we had heard little about American troops, involvement in the war until told of significant losses on their part in action to the south of us.

During the day we have a quiet and comfortable time in old German positions that are roomy and accessible but at night we are troubled with bombs and gas shells. Last night we set out with a stretcher case. Lucky for him we were able to dress his leg wound successfully. He had been losing a lot of blood but was now fairly comfortable. In the darkness, handicapped by our gas helmets, whose lenses are difficult to see out of, even in daylight and further, puzzled by the strange country, we walked in a circle. We were pulled up by a German machine gunner who opened up in front of us. He then must have drummed up artillery for gas shells started plopping around us. We lost no time in fixing our masks on properly, taking gas tablets and seeing to it that our 'case' did the same. We then turned about and headed in the opposite direction with the first light that was just twinkling in the east at our backs. It was full daylight before we safely delivered our 'carry' at the Relay Post.

Wednesday 2 October 1918

We were still up at 'sparrow fart', as the Australians describe dawn, but quite unnecessarily as we weren't needed. Our Division was being relieved so we could have got our heads down straight away. We grabbed a few hours of 'shut eye' when we returned to Barastre in an Ambulance wagon, dozing in the empty blood-stained stretchers in spite of the rough ride.

Thursday 3 October 1918

An interesting morning. We were paraded just after breakfast so that we could be given the news that Bulgaria had surrendered. The information was delivered to us by an Officer who spoke perfect English. He had been fighting in a Russian unit in France Most of us were not aware that Bulgaria had been fighting for the Germans. Nonetheless one of Germany's allies had surrendered. Things must be hotting up.

After the parade we were treated to a second breakfast. The first had been rushed bully, biscuit and water. We had the most delicious porridge I have ever tasted. Bacon

240

sandwiches in such abundance, we were told to 'fill our boots'. Sometimes the catering lads with their field cookers could produce really good grub. We could certainly have marched a day on what we had for that breakfast.

Our main job at Barastre is helping to run the Rest Centre and it ought not to be surprising what a hot bath, clean clothes, clean sheets, early restful nights and three hot meals a day thrown in, could do for a fella. The lads came in 'dead beat'. It was a treat to see them go out after a few days 'bright-eyed and bushy-tailed'. The only fly in the ointment being that they were going back into the sausage machine.

CHAPTER 14 - ANOTHER HOME LEAVE

Wednesday 9 October 1918

Our Ambulance will move up into action today. I shall miss it because I received my leave pass and travel warrant and I start on leave at two o'clock this morning. To get to the train I had to get to Bapaume by five o'clock. What traffic there was, was moving east and it did not make any difference what running around I did, I couldn't find any transport. The train was (unusually a leave train) going direct to Boulogne and if I missed it I would miss the ferry.

Behind the Rest Centre, among the wheel chairs and wheeled stretchers, there were some bikes, locked up, that belonged to the Signals. There was no-one about so I forced a lock with a bayonet and borrowed one. 'Needs must when the Devil drives'. I mounted it and I was off like a competitor for the 'Tour de France'. I made the six miles to Bapaume in just under an hour. I would have been quicker but I had no lights and just outside the town I was stopped by a night duty M.P. who, shining his shaded lamp on me, asked me for my pass and warrant, saying, 'Who are you then, the blanking demon cyclist deserter?'. He saw I was 'bony fido' and I shot off, free-wheeling down the hill. I was soon at the railhead and on the train. I left the bike with a note on it asking that it be returned to Barastre Rest Centre. A few years ago I would no more have thought of stealing than lying. Now I did both.

Friday 11 October 1918

I arrived at Boulogne yesterday after a journey rattling over lines in the process of being repaired. In the early light you could see the gangs of railway men stand back to let the train pass. It was difficult to see if they were Army or civilian. Rattling or not the train arrived, full of it's leave-taking troops, in time for the first boat. There was the usual long queue to get on and the standard vetting by M.P.s. This time they were not only vetting passes but looking in knapsacks. Mine was full of rations that I was taking home as my contribution to the difficulties of shortages. It was bulging with plunder. I was singled out. But lucky for me they didn't up-end the sack as they were doing with others. The quayside was littered with tins of butter, bully and bacon as they clattered on the stones out of emptied sacks. In the top of my sack there were books over the layer of spare clothes covering my 'booty'. The books fascinated the M.P. assigned to search my sack. 'What are you then, a blanking scholar?' We are taking some right 'Jessies' in these days. On your way'. I was rescued from discovery by literature.

The boat was as always a melée of confused searches for decent places to squat. I showed my Red Cross in the sick bay and was allowed to snooze in a corner. It was a short crossing and I was soon in Folkestone, boarding a crowed train to London. In London I was in time for a train to Yorkshire that wasn't overcrowded. I changed at Leeds for Halifax and I eventually found myself walking up to the cottage in the late evening. The autumn weather had brought a cooling to the air.

Little seemed to have changed. As I walked up the path to the door I saw a simple note pinned to it 'Gone to Hull'. ----- 'Home is the sailor, home from the sea, and the hunter home from the hill'. But what about the blanking soldier? What a home-coming.

The key to the door was on a string through the letter box and I turned the lock and walked in. There was nothing in the larder, and only cold grey ashes in the grate. It was obvious that nobody had been home for days. I took the few sticks and the odd nuggets of coal that there were in the bucket. I lit a lamp and made myself a fire in the grate and put on the kettle to boil. With a few pinches of tea and my own condensed milk I made a brew. After that I heated up a tin of pork and beans, ate them out of the tin and then had an early night in a cold bed. I felt very sorry for myself

Sunday 13 October 1918

I felt better when I got up and after making myself a cup of tea I ate the last of the pork and beans with some of my tinned bacon for breakfast. Although it was Sunday and I was at home I didn't go down to Luddenden Church but made my way to Halifax where, in spite of it being 'The Lord's Day', the streets were thronged with workers and the uniforms of the various forces on leave. I went straight to Sykes's mill and asked after Tilly. She wasn't in work that day and, it was supposed, at home. I made my way to her Nan's house but as far as I could see, she wasn't there. I was told by a neighbour that the old lady had died some time before. Tilly had not told me. I thought this as strange as the attitude demonstrated by the neighbour when I enquired.

I scribbled a note for the neighbour to tell Tilly that I'd been but before I could deliver it, any mystery was almost immediately solved for as I made to do so I was confronted by a distressed but very obviously pregnant Tilly. The curious thing was that I was not shocked. I only experienced a momentary anxiety that the child she was carrying might be mine. But then I quickly dismissed this thought. I hadn't seen her for over a year. What could you expect? At least we weren't married and what had happened to Tilly we heard about all the time 'over there', and to married women sometimes. News of pregnant wives at home drove serving husbands crazy. Many a marriage foundered on the arrival home on leave of the irate husband.

We went into the house and I got the whole story through sobs as Tilly collapsed in a heap on the sofa. All I could do, as she wept out her misery, was to put my arm around her and assure her that I understood, that she was not to worry and that I hoped she would be happy. Her Nan had died, she told me, and left her all alone, choking on each word like a little child, and she had taken over the tenancy of the house. She had met a man who had been discharged from the West Yorks because of wounds. He had taken his old job back at the Mill and that's where they had met. She had become pregnant and so they had married a few months before. There wasn't really anything for me to say. It was done. She hadn't the heart to tell me by letter.

I wasn't unhappy when I left her, still grieving, on the doorstep. My thoughts were mixed and the one that came out of the mixture was that I probably would not have married her myself, and I was ashamed to think it. I looked back as I closed the gate and saw that her pregnancy, though she had put on weight, and her breasts were larger, had not made her any the less beautiful. I hurried away because I didn't want to be there if the new husband arrived home. It would have been too embarrassing even if, as Tilly told me through her tears, that he knew all about me.

I went back to our house and packed up, making sure I didn't forget my sack of groceries. I locked the door and went for the train to Leeds then Hull. It wasn't difficult to be philosophical about Tilly. A year is a long time. For me what I thought was that I'd had a sweetheart. I'd had someone, a girlfriend, who would have cared had I 'copped it' and I had the memory of our love making. She had been my first love. Before leaving her I'd made her promise to stop smoking and to try to learn her letters, both for the sake of her new baby.

I arrived at Hull through Leeds, Selby, and Goole . It was very late when I knocked on the door. Dad, Maud and Phyllis were very surprised to see me as I'd not been able to give them any notice of my coming home. The note on the door was not for me but the coalman.

Phyllis served me the stew that was left from their meal and as a candle was lit to take me up to bed Phyllis said enigmatically 'We'll talk in the morning'.

Monday 14 October 1918

I didn't sleep in late as they had wanted me to, but instead I was up for a breakfast of bread and jam and tea. The eggs to go with my bacon were not forthcoming because of rationing shortages. Phyllis told me, as I sat at the table, that she had known about Tilly but she did not want to upset me as she thought I would have enough to put up with. It occurred to me that nobody had told me. Mates were always getting letters from home telling them that their girlfriends or their wives, for that matter, were 'putting it about'. The letters were usually signed 'a friend'.

Phyllis said I was better off without her and it was no use arguing with my sister. She didn't understand how I felt. Dad, as always, kept his counsel, and put his boots on and went off to work. Phyllis herself then told me that both she and Maud were getting married to chaps they had met at the Mill. I didn't know either of their prospective husbands. They were still in Halifax. As I was unlikely to get another leave for a long time there wasn't much chance that I would get to the weddings. Of course I wished them both well, but things here seemed so distant from me. News, even personal family news, hardly registered on me. I needed to get out so I decided to go to Beverley for the day, and I would walk taking a short cut by going over the river at Wawne.

The town was quite lively when I got there with lots of soldiery from local camps and the Victoria Barracks of the East Yorkshire Regiment. I went in the Push, a pub in the town square, initially for a quiet drink but got up with two lads in the E.Y's who, like me, were on leave from France. What with telling the tale and swapping views on when the war would end and feeling more at home with them than with anyone I had met so far, I drank more than I intended to.

We walked back to the Barracks together and they arranged a meal for me from their Cookhouse. I stayed all the afternoon, yarning about narrow escapes and good nights out and fallen comrades. I began to get concerned about the journey back. Having spent up in the Pub, I hadn't even the train fare and I didn't fancy the walk back. I needn't have worried. One of the lads was billeted in Hull and he was returning on his motorbike. I went home on the back of that.

Everybody was in bed when I let myself in and it did not take me long getting there myself.

Tuesday 15 October 1918

Dad had to go to work and Phyllis and Maud back to Halifax, so I told them I had decided to go to Hornsea for a couple of days. I caught the train at Paragon and as it rolled through the East Yorkshire countryside I could only think of the rolling post-harvest fields as pock-marked with shell craters. I saw its villages and farmsteads ruined as in France. Really this country knew nothing of what was happening in France. The land did not know, nor did the people.

My stay in Hornsea was not a success. There is really nothing sadder than a seaside town out of season. I drifted from pub to pub and the only treat I enjoyed was fish and chips. I was assured that the fish was sea fresh, straight off the cobles of the inshore fishermen of Hornsea, who land their catch on the beach. I had no trouble finding lodgings but when the landlady asked my name and unit the new conditions in England were brought home to me.

I sat in the parlour quite comfortable in front of a big fire, and I was just settling down for a snooze in the roomy armchair when a policeman was shown in by the landlady, who then hastily left the room and closed the door behind her. The 'bobby' wanted to see my leave warrant. My busy-body hostess had suspected me of being absent without leave or even a deserter and had called in a policeman.

When he saw that I had a pass, he apologised and left. I felt insulted and disappointed. I decided not to stay the night and I paid what she thought I owed her and I went out to catch the train home. When it arrived in Hull I got off and passed what was left of the night at first in a pub and then in a picture house. When I got home I went straight to bed but not before having to explain the reason for my early return.

Sunday 20 October 1918

The last few days I have been getting up late and passing the time by walking into town and catching the tram and exploring various parts of Hull. I spent a day on Hessle Road but that once lively quarter is subdued because of the restrictions on fishing. I went into my old firm but I didn't get the welcome I expected. It made me doubt that the promise made to me when I left, that there would be a job for me on my return, might not be fulfilled. It was depressing to learn of how many of my old mates would not be coming back.

At home I take my mind off things by busying myself around the house and garden, such as it is, and getting my Dad's meals ready for him when he comes home from work. I don't think that my being here has cheered him up. He has got used to the solitary life. Phyllis said she found the same when she returned from Halifax to make sure that things were going well with him. She was quieted with the words, 'You're not to worry. I am coping quite well by myself'. On Saturday night I decided to go to a picture house and I asked Dad to come with me, but he preferred to stay in to put his feet up with a mug of tea after his dinner.

I went to St Mary's Sculcoates this morning but did not take Communion, nor did I really recognise anyone in the congregation. The Vicar gave a sermon and he talked about the war a lot, but what he did say went over my head.

Tuesday 22 October 1918

I had a good swim today in Beverley Road Baths. First of all I luxuriated in the hot water of the slipper baths and dried myself off and went to the main pool where I did two lots of a quarter mile. I then went home and made an attempt at resurrecting the bike that had been brought back from Halifax but it was too far gone. The tyres have perished, the tubes are rotten and there is so much rust around the brakes and hubs that it will take some time to get it off. It is a job I will have to cope with more completely if and when I come back.

Wednesday 23 October 1918

It is the last day of a leave that I am only just beginning to enjoy as it is coming to an end. I said 'good bye' to Dad and he said to me as I did, rather strangely, 'I will see you when you come back soon. You know you will come back, don't you? I know you will'.

He then shouldered the bag he kept light tools in and his packet of sandwiches and went off down the terrace, waving his hand in the air, without turning round. I hope he is right and I do come back.

I thought to go to Halifax to say 'Au revoir' to Phyllis and Maud and also to give a different impression than the one I'd given them when I first arrived. I want to say how pleased I am that they have found someone. I decided against it. I shall write to them both. If there was any problem with train times it might result in me reporting late if I had to go to London from Leeds. I caught the London train and it went along a Humber River busy with craft carrying, I suppose, materials for the war. The train was full of civilians and servicemen and women. I couldn't find any place on it where there wasn't a smoker. So I exercised one of the skills I'd developed during my service and went to sleep.

The train was late and did not get to London until the early hours of the morning and I reported to Victoria and was told where to catch the train to Dover.

Thursday 24 October 1918

I arrived at Dover just before dawn and after a few hours in the town, where everything seemed open in spite of the late hour, I embarked for Boulogne. The crossing was delightful as I woke up from a doze into bright sunshine. We were convoyed by a Naval Airship which droned above us like a huge wasp.

CHAPTER 15 - BACK IN TIME FOR THE ARMISTICE

Friday 25 October 1918

Myself and others returning from leave spent a very uncomfortable night in the wireless Rest Camp at Boulogne and with no breakfast to speak of, save a few crumbs of biscuit and water, we entrained for the Line. I didn't expect such meagre rations otherwise I would have prepared myself. Our train of goods trucks and vans was nearly a mile long and took eight hours to reach Achiet-le-Grand. I slept for most of the journey apart from waking up at a stop where we were given tea and enormous sandwiches of pressed pork and cheese. For the last part of the journey I slid the door open a little and looked out at the barren war-torn countryside with its seemingly endless treeless waste and its unrecognisable piles of rubble that were once villages. Everywhere there is the rubbish and junk of war, broken guns, wagons, wooden boxes, smashed equipment and belts of rusting barbed-wire now uselessly guarding deserted trenches.

Saturday 26 October 1918

Last night we stayed at what was called Achiet-le-Grand Reception Centre. What a reception, it was very cold, there were no blankets and most of us lit fires around which we sat chatting with the smokers smoking until daybreak. The experience I'd had on leave, judging from conversations, was a common one. Most were of my opinion: it did not seem real.

When the rations came at last, there was a wild scramble for them. Four to a loaf were the instructions with bully and Maconochie's which we warmed up on our fires along with water for tea.

We entrained again and rattled slowly over our old battlefield to Gouzeaucourt. This was the railhead so after a short march, during which we crossed the ruined Canal du Nord on planks, we were offered another so-called Reception Centre at Bantouzelle. We spent another cold sleepless night there and by this time there wasn't a man amongst us who wasn't blanking fed up and near to, without putting too fine a point on it, mutiny.

Sunday 27 October 1918

We drew two days' rations and a crowd of us set off on foot to find our Division. There was no-one above Lance-Jack with us.

The country now began to improve, there were good roads and houses with roofs intact. Gardens were well tended and the country around untouched by war.

After a long disorganised march we reached Caudry. The march was too much for some who, after nights without sleep in freezing billets, fell by the wayside and had to be picked up by wagon.

We only stayed long enough in Caudry to enquire of a Military Police Post where our Ambulance was billeted then we set off and reached our unit just after dark. Caudry was the first decent town we had been in with people recognisable as civilians. It was jolly fine to hear the calls of familiar voices and the shouts of 'chaff' that was the welcome of old pals. After a good hot supper with hot tea and a game of cards for old times' sake, I turned in to sleep. Wrapped up warm on a straw mattress, it was the first for four nights.

Monday 28 October 1918

The villages around here are hardly damaged and there are lots of civilians about, picking up their lives after years of occupation. But the memory of that wide belt of ruined country remained. For me it seemed to confirm the experience I'd had on leave and to cut us off from home.

Saturday 2 November 1918

The four days of sleeplessness, of poor rations and the Army not giving a blank for us have been made up for in a pleasant rest at Béthencourt. We have been given plenty of time to prepare for our imminent entry back into action. The billets are comfortable, warm and roomy. Our meals come from a well-run Field Cooker and I get the strong impression, though I maybe wrong that the people who administer our Field Ambulance and were responsible for the 'balls-up' of our reception are trying to say 'sorry'.

Sunday 3 November 1918

'Stand to' was well before sunset this evening as we set off from Béthencourt for a long march to Le Quesnoy, north east of Cambrai. The march was made unpleasant by over frequent halts when we had to stand in the rain while messages were passed back and forth as to the position and strength of the Germans up ahead. It was quite obvious, even to us who are not supposed to have a Military mind, that we had set off too early. We should have waited until the next day. 'Ours not to reason why'.

We reached Le Quesnoy at two o'clock in the morning in pouring rain, and soaking wet-through we were ushered into a large complex of barns. They were un-damaged and leak proof but that is all. We were too beat to even scrounge around for firewood to make a fire that might boil our water and dry our clothes. We simply fell down, in our boots, our drenched uniforms a witness to how inefficient our gas-capes were in keeping off the rain.

Monday 4 November 1918

We woke and weren't expected to fall in until eight thirty. What changes are taking place. There was hot water, braziers to dry clothes and a Field Cooker that made coffee, bread and bacon.

The weather is splendid today and it was possible to stand outside and have a strip wash. So scrubbed and tidied up, with uniforms more or less dry, the inner man fed and watered, we are standing by, well equipped and ready for action up with the Devons.

Thursday 7 November 1918

At sunset on Monday my squad of four joined the Devons and we marched to Louvignies. It is a small village and not much damaged. There is a shell hole here, marks of machine gun bullets there. We rested in the village until daybreak. I found an outhouse with no door but it was better than squatting in the road or lolling on the banks at its side. I was able to get sleep of sorts before we were called at daybreak to form up for a march that moved us up into the Mormal Forest. We strode purposefully over cross-country tracks, stumbling on roots and slipping in grass in the teeming rain.

At noon we halted for the rest of the day and the night. We constructed 'bivvies' as best we could with our ground sheets, using the low branches of forest trees. As we were able to use a tarpaulin from the Ambulance ours was big enough to cover the squad. In borrowing the tarpaulin I saw that there was also fodder there for the horse. I liberated a bale of hay and we were glad to roll in its sweet smelling dryness in our wet clothes.

At daybreak on Wednesday we moved up again, hurriedly downing water, biscuit and bully. There was first a cross-country struggle through stiff, muddy, valleys then some kilometers on a high road through the Forest. On this road we came across two mine craters and we had to struggle to get our wheeled stretchers across them.

About seven p.m. we got in touch with Fritzy for the first time so we hung on near the River Sambre until night fall. The firing, heavy and light artillery with some long range machine gun mixed up with it, was enough to give us a few casualties. The continuing rain made conditions bad and we had to carry and wheel our stretcher cases back nearly four kilometres. When we got to this point Ambulance cars were able to come up and collect them but they could get no further.

After dark the river was bridged and the German rear guard moved back and we took possession of the first village on the opposite side. We rested there until day break. I am no military tactician but it seemed to me that the Germans were making an orderly

251

withdrawal at their own speed and would not engage us if we did not come too close. Men were being killed and wounded on both sides just because some high-ranker wanted to see some action or was carrying out orders to harass the German withdrawal just a bit too enthusiastically. Luckily for me and my squad we were relieved and marched back to where the Ambulance cars were and went with one of them to rejoin our Field Ambulance.

We had a night's rest at Headquarters and then joined another advance to Pont-sur-Sambre where we rested in a house cellar awaiting further orders. The house was undamaged and the residents were a bit surprised that we should ask for the shelter of the cellar for they had only just repossessed it after the Germans had used it as a billet. I must say that it was obvious that the Germans had left it in a very tidy condition. That must have been the case because the family that lived in it had only just returned. We only wanted the cellar but they were still worried that the Germans would regard their newly regained house as a target.

The weather is bad, squally rain and cold winds. These conditions however are not dampening the ardour of our brave boys. There are some military 'experts' who are convinced that Fritz is drawing us forward so that he can come back when our Lines are too extended and so we should take our positions much more seriously. I will believe that when it happens.

All around is bustle. Artillery that is obviously newly painted under tarpaulin cover rumbles with its tractors through the town. Infantry, smartly uniformed under capes, tramps on clean boots behind the wheeled columns of long guns. Cavalry detachments trot along the main road with their gear jingling, boots and saddles polished, and horses gleaming and looking very well fed. The Cavalry is in force on the highway where it has wanted to be for the last four years. A complete Army Corps is on the move.

We are not losing many men from the enemy's well ordered and well controlled rear guard but even the few casualties we are getting, I say again, are quite unnecessary. If we are moving towards the end of things, as every conversation begins with, no matter who you talk to or who you are, I am keeping my head down. I am not 'copping a packet' just as Jerry throws the towel in. Not after all I've been through. Not on your life. As I write this we get a report that the squad which relieved us at the Devon's last position yesterday came in for just the kind of bad luck I wish to avoid. A stray shell that dropped near them while on a 'carry' killed one man and seriously wounded another.

Saturday 9 November 1918

We buried our dead comrade in the Communal Cemetery at Pont-sur-Sambre. I didn't know him well. He was one of a recent intake of replacements, poor sod. The luck of the draw.

We have moved forward to Limont-Fontaine, a small settlement clustered on rocky hills. The civilians here are busy patching up their houses and moving back in. Ladders are up against walls. Tarpaulins, probably lifted from Army stores and sold by unscrupulous Quartermasters, are being roped over holes in roofs, and smashed windows are being replaced. As we pass, sticks of furniture, mattresses and bed-heads are being lifted off carts and carried down pathways into open front doors. The returning population is in a state of pleased wonder as they shout what sounds like 'Tres bon Tommy'. They put up their thumbs and hold their babies aloft to show us. We are the conquering heroes who have delivered them free from the Germans. 'It was roses, roses all the way'. Except, of course, being November there weren't any roses.

The only signs of the enemy as we advance are a few broken limbers and blasted guns with their wheels askew, with the horses that pulled them dead in the road. In the farmyards that we passed the poor peasantry's recently shot cattle could be seen lying in dung heaps.

We halted, awaiting orders, within sight of Mauberg, the biggest town in the district. It has been fortified for centuries and now has modern additions. It was part of the B.E.F. concentration in 1914.

Sunday 10 November 1918

There was a church parade this morning and the Padre prayed for the defeat of the Germans and for the final victory of our glorious alliance. He made special mention of the Americans, including them in his references to the triumph of European civilisations. I suppose that excluded Germany and Austria. So much for Beethoven and Mozart. I have to be in the right mood these days to take Communion and I didn't like the sound of this Padre. He sounded more like a Bishop.

The weather is very good, for after the squalls came bright sunshine with a warmth in it quite unusual for the time of year. Under a beautifully blue sky we moved back to Pont-sur-Sambre where there was a very good dinner waiting for us. After eating, me and my squad went to an entertainment. Nobody paid any attention. The only talk was of a rumoured armistice. The skeptics among us could only chorus what we usually sang when we thought someone was talking 'bullblank', 'Tell us another one, just like the other one, tell us another one do'. To hear such optimistic talk when you had as much service in as we did, we privately thought depressing. We'd heard it all before.

Monday 11 November 1918

Reveille at six and another hot breakfast. They can keep this up and there will be no complaints.

We formed up after conducting our ablutions, shave etc. in plentiful hot water and moved back further to Gommegnies, back near the Mormal Forest.

I am ready to be confounded. I am ready to eat my words. The armistice that everybody and his dog has been talking about for days seems to be 'pukka'. Nobody has officially delivered any message to us. Anybody above the rank of Lance Corporal that we consult, including the Officers who will deign to talk to us, hint of the possibility but will not confirm it. I suppose, because we haven't got anything to shoot with, they don't have to tell us to 'cease fire'. We find it very frustrating that nobody will let us know for certain. We can only judge by the atmosphere that is pervading all activities. There is a sort of calm in the air. It could of course be my imagination and my hopes.

We have other things, as scrounging soldiers, to think about. We are busy along with the civilians, raiding the huge dumps of charcoal left by Fritzy. On these cold nights it is very welcome in our billets.

Sunday 17 November 1918

It is a week now since what seemed like certain news of the armistice but we are still marking time here and awaiting official news of peace. This last week has been a confusion of orders to be ready for a move and orders countermanding. We have not known whether we were on our blanks or our elbows. Officers of various seniority have been running round like blue blank flies. Infantrymen have hesitated outside our billet and then moved on. Orders not to go into the town have been delivered and then repealed. In the years I've been in the Army I have never known such confusion. It is a bloody good job that we are not under fire.

Thursday 21 November 1918

I have had to get out of it and off my own bat I decided to go for a walk round. I am certain I shall not be missed. I have just returned from a thirty kilometre round trip. I took a stroll to Malplaquet, where the English and Germans beat the French in 1709. The Germans were our friends back then.

Yesterday I went to Le Quesnoy where I had a pleasant time visiting a Divisional Cinema. There was a newsreel but no mention of the armistice. I then went on a visit to a B.E.F. Canteen in search of grub but my search was fruitless. If peace has come it has not produced a surfeit of rations.

Sunday 24 November 1918

We are still resting at Gommegnies and during the week a rather interesting education scheme has been set up. Day and evening classes in English, English literature, French, arithmetic and history are on offer. They are said to have been designed to polish off some of the 'rust' if we are to return to civil life soon. Assuming, that is, the war is really over. To join the classes there is the simple formality of making a request to the M.O.

Sunday 1 December 1918

At Gommignies the only thing I find interesting is school. In English literature we are reading the works of John Milton. 'When I consider how my light is spent'. After four years of route marches, drills, fatigues, practices and guard duties I'm not as enthusiastic as I used to be. The school has not been greeted with any enthusiasm as far as some of my acquaintances are concerned. 'I left school to join the Army, now I'm back at blanketty school again', is the general comment of those who have opted for school to get out of other duties.

When we have time, and we seem to have it now in abundance, we visit Le Quesnoy, which is now crowded with Army and civilians trying to return to normal life. I get the impression sometimes that we are in the way. The war is almost over and we are not needed anymore. The time when I get this impression most strongly is when we stand around in a group pooling our cash, trying to drum up enough to pay the increased prices being asked for everything, and I mean everything. When civilians feel that they can be impatient with soldiers is when soldiers should realise that its time to go. Kipling got it right, 'It's Tommy this and Tommy that'. I don't think I am alone in thinking what I do. There has been a sharp increase in altercations between squaddies and civvies, the product of this impatience. We have been told to be on our best behaviour.

Sunday 8 December 1918

The weather is dull but not too cold, nor is it wet.

We are keeping boredom at bay by participating in games of football and rugby union. We spend happy hours and happy afternoons following the teams. We ride to our 'away' matches in two of the horse Ambulances no longer needed for the purpose they were designed for. Unless of course Fritz does the about turn our Officers and betters say we must guard against and be prepared for. The ride we cover is about ten kilometres. It is pleasant fun and a change and everyone is cheerful. The matches are something of an amateur scramble but always enjoyable. After tea with the opposing side during which everyone congratulates everyone else on their sportsmanship, we are all convinced that we are great fellows. In the words of the poet, 'It matters not if you won or lost, but whether you played the game'.

We return in the darkness in our Ambulance and I drive for our squad, all singing to the steady beat of the horse's hooves.

The King visited Le Quesnoy during the week. Fortunately for us we were not involved in the formality of the visit. That was for the spick and span Cavalry and the spit and polish Guards Regiments. A small party went down to see him and his entourage and I happened to be there with the football team and I just managed to catch a glimpse of black shiny carriages with a gleaming horse flesh Cavalry escort as it passed a street end.

In the evening, cosy round the brazier fire of our billet, a visitor from another Ambulance told us to expect a move.

Friday 13 December 1918

Straight after breakfast we mounted waiting lorries and drove through Bavay to Faisnieres sur Hon, a jolly little village on a jolly little hill. We are comfortably lodged in some sort of warehouse shed that smells of leather. We have no time to get used to it for it was only bed and breakfast. We had a wash and a shave and then, quite unusually and surprisingly, a 'short-arm' inspection by an M.O. we'd not seen before. We then moved on to Mauberge.

Saturday 14 December 1918

We learned today that the inspection was because there has been an outbreak of venereal disease in the town. As one voice we chorus: 'Nothing to do with us'. Later on the M.O. who had presided over the anti-V.D. inspection came round and we were herded into a hut for him to give us a talk It was the usual stuff about personal hygiene, and treating young women as we would expect our sisters to be treated, and what shame would descend on us if we went home after having a 'dose' plus the fact we would be on a charge . He left after delivering his 'pep' talk and then, not wishing to miss an opportunity with a captive audience, a somewhat, I thought enebriated, CSM came in and gave us the benefit of his wisdom. He began, without any preamble, by saying: 'You lot are like to put yourselves where I would not put the end of my walking stick so I have this advice for you and any of the women of your acquaintance. For you lads, keep it in your trousers and you won't go far wrong, and for the lasses, keep Toby out. And after that if you can't be good be careful.' He then made his exit pausing as he reached the door to turn and say: 'We are all men of the world so if you want to get the dirty water off your chest , there is always Mrs Palmer and her five lovely daughters.' He slammed the door unnecessarily forcefully and in the brief silence that ensued a very young new recruit said quizzically from behind his glasses: 'Corporal, do you know where this Mrs Palmer lives then?' There was uproar. I have never heard since such spontaneous laughter.

The weather improves and we have a fine sunny day towards to end of our move. Our section is billeted in, of all places, a concert hall. We are in a large windowless space, under the stage, and as there is to be a concert tonight we don't expect to be able to sleep.

The civilians in this 'County Town' are initially very pleased to see us, but become less pleased when they see we can't pay the famine prices for their coffee, cocoa, cognac, vin blanc and le plonkay. Once again we are only in town for bed and breakfast.

Sunday 15 December 1918

We marched to Grand Remy after waiting for motor transport that didn't turn up. At Grand Remy we settled in very comfortable quarters in an empty convent. The nuns fled south at the beginning of the war and have not yet returned. It had been used by Jerry as a hospital but all his stuff had been cleared up apart from a few signs in German Gothic script that were taken down as souvenirs.

As we settled in, the Padre came in to tell us to get scrubbed up and tidied as there was to be a Grand Ball in the village hall and we were invited. We did not need asking twice.

In best bib and tucker, which really only meant a brushing off of our khaki, we turned up to the brightly lit hall. Sandwiches, cakes and a very nice fruit punch that smelled of alcohol waited for us, along with most of the population of the village. To the music of fiddle, brass and drum we were taught country dances whose style permitted you having your arms around the waists of young girls and village wives, if only for brief seconds. We had a lovely time and met some very nice people who did not want to sell us anything.

CHAPTER 16 - RUMOURS OF DEMOB

Tuesday 17 December

We left the convent and marched to Péronne near Bingehe, a busy mining town. There, there was little evidence of war. It had electric cars, brightly lit shops, well stocked for the season and full of Christmas decoration. The cafés were comfortable and built for the job, not the converted front rooms of houses that we were used to. The normality of the lamp-lit streets illuminating the passers-by shopping for the holiday reminded me of home. For the first time since the rumoured armistice I cannot now imagine the war starting again. The Germans are out of France and Belgium and well behind their own frontiers and won't be coming back. I think the war is over but nobody we come across has been officially informed. The impression we get is that Jerry might re-organise and make the same attack as in March 1918.

Wednesday 18 December 1918

We set off on a miserable day. Motor transport would have been very welcome as the rain poured as we marched along. There was general agreement not to rest too long just to get out of it. We marched into Bois d' Haine-par-Manage and gratefully accepted the civilian billets that were waiting for us.

Myself and the other three of our squad sat in our underwear after protesting to the lady of the house, who had insisted on us taking off all our clothes so that she could dry them on the green coloured tiles of the great stove that glowed in her kitchen. I got snatches of what she said as she showed photos of two soldiers that were obviously her sons. I suppose she was saying, 'You haven't got anything I haven't seen before'. We needn't have worried, our 'harvest festival' long combinations saw to it that 'all was safely gathered in'.

We sat there drinking hot coffee and warming our toes. The lady and her husband were about the same age as my Dad and late Mam and they made me think very nostalgically of home.

Later in the evening she made us a great bowl of golden chips and we ate them after dipping them in a dish of salty creamy sauce. After that supper she showed us to our room. There was no bed, just an enormous down mattress on the floor, covered by a great white eiderdown. The four of us fell into what was to be a very comfortable sleep.

Thursday 19 December 1918

Our host woke us early for parade and gave us our snuff-dry uniforms that looked as if they had been pressed. After a breakfast of sponge cake, bread and jam and great bowls of sweet milky coffee, we said goodbye and joined the march to Nivelle. The weather was dry, so much more comfortable, and our vigorous left-right tramp soon covered the relatively short distance we had to go.

Our billets in Nivelle were not as comfortable as the day before. We were lodged in an empty cold cavernous school hall lit only by our guttering candle ends. We went to sleep on cold Army rations. The rumour is that we are to march up to the German frontier.

Friday 20 December 1918

Breakfast was as cold as supper and it didn't give us much enthusiasm for the journey to our next stop, Cour St Ettiene. Once there we were billeted in a civilian farmhouse. Once again it had rained all day so we were wet through. Our billet however had a great open log fire that crackled and flamed as our jackets, great coats, shirts and socks steamed as they hung from the great beam over the chimney piece.

I made good friends with the very sociable family that we were billeted on and I would have liked to have stayed longer. While my mates talked socialism to Madame and Monsieur I played cards with Madamoiselle, the daughter of the family. She was about fifteen and very pretty. She wanted to learn English and I wanted to improve my French conversation. The evening's pleasure was added to by Monsieur's generous offering of his home made beer. As glasses emptied they were filled.

Saturday 21 December 1918

Our hosts insisted on rising with us and presenting our dry clothes folded and brushed. Though before six they had prepared us a breakfast of cheese, bread and coffee which we ate before the fire. We then washed and shaved in the copious hot water provided. Even the 'cabinet', though only a bucket and seat, was inside in the warm.

As we weren't to be paraded until eight-thirty we sat together with them and I talked to the daughter who sat in a pink dressing gown with slippers to match. Her hair was in a long plait and I lost my heart to her Belgian-accented English and her pretty face. We very reluctantly said our good-byes and set off on the march to Petit Leey.

We arrived at Petit Leey to be told that although there were civilian billets on offer we were to use empty barns with straw on the floor. This made us suspicious. Civilians got a billeting allowance. The barns, we surmised, were 'buck shee'. 'So who was pocketing the billeting allowance'?. A group of us decided that at the next stop if civilian billets were on offer we would occupy them and take the consequences.

Sunday 22 December 1918

We eventually reached our destination, which was a small village called Chateau Duy. Sure enough, civilian billets were on offer but we were told we would be billeted in the attics of the empty chateau. There was no water except in the outside yard, no latrines except in the grounds, and all there was to sleep on were our blankets. We mutinied and of our own accord we moved into the civilian billets that were available. The Sergeant Major in charge of billeting was apoplectic with rage and he threatened us with dire consequences. Significantly he did not follow through by putting us on a charge. That would have meant being disciplined by an Officer. We were convinced that he was on the fiddle.

The chateau is a fine stone building surrounded by a moat which extends into a pretty lake in front of the house. The village is scattered but the houses are well built and were obviously prosperous in normal times. Six of us who took a good share in speaking up for civilian billets now share three of the houses and we all meet for meal times in the largest house. Madame is a very good cook and with her garden produce, which includes chicken and rabbits, treats us, including our ration donation, to some topping dinners. My mate and I have a nice little bedroom on the ground floor overlooking the flower garden and it is easy to get up in the morning when there is a stove burning in the next room and hot coffee is waiting. The daughter of the house is only seven and Madame has already promised me that I shall teach her to read and write for she has had no schooling during the German occupation. Monsieur, a big hearty man, who goes to work in Namur every day has promised to show us how they dance in Belguim.

Thursday 26 December 1918

It has been a very merry Christmas. On Christmas Eve we sang carols after a slap-up Christmas tea. On Christmas Day we had dinner at the chateau and then spent a quiet afternoon before once again tea and a very merry evening at our billet. I spent some of it teaching Denise, the little girl, the words of English Christmas Carols. She learns very quickly. The weather is fine and cold.

Sunday 29 December 1918

A very wet day, but in spite of the weather 'we six' have had an interesting time in Namur. We were up at the un-godly hour of four a.m. to catch the train. We were accompanied by the gentleman from the house where we dine. He is to show us around. In the train we caught there was no light so candles were lit and stuck wherever there was room. All the seats were full and in the flickering candle light it looked as if we were off down some mine or other.

In less than an hour the train had covered the five kilometres to Namur and we emerged from the station as the sky lightened. Rain came with the daybreak. Before we started our tour we had coffee and cognac in a café and then took our first trip which was to the Citadel. Up the winding road and under tunnels took us to the top where we looked over the walls into a hole which Monsieur told us was all that remained of the English hotel, burned by the Germans in 1914.

The view from this height, even under leaden skies, was splendid. Straight below was the river crossed by bridges, and flat well-cultivated country could be seen for miles stretching away toward the frontier. After walking down the hill we called for a glass of beer in an estaminet on the river bank, then our guide took us to look at the battle-scarred bridges and the Cathedral, past the fleets of barges tied up on the river banks. After that to a café near the station for dinner. After dinner we adjourned to the 'pictures' where we sat round small tables, sipping drinks as we watched the show. At the end of the show it was time for us to take our seats in the train. By the time we reached the village it was dark.

There was then the matter of settling finances with Monsieur, as he had acted as treasurer all the day. Then wet and tired, but happy, we dispersed to our billets.

Wednesday 1 January 1919

I spent a quite enjoyable day in my billet helping Madame with the garden and 'Ma Grande Denise' with her A B C.

Later in the evening at a neighbour's house, where the fiddler was mounted on a stool in a corner, we danced and sang most of the night.

Sunday 5 January 1919

The weather is cold and wet. Things are rather quiet. There is not much activity at all. No parades, drills or fatigues. I am very disappointed that the education scheme has dropped through owing to lack of support. They can't be blamed, the chaps want to be getting home, not being 'educated' out here. My education scheme however, for little Denise is going strong, and we are rare pals. Other than this I busy myself with my own reading or rugger practice and, recently, nearly six hours dancing.

Thursday 9 January 1919

We played the 14th and 15th Ambulance at rugby in a village near Gembloux. As the other team were short of a man I played in their pack and helped them to beat my own team. We arrived too early for this match and I think that the hour we spent in an estaminet drinking coffee and cognac, did our team no good.

Sunday 12 January 1919

The weather is fine. Today there was nothing on the programme and we spent it talking about the de-mobilization programme that we have heard of, but none of our men have gone yet.

Sunday 19 January 1919

We have sent thirty men home during this week. Things are very quiet. The weather is bright and frosty.

Sunday 26 January 1919

No men have been sent home this week so our lot are not feeling so hopeful. The weather is frosty and it has started to snow. I am passing most of my time teaching little Denise and she gets on well with her lessons. My looking after Denise is a welcome relief for Madame for she is suffering from a painful abscess in her mouth. When Monsieur gets home from his work in Namur each night he brings home new news about the British Forces occupation of Germany.

Sunday 2 February 1919

The ground is now covered with frozen snow and we have a wintry landscape. My mate and I have just been awarded seven days C.B. for missing the nine o clock parade. Our excuse that we had been out all night dancing and Madame, thinking that we should be tired, let us sleep until twelve o clock. It did not cut much ice. The Sergeant Major had obviously got it in for us, for to keep us busy he instructed the joiner to make a snow plough which we were to pull. The laugh was on him. The snow melted during the night. So we are doing our C.B. in the cook house, splitting wood to keep the fires going. This evening we are going dancing, bugger the C.B.

Sunday 9 February 1919

The day is fine and frosty. One of my pals has received his papers and is going home next Tuesday, so this evening's dance in the next village will be his last.

Wednesday 12 February 1919

A party of us were ordered to the Adjutant's office to receive our papers. At last that long looked for 'ticket', but like most things I was not particularly pleased with it when I had got it. I was very sorry to leave my kind friends and comfortable billet at Chateau Duy. Madame cried and my little Denise, Ma Grande Denise, was very upset. She promised to write and I promised to write and to come back one day. Monsieur had gone to work when I left so I was not able to say good-bye to him. We set off for the Cavalry Barracks at Namur where I and several companions who are travelling the same way, are to be billeted for the night.

The journey down to Namur was quite pleasant. A Horse Ambulance carried our kit, but as it was a bright frosty morning, we walked. We passed a boy's school, set on a hill, and were heartily snow-balled by the scholars. Near to Namur we saw Zeppelin sheds. They were well built gigantic structures with huge sliding doors and anti-aircraft guns mounted on the roof.

Friday 14 February 1919

We boarded a troop train after a crowded and uncomfortable night in the Cavalry Barracks and took an uneventful journey to Charleroi, where we stayed the night in the train. I was feeling somewhat low so I turned in early.

Sunday 16 February 1919

I woke up cold, cramped, sore and hungry to find that the train had moved during the night while I was asleep. It was in sidings near Tournai . After some hours standing we pulled slowly into the much battered station and I slipped off into the town to get some coffee and breakfast. I rushed back to the station, worried that I might miss the train if it set off again. I needn't have worried, the train didn't set off for hours and then when it did, it moved slowly and stopped every few miles. Eventually it got going and we passed Lille, Armentières and the ruined countryside of Northern France.

Monday 17 February 1919

After another uncomfortable night in the train, living off cold rations, we arrived at Dunkirk and were marched to a camp that ought to have been condemned as unfit for human habitation. The barrack room and its facilities were filthy and had it not been for the fact that we had had no hot food for days we would have given the cook-house a miss.

Tuesday 18 February 1919

Without exception we got up in a very grumpy mood, which must have got through to those in charge, for after a kit inspection and brief medical inspection and a bath we were moved to a cleaner camp near the sea.

Wednesday 19 February 1919

I decided to take advantage of my stay in Dunkirk and after visiting the town, which is a very interesting old place and not as badly damaged as I expected, I walked along the beach to the place where we bathed the first time I was here shortly after Tom's death.

Thursday 20 February 1919

The weather is dull and very cold and occasionally it rains. We embarked today in a large troop ship for Tilbury Dock. The conditions on board were very uncomfortable and although the weather on deck was a bit breezy I preferred it to the conditions below.

Friday 21 February 1919

We spent the night in the Channel and were landed by tender at Tilbury. 'Old London River' looked cold and drab as we came up it this morning. There was, though, a warm welcome at the station. Hot cups of tea, sandwiches, buns and chocolate were on offer to us before we entrained for Clipstone Camp, back to the North Country

Saturday 22 February 1919

Late last night we reached Clipstone and supper. Most of the night we were on the move passing various inspections. Those who elected to take civilian clothing were measured and fitted for their suits. The other option was to draw two pounds in lieu. I chose the money. We had little or no sleep going through this organisation, so by daybreak we were all settled up and ready to catch the trains for our respective homes.

Myself and a group of others were taken by lorry to Doncaster Railway Station. There we split up, some for the North, some for the West and others along with me for the East.

Our train was slow, stopping at every station, but I knew I was heading home when after passing through Goole it rattled over the bridge on the River Ouse, stopped at Staddlethorpe, then Brough, and finally made a long flat curve along the River Humber to Hull. In the carriage with me, lads like me but strangers to each other had passed the time telling stories of their adventures. As we reached the end of the line their conversation had changed to speculation on what they would do now. They would be back in their old job 'or know the reason why'. They would settle down with the 'girl they had left behind'. I kept my counsel. I thought only that I had come through when many of my mates had not. I wasn't the man I had been when I went in. For me it had been:

The adventure of a life time and I for one was better for it.